Shooter's Bible

SMALL ARMS
Lexicon
and concise
Encyclopedia

Shooter's Bible

SMALL ARMS
Lexicon
and concise
Encyclopedia

by Chester Mueller
and John Olson

FIRST EDITION
1968

Library of Congress Catalog Card Number 67-30798

Preface

"Lexicon" is defined in the Random House Dictionary of the English Language (unabridged edition, 1966) as "the vocabulary of a particular language, field, social class, person, etc."

To assemble in one place the many terms that comprise the "firearms language" together with brief encyclopedic definitions is the object of this work.

Compiled herein are over three thousand common and uncommon words, phrases, and names relating to the art of shooting and encountered in the public press, in firearms literature, on the range, in the field, and in the gunsmith's shop, together with approximately 500 illustrations to assist in understanding the written descriptions.

Included are:

Definitions given with concise descriptions to explain generally accepted meanings and uses in the firearms art. In the case of words that have more than one meaning only the definition relating to firearms is given.

Pronunciations in phonetic form, are given for words of uncommon spelling or usage. Wherever the letter "i" appears as a syllable in such phonetic spelling it is pronounced as the "i" in "ill".

Antique weapons frequently referred to in firearms literature.

Military weapons to the extent of those more commonly known to the civilian shooter.

Names of firearms, ammunition, equipment and accessories that have achieved fairly widespread popularity.

Biographical briefs of the better known contributors of past years to the development of firearms.

Appendix with tables, formulas and facts of interest useful to the firearms industry.

While locally used words, terms and expressions are included to some extent, some regional favorites may have been overlooked.

Obviously, this is not a book to read from cover to cover, but one that should be used as a handy reference source, called upon to furnish a definition or background information when an unfamiliar term or phrase is encountered.

While compiling this work we often wished that we had something to compare it with — a form of check list to assure the inclusion of *every* possible term relating to the firearms field. Surely, most dictionary compilers have someone else's dictionary to use in this manner. Because this is the first book of its kind published, we have had to start literally from "scratch" and for that reason some errors, omissions and oversights are to be expected. Perhaps we are a bit too optimistic in feeling that these instances will not prove numerous.

Chester Mueller and John Olson

South Hackensack, New Jersey
December, 1967

Acknowledgments

The authors freely acknowledge their indebtedness to the many competent and knowledgeable writers whose works have served to define or clarify words and terms of uncertain or obscure meaning.

For their cooperation and assistance in furnishing technical advice, photographs, art work and, or, information, the authors especially want to thank the following organizations and individuals:

Mr. W. Woodin of The National Rifle Association, Mr. Earl Larson and Mr. E. S. McCawley, Jr. of Remington Arms Company, Mr. Fred Moulton of the American Rifleman Magazine, Mr. William E. Lennox of Frankfort Arsenal, Mr. J. Philip O'Hara of the Follett Publishing Company, Mr. Al Groody of Groody Advertising, Messrs. William Amestoy, Robert Storms, Herbert Weinberger, Herman Koelling and Larry Knauer of Stoeger Arms Corporation, Mr. Malcolm Lyle of Holland & Holland, Ltd., Mr. Charles DuBuisson of Savage Arms Corporation, Mr. Harry Hampton of the Sporting Arms and Ammunition Manufacturer's Institute, Mr. William H. Tantum of the National Shooting Sports Foundation, Mr. George A. Virigines of the Mid-West Fast Draw Association, and to the Lyman Gun Sight Company for the use of material appearing in the Lyman Reloading Handbook.

To Mrs. William Moldt and Mrs. Christian F. Scherer who patiently typed and many times retyped the subject matter of this manuscript the authors extend their sincerest thanks and appreciation.

DIRECTORY OF CONTENTS

A

aberration

in optics, the deviation of light rays from a single focus, or, the convergence to a different foci by means of a mirror or lens of light rays coming from a single point. Its effect is to lessen the distinctness of images.

abrasion

the wearing away of a surface by friction. Caused in the bore of a gun by use of improper cleaning materials as well as the normal effect of bullets pressing thru the bore.

abrasive

a substance used to wear away a surface by friction. It may be either a natural or artificial substance and, may be used in making grinding wheels, abrasive cloth, abrasive paper, etc. Natural abrasives such as emery and corundum have been largely replaced by artificial abrasives of the silicon carbide or aluminous types.

absolute deviation

the distance between the center of the target and the point where projectile hits or bursts.

absolute error

1. the shortest distance between the center of impact of a group of shots and the point of impact of a single shot.

2. the error of a sight in relation to a tested, correctible, master service sight.

abutment

the block or framework at the rear of a cannon that receives the rearward thrust of discharge.

Acacia (uh KAY shuh)

an American tree yielding a wood similar to American black walnut in weight, color and density. It is very hard and durable—often mistaken for walnut. Until recently it has been little used for gunstock work, however the growing scarcity of walnut has enhanced its importance to the firearms industry.

acanthus (uh KAN thuhs)

an engraver's and wood-carver's ornamentation, patterned after the acanthus plant which is common to the Mediterranean region.

accelerate

to speed up or cause to go faster, thus a projectile from its stationary position in a gun barrel is accelerated by the rapidly expanding gases of the explosion of the propellent powder to the velocity attained at the muzzle.

acceleration

the change of velocity (speed), or the rate of such change.

acceleration of gravity

the rate of change of velocity caused by the action of gravity upon all freely falling bodies, usually expressed in feet per second. At sea level, latitude 45°, it is 32.174 feet per second.
See "bullet drop"

accelerator

a part of the mechanism of certain types of automatic weapons that speeds up the action. In chemistry it is a substance that hastens a reaction, such substance being called catalyst.

accuracy

freedom from error. In firearms it is dependent upon the design of the weapon and the ammunition; in the use of firearms upon the shooter, weather, terrain, and target. In the case of shotguns, even distribution of the shot pattern is rated over accuracy in evaluating the result.

accuracy life

estimated average number of rounds that may be fired in a particular gun before it becomes inaccurate because of normal wear.

accuracy of fire

the closeness of a grouping of shots around their center of impact.

accuracy of practice

a measure of the precision of fire in terms of the distance of the center of impact from the center of the target. Also called accuracy of the shoot. A term more commonly used in artillery firing.

achromatic *(ACK-row-MATic)*

in optics, refracting light, giving images almost entirely free from extraneous colors.

achromatic lens

a lens consisting of two joined glass elements, free of chromatic aberration or color fringes in the image.

acids

substances whose molecules ionize in water solutions to give the hydrogen ion from their constituent elements. The strength of an acid is proportional to the concentration of hydrogen ions present. Acids are characterized by their sour taste and ability to redden litmus, a dyestuff.

ACP *(A.C.P.)*

abbreviation for "Automatic Colt Pistol"

Acraglas

the registered trademark for Bob Brownell's chemical bonding or "bedding" compound. Mixed with a catalyst and a coloring agent, the paste mixture is strategically applied to the barrel and receiver channels of the rifle stock. Designed to improve the accuracy of a given rifle, the application of this, or other similar preparations, is generally termed "glass-bedding".

action

the breech mechanism of a firearm by which it is loaded, fired and unloaded. The term action is broader than the term lock which designates only the firing mechanism, not the loading and unloading mechanism.

action bar flats

See "water table"

action shortening

the practice of shortening a bolt action rifle receiver by removing a portion of the rails between the forward receiver ring and the rear receiver bridge and by welding the remaining portions of the rails together again. At one time this was frequently done (by highly qualified gunsmiths) to convert a given rifle from a large caliber to one that was considerably smaller.

actuator

part of the receiver mechanism in certain types of automatic weapons; trigger actuator. The actuator slides forward and back in preparing each round to be fired.

Adams, Robert

an English inventor and gunmaker, best known for the solid frame, double action percussion revolver he patented in 1851. It was the first successful solid frame revolver and afforded England means for competing with the U. S. Colt revolver.

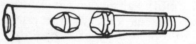

adapter

1. a part or piece to permit parts of different size or shape to be fitted together.

2. a part that modifies a weapon for a different use. For example, adapters used with a 45 calibre pistol enables its use with .22 calibre ammunition.

3. grip adapter — a device frequently employed on revolvers or automatic pistols to enlarge the gripping surfaces.

adhesion and friction

adhesion is the sticking together of two substances in contact with each other while friction is the resistance of the relative motion between two bodies in contact with each other. Adhesion is independent of the pressure between contacting bodies while friction increases with pressure. Lubricants increase the adhesion and decrease the friction. This is noticeable in handling small, oiled gun parts that tend to cling together but may readily be slid over each other.

adjust

to correct the sighting of a gun so that its projectile will hit the target.

adjusted elevation

after observation of fire. The correction of the elevation of a gun to cause its projectile to hit the target. A term used in artillery firing.

adjusted range

the range of a gun corrected by observation of fire so that succeeding shots will hit on or close to the target. It is a term commonly employed in artillery firing.

adjustment fire

gunfire utilized for the purpose of obtaining information upon which correction of fire may be made. It is a term commonly employed in artillery firing.

adjustment of fire

the correction of the setting of the gun, or the setting of the fuze of an artillery projectile, to bring the projectile on target. It is a term commonly employed in artillery firing.

afgan stock *(AFF gan)*

a deeply curved stock having an unusually narrow butt, produced in Afghanistan for crude muzzle loading guns.

aggregate match

a score found in target competition by totaling the scores from two or more match stages or individual matches.

aim

to align the sights of a weapon on a target.

aiming circle

an instrument used for measuring horizontal and vertical angles in artillery and machine gun fire.

aiming device

an attachment for a firearm for correcting its sight alignment. Also used in training to enable the instructor to detect errors in the sight alignment of a firearm.

aiming disk

a rigid circular disk with a bull's-eye and a pinhole in its center, attached to the end of a wooden staff. It is used for instruction purposes in sighting and aiming.

aiming group

the pattern made on a surface by a series of marks, to test the ability of a trainee to properly sight a gun. The trainee directs an aiming disk to be moved over a surface until it is aligned, in his judgment, with the sights of a fixed firearm. The position of the disk is marked by making a pencil dot on the surface thru the hole in the disk. Three such marks will constitute an aiming group.

aiming point

1. the target when it can be seen by the shooter.

2. a point both fixed and visible if he cannot see the target, sometimes called the auxiliary aiming point, which he can use to direct his fire at the unseen target.

aiming post

a stake used as an auxiliary aiming point in obtaining the proper direction and elevation of a gun. Sometimes also called aiming stake. It is a term commonly employed in artillery firing.

aiming silhouette *(SILL o et)*

a target outlining the form of an animal or man for use in small arms practice.

aiming stake

See "aiming post"

air

a mechanical mixture of gases composed by volume of 78 per cent nitrogen, 21 per cent oxygen, and 1 per cent argon. At 32 degrees Fahrenheit and 14.70 pounds per square inch pressure, pure air weighs 0.08073 pounds per cubic foot. At the same temperature and pressure a pound of air occupies 12.387 cubic feet.

air gun

a gun that uses the pressure of compressed air or a gas (usually carbon dioxide, CO_2) to propel a pellet or B-B. Originally called wind guns in the 17th and 18th centuries, use of the term air gun began about 1800.

air hardening steel

the discovery by Robert F. Mushet in 1868 that a steel allowed to cool slowly in air rather than quenching was harder as a result, led to modern high-speed production. Also called mushet or self-hardening steel.

air pistol

a hand gun using compressed air or a gas to propel a pellet or B-B from its barrel.

air resistance

the resistance of air to the passage of a projectile through it. It is one of two principal forces that act upon a projectile after it leaves a gun, the other being gravity.

air rifle

a rifle using compressed air or a gas to propel a pellet or B-B from its barrel. As early as 1750 a 13-shot compressed air gun, 31 inches long, with its stock serving as an air flask was designed by Contriner of Vienna.

air space

the space in a loaded cartridge case that is not occupied by the propellent powder or the bullet.

air speed

the speed of a projectile with reference to the air through which it travels instead of with reference to the ground over which it passes.

air spiral

a term used to describe the imperfect flight of a bullet through the air caused by its unbalanced form, i.e. its center of gravity is not coincident with its center of form. The flight may be likened to a corkscrew path through the air. Other terms used to describe an imperfect flight are "wobble" and "tipping".

air target

any target in the air that may be fired on from an aircraft or from the ground.

A.I.S.I.

abbreviation for American Iron and Steel Institute.

alarm gun

a term once in general use to describe a gun that fired blank cartridges. Typical gun so called is the American Cartridge Alarm Pistol, patented in 1874, firing a blank .22 caliber rim fire cartridge.

alibi

in target shooting, a circumstance which, under applicable range rules, nullifies the shooter's score and permits him to fire a substitute round.

align, aline

to bring into line such as lining up the front and rear sights of a gun.

all-around traverse

turning a gun horizontally in a complete circle without changing the position of its tripod or mount.

Allen, Ethan (1808-1871)

a New England gunsmith and inventor, who was successively in the firms called Allen & Thurber, Allen & Wheelock and Ethan Allen & Co. He is famous for his inventions relating to the pepperbox pistols, his earliest being patented in 1845. At one time these pistols were more popular than the Colt revolver. He was not the Ethan Allen of Revolutionary War fame.

Allen & Wheelock
the name associated with a single shot rifle, firing a rim fire cartridge, made by the company of that name, used during the Civil War.

allowance
means the dimensional latitude permitted between parts that are designed to fit each other. The allowance depends on the class of fit desired such as a forced fit, running fit, etc., and is important in the design of firearms. It should not be confused, as it often is, with "tolerance" which is the dimensional latitude provided in the manufacture of a part.

alloy
an intimate mixture of two or more metals melted together to form, for all practical purposes, a new metal. For example, brass is an alloy composed principally of copper and zinc, sometimes containing small amounts of lead and iron.

altimeter *(al TIM it er)*
an instrument for measuring altitude. For effect of altitude on sighting a firearm see "altitude".

altitude
the perpendicular elevation of an object above a designated level surface such as sea level. Contrary to popular opinion, variations in atmospheric density have little or no effect on sighting or trajectory, according to a noted authority.

alumina
the common name for the chemical aluminum oxide which occurs naturally as the mineral corundum. Used as an abrasive, it constitutes a large part of emery. Wheels made from alumina are recommended for grinding metals having a high tensile strength, such as steel.

aluminum, aluminium
a bluish silver-white metal characterized by its lightness and resistance to oxidation. Aluminum castings are employed in the manufacture of small arms and when so used aluminum is alloyed with other metals.

amalgam
an alloy of mercury with one or more metals.

Amateur Trapshooting Association
a national organization of those interested in trapshooting, founded 1923 and having headquarters in Vandalia, Ohio. Responsible for the rules, shooting procedures and handicapping of American trapshooters. Abbreviated as ATA.

amatol *(AM a toll)*
a high explosive made of a mixture of ammonium-nitrate and TNT, used as a bursting charge in high explosive projectiles.

American Enfield
See "Enfield, American"

American Iron and Steel Institute
a national organization of individuals and basic manufacturers in the steel industry founded in 1908, having its headquarters in New York City. Its steel specifications are a standard for the industry.

American Ordnance Association
a patriotic, educational, scientific, non-political and non-profit-making organization of American citizens dedicated to scientific and industrial preparedness for the common defense. Founded in 1919 its headquarters is located in Washington, D.C. It publishes the bi-monthly magazine "Ordnance".

American Primer
See "Boxer primer"

American Rifleman, The
the official journal of The National Rifle Association, published monthly for its members.

American Single Shot Rifle Association
founded in 1946 and composed of persons interested in single shot rifles of the period between the Civil War and World War I. Headquarters are in Berwyn, Illinois.

American Society for Testing Materials
abbreviated as ASTM, or A.S.T.M., founded in 1898 to promote the knowledge of materials of engineering and the standardization of specifications and testing methods.

American Society of Mechanical Engineers
a national organization of engineers founded in 1880 and having its headquarters in New York City. It has codified steel specifications which are published and known as ASME specifications.

American Standards Association
abbreviated as ASA, founded 1918 to serve as a clearing house for voluntary coordinated national efforts to establish standards in safety engineering and industry covering a wide range of applications within these areas.

American walnut *(Juglans Nigra)*
wood from the American Black Walnut tree which may be found throughout the continental United States. Varying greatly in quality, American Walnut in the better grades is an ideal gunstocker's wood because it is hard, strong, close-grained and is easily worked. When quarter-sawn from a stump cut, American Walnut often has spectacular figuring and results in an unusually attractive stock for rifle or shotgun.

ammonal *(AM uh NALL)*
a high explosive made of a mixture of ammonium nitrate, TNT, and flaked or powdered aluminum, used as a bursting charge in a high explosive projectile and producing a bright flash on explosion.

ammonium chloride
See "sal ammoniac"

ammonium picrate
See "explosive D"

ammunition
a generic word covering the materials used in discharging every kind of firearm or weapon that hurls a projectile. Including, but not limited to, powder, shot, bullets, shrapnel, cartridges, primers, fuses, bombs, grenades, mines and pyrotechnics. Ammunition is classified in many ways, — by composition, size, intended use, effect, etc.

ammunition bag
a bag usually of canvas, containing pockets in which a supply of ammunition may be carried.

ammunition belt
1. a fabric or metal band with loops for cartridges that are fed from it into a machine gun or other automatic weapon. In this meaning usually called a "feed belt".

2. a belt with loops or pockets for carrying cartridges or clips of cartridges. In this meaning usually called "cartridge belt".

ammunition clip
See "Cartridge Clip"

ammunition data card
a card put into a box or container of ammunition to identify it by type and composition and in some cases to furnish instructions for handling.

ammunition dump
a temporary storage place for military ammunition in a combat zone.

ammunition lot number
a code number identifying a particular quantity of ammunition with its manufacturer. The number is assigned to each lot of ammunition when it is manufactured. Particularly important to target shooters who wish to avoid any possible minor variation in loads when in competition.

amusette *(AM you SET)*
an early breechloader, mounted like a cannon but fired like a musket. Made of brass and firing a half-pound ball.

anemometer *(AN i MOM i ter)*
an instrument for measuring wind pressure or velocity.

angle
the space between two lines that come to a point, specifically the measure of the distance one line would have to be rotated about such point to make it lie on the other line. The measure of an angle may be made in degrees, minutes, and seconds or in mils. See "mil".

angle of approach

the angle between the line along which a moving target is traveling and the line along which a gun is aimed. A term commonly used in artillery firing.

angle of clearance

the angle between the line along which a gun is aimed at a target and the line along which the gun should be aimed in order for a projectile fired from it to clear any obstruction between the gun and the target. A term employed in artillery firing.

angle of convergence

the angle formed by the intersection of the lines of sight from the two eyes of the observer; from the two eye pieces of an optical instrument; or from two points of observation. Also called angle of parallax.

angle of deflection

the angle between the axis of the bore of a gun and the line of sight when the gun is laid for direction. A term used in artillery firing.

angle of departure

the vertical angle between the line from the muzzle of the gun to the target and a line along which the gun is pointed at the instant the projectile leaves the muzzle.

angle of depression

the angle between the horizontal and the line along which the gun is pointed when it is pointed below the horizontal. Also called negative angle of site or depression angle. A term employed in artillery firing.

angle of elevation

the vertical angle between the line from the muzzle of the gun to the target and the axis of the bore. Also simply called "elevation".

angle of fall

the angle at which a projectile falls. It is the angle between the tangent to the trajectory at the level point and the base of the trajectory.

angle of impact

the acute angle between the tangent to the trajectory at the point of impact of a projectile and the plane tangent to the surface of the ground at the point of impact. It is the angle at which a projectile strikes the ground or a target.

angle of incidence

it is the acute angle between the tangent to the trajectory at the point of impact of a projectile and the perpendicular to the surface of the ground at the point of impact, thus it is the complement of the angle of impact.

angle of jump

the angle formed between the line along which a gun is aimed just before firing and the line along which the gun is pointed at the instant the projectile leaves the muzzle. Also termed "jump".

angle of parallax *(PARA lacks)*

See "angle of convergence"

angle of position

also called angle of site or just "site". A term common to artillery firing.

angle of site

the vertical angle between the horizontal and a line joining the target and the muzzle of a gun. Also called "angle of position" or just "site". A term common to artillery firing.

angle of traverse

the horizontal angle through which a gun can be turned on its mount.

angstrom *(ANG strom)*

a unit of measurement of the wave-length of light, equal to one ten-millionth of a millimeter, or .00000001 centimeters, about 4 one-billionths of an inch.

angular magnification

an increase in the apparent size of an object by optical means.

annealing

a process to soften metal involving the heating and, usually, relatively slow cooling of a metal to change certain of its properties — the exception being brass which must be cooled rapidly in the annealing process.

Annie Oakley
a free pass. The resemblance of a punched free pass to a playing card with its spots shot through, one of the stunts performed by Annie Oakley Butler (1860-1926) a famous rifle shot who travelled for 17 years with Buffalo Bill's Wild West Show.

annular rim

1. a circular rim.

2. a ring containing a primer composition encircling the body of a Crispin cartridge ahead of its base (year 1865) that not only acted as a primer but as a gas check. The charge was ignited when the firing pin struck any point on the ring. Thus the fulminate was presented for activation by the firing pin irrespective of the seating of the cartridge.

anodizing
an electrolytic process that causes the anodic-oxidation of a non-ferrous metal thereby protecting it from corrosion and abrasion.

Anschutz
sporting and match rifles known by the name of their German manufacturer.

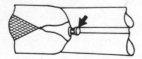

Anson fastening, forend
a method for fastening the forend to side by side double barrelled shotguns developed by William Anson, an English gun designer, in 1872.

anticorrosive
resistant to corrosion. In firearms, the resistance to the effect of acids on the metal parts of a gun or the quality of protecting against corrosion of such parts.

antigallic brown (ANT i GAL ick)
a process for re-browning antique firearms. Antigallic brown consists of a mixture of antimony trichloride, ferric chloride crystals, gallic acid and distilled water.

antimony
a brittle lustrous white metal element whose chemical symbol is Sb. When added to lead or a lead alloy it adds strength and hardness. A small quantity, say two tenths of one percent, added to lead, produces the common lead shot composition.

antique (an-TEEK)
old or ancient. Firearms manufactured prior to 1900 are generally considered antiques altho certain firearms laws may specify otherwise.

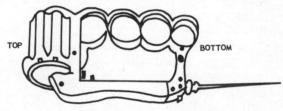

anvil
a rigid metal part of a primer assembly against which the priming charge is compressed by the blow from the firing pin against the primer cap.

AP
abbreviation for armor piercing or automatic pistol.

apache pistol (uh PASH)
a combination of a revolver, metal knuckles and a dagger or knife. It has been the favorite weapon of the Parisian gangster called an apache, pronounced in French as shown here.

aperture
an opening or hole such as found in a peep sight.

aperture sight
a metallic sight, usually a rear sight, having a small hole to look through in aiming the gun to which it is affixed. Also called a "peep sight".

apogee *(AP o gee)*

the highest or farthest point in the orbit of an object, generally one flying in space. It is the opposite of perigee.

appeal

a procedure employed in target shooting when a competitor feels he has been improperly classified or excessively handicapped. The competitor appeals for re-classification to the officials of the match and/or to the protest committee of the organization sponsoring the match.

apple wood *(genus Malus)*

the wood from any one of the many varieties of apple-bearing fruit trees. The heartwood of the apple tree has many desirable stock-making characteristics but, because it is not widely marketed, it is seldom used by stock makers. Apple wood is durable, close-grained and attractively dark red-brown in color. It is easily carved and checkered.

approaching target

a target moving towards the shooter.

apron shield

a shield of steel attached to an artillery piece to protect the gunners.

arabesque *(ARR ah BESK)*

a pattern of ornamentation practiced by European gun-engravers. Originating with the Moorish influence in Spain, this form of engraving employs a highly complex geometric design consisting of interlaced scrolls occasionally accompanied by floral patterns.

arbor

a tool used in gunsmithing being a shaft or bar for holding cutting tools.

arc welding

See "welding"

Arisaka

The popular name for the Japanese Army's Type 30, 6.5 mm (1897) rifle, Type 38, 6.5 mm (later (7.7 mm) official rifle from 1906 to 1945, and the type 44 (1911) cavalry carbine.

Arkansas Stone

a natural stone of pure silica used as a means for sharpening fine tools and finishing metal parts such as sears, triggers, etc. Used with oil or water.

arm

1. a weapon designed for sporting purposes.

2. a weapon for use in war and in this meaning usually called arms.

3. to supply with a weapon or weapons.

4. to put a fuze in a bomb or projectile in condition to cause it to explode at a designated time or at impact.

armament

the total of the arms and weapons with which an instrumentality of war may be equipped.

armor, armour

a protective covering for individuals or ships, tanks, vehicles, etc., usually consisting of steel chain or steel plates. (While historians generally credit the French for first employing metal armor on ships in the year 1835, an earlier utilization is recorded by the Koreans who claim that their Admiral Yi Sun-sin used a metal clad "Turtle ship" to rout the Japanese navy in the year 1593.)
The first French naval armor was made from wrought iron. The Koreans, it is believed, used a form of brass.

armor-piercing

a projectile designed to pass through armor.

armor-piercing bullet

a bullet designed to pierce armor. Use of a hardened steel core is favored for small arms ammunition while in larger calibers a heat-treated high carbon alloy steel is used with a very hard head for penetration of the armor and a tough body to withstand the strains imposed by the twisting action of the projectile at angles of impact oblique to normal. To improve penetration in face-hardened armor plate an armor-piercing cap is attached to the head of the projectile together with a windshield of steel or aluminum.

armorer, armourer

one who repairs and services small arms, more popularly called a gunsmith. The term originally applied only to the artisan who made and repaired suits of armor and similar metal accouterments.

armory

a place or building where arms are stored or where drills and reviews are held. Sometimes also used in referring to place of manufacture of firearms, such as Springfield Armory.

arms chest

a box or case used as a portable locker for holding or transporting small arms.

arms locker

a chest or cabinet in which small arms are stored or displayed.

arms rack

also termed gun rack. Shelving or other means to store small arms or to display them.

arquebus *(ARE kwee bus)*

an early military musket also called harquebus. The word is derived from the French who in turn adopted it from the Dutch or German word meaning a gun with a hook. Originally the word was applied to a heavy matchlock gun supported on a hooked staff or forked rest. Later it was also used in referring to a wheellock gun.

arquebusier *(ARE kwee bus EAR)*

in early times a soldier armed with an arquebus.

arsenal

1. a manufacturing or storage facility for arms and ammunition. Best known in the United States for their development work are Frankford Arsenal, Picatinny Arsenal and Watertown Arsenal.

2. a term often applied to the collection of weapons owned by an individual or a group.

artificer *(are TIF i sir)*

one who makes or contrives; a term formerly in common use to describe one who worked in an arsenal on shells, fuses, etc.

artillery

1. in the military sense guns of larger caliber than machine guns.

2. equipment, supplies, ammunition and personnel involved in the use of such guns.

3. science of using guns larger in caliber than machine guns.

artisan *(ART i san)*

a person trained in a mechanical art or trade. A gunsmith is an artisan.

ASA

abbreviation for American Standards Association.

ascending branch

part of the curved path of a projectile extending from the muzzle of the gun to the highest point in its trajectory. From the highest point to the point of impact it is called the descending branch.

A.S.M.E.

abbreviation for American Society of Mechanical Engineers.

assault gun

any of various sizes and types of guns that are self-propelled or mounted on tanks and are used for direct fire from close range against a target that requires accurate placement of gun fire.

assembly

a group of parts put together to form a single

unit, such as a "bolt assembly", "primer assembly", etc.

ASTM, A.S.T.M.
abbreviation for American Society for Testing Materials.

Astra
the name under which pistols and revolvers are manufactured by Unceta & Company of Guernica, Spain.

ATA
abbreviation for Amateur Trapshooting Association.

atmospheric pressure
the pressure at any given place in the air surrounding the earth caused by the weight of the vertical column of air immediately above it. At sea level it is taken to be 14.7 pounds per square inch the same pressure that will support a vertical column of mercury 29.92 inches high. Differences in atmospheric pressure have an insignificant effect on the accuracy of firearms but may have an appreciable effect on the shooter.

attitude
posture or position in preparation for some action or indicative of a state of mind or condition. Thus a loaded, cocked gun is said to be in firing attitude.

auto
a shortened expression for autoloader or automatic.

autogenus fusing
the technical name for welding.
See "welding"

autoloader
an autoloading firearm.

autoloading
self-loading. A gun that is autoloading has a mechanism that ejects the used shell, puts a new one in the chamber and prepares the gun to be fired, but does not fire it.

automatic
1. in firearms, a term meaning a repetitive mechanical action; as applicable to "machine gun". An automatic firearm ejects the used shell, inserts a new one and continues to fire until pressure on the trigger is released. It is completely self-acting, unlike "semiautomatic" which means partially self-acting. In military circles, the term "automatic" is strictly employed in referring only to firearms that fire repeatedly with one squeeze of the trigger. Similarly, the term "semiautomatic" describes a weapon that is self-loading but which fires only one round with each squeeze of the trigger. The sporting world erroneously uses the term "automatic" in referring to semiautomatic weapons, primarily because there is no sporting application for a true automatic weapon.

2. a term also used, although improperly, to describe autoloading, i.e. semiautomatic, pistols.

automatic feed mechanism
a mechanism in an automatic gun that puts fresh cartridges into the chamber, ready for firing.

automatic fire
continuous fire from a fully automatic gun until pressure on the trigger is released. Semiautomatic fire requires a separate squeeze of the trigger for each shot fired.

automatic firearm
same as "automatic gun".

automatic gun
a firearm or cannon that fires continuously until pressure on the trigger is released. The term is synonymous with automatic firearm and automatic weapon.

automatic machine gun
See "machine gun"

automatic pistol
a pistol having a mechanism which utilizes the pressure of the exploding propellent powder to eject the used case, insert a new cartridge and prepare the pistol for the next shot. While actually a self-loading or semiautomatic weapon the term "automatic" is generally, although improperly used to describe such a pistol.

automatic rifle

a rifle having a mechanism which utilizes the pressure of the exploding propellent powder to eject the used case, insert a new cartridge and prepare the rifle for the next shot. Some models permit the shooter to elect either full automatic or semiautomatic fire.

auxiliary aiming point

a point or object used for laying a gun on a target that cannot be seen. The gun is adjusted so that when the sight is aimed at the auxiliary aiming point the gun is laid on the target. A term employed in artillery firing.

auxiliary cartridge or chamber

an adapter that permits a small cartridge to be used in a larger chambered gun. Thus .22 caliber cartridges or pistol cartridges may be fired in rifles having chambers larger than the calibers of the cartridges. It generally consists of a hollow case of the rifle cartridge size having an open end into which the smaller caliber cartridge may be removably secured. A floating firing pin communicates the blow of the rifle's firing pin to the cartridge base.

axis

1. a real or an imaginary line passing through an object and about which the object turns or seems to turn.

2. a centrally located imaginary line about which parts are, or a mass is, regularly located. Such central line in the bore of a gun is its axis.

axis of sighting

an imaginary line through the sights of a gun.

axis of the bore

the imaginary central line of the bore of a gun.

azimuth *(AZ i muth)*

the measure of an angle to express horizontal direction from north. Such horizontal angle is formed by a north and south line passing through the observer and a line from the observer to the observed point. The north-south line may be to true north, magnetic north or grid north. The angle may be expressed in degrees or mils and is measured clockwise from the designated north. It is employed in artillery firing.

azimuth circle

an instrument for measuring azimuths. It is a graduated circle and may be mounted on a sight, gun carriage, etc.

azimuth deviation

the angular difference between the line running from the gun to the target and the line running from the gun to the point where the projectile strikes.

azimuth difference

See "parallax"

azimuth scale

a graduated angle measuring device on instruments, gun carriages, etc. to indicate azimuth.

B

Babbitt, Isaac *(1799-1862)*

of the United States, a goldsmith by trade who produced the first of the various alloys that bear his name. The first was an alloy of tin with a small percentage of copper and antimony.

babbitt metal

the name applied to a large variety of white metals used as linings for bearings. Named after Isaac Babbitt who, in 1839, obtained a patent for a type of bearing enclosing a soft metal alloy of copper, tin, and antimony. The compositions today may also contain small quantities of other elements.

back blast

rearward blast of gases from the breech of recoilless weapons upon discharge. Also sometimes called breech blast.

backing targets

used in precision competition when a number of rounds are to be fired at the same bull's-eye. Because a closely grouped sequence frequently results in one irregular hole in the match target, a moving backing target is required to verify the number of rounds fired. The backing target is generally placed some distance directly behind the match target and it is numbered to coincide with it.

backlash

1. a rebound or recoil in loosely fitting parts. Also used in referring to the movement of a trigger beyond the point where the firing pin or hammer has been released or to the failure of a sight adjusting screw to continuously move the sight as it is rotated.

2. lost motion in moving parts.

back plate

a plate at the rear of the breech mechanism of certain automatic guns.

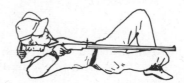

back position

once a popular shooting position in which the shooter lies on his back with feet in the direction of the target, supporting the muzzle end of the rifle on his leg or foot and the butt in one of several ways.

backstop

an artificial or natural bullet stop on a firing range, located behind the targets.

backstrap

that part of the frame of a pistol or revolver that forms the rear of the grip.

back thrust

the pressure exerted on the breech block or bolt by the head of the cartridge case when a firearm is discharged.

back-yardage

common to the sport of trapshooting, refers to those positions employed in handicap shooting from 24 to 27 yards.

Bacon, Roger *circa 1214-1292*

a famous early English experimenter with gun powder during the years 1230 to 1248 who, in 1248 wrote an historical manuscript describing the composition of gun powder but not claiming to be its inventor.

baffle

1. a wall or screen to deflect or control the flow of a gas or liquid. Used extensively in gun muzzle brakes.

2. screens lining the walls of an indoor shooting range to deaden sound.

Baker

a muzzleloading flintlock rifle introduced in England in 1802. It followed the smooth bore Brown Bess and was the British service rifle for almost 40 years. In the latter years many were converted to the percussion system.

Baker, Ezekiel *(1758-1836)*

an English gunsmith, producer of the Baker military rifles, and inventor of improvements in locks and in the manufacture of bullets.

balance

1. in shotgun design the relationship between design and ballistics.
2. in firearms use, the mechanical balance or distribution of weight.

ball

the forerunner of the "bullet" and so named because the early firearms projectiles were spherical in shape. Today, reference to "ball ammunition" means a round of ammunition having a single bullet of any shape.

Ball, Albert *(1835-1927)*

an American mechanical genius and versatile inventor having been granted some 135 patents. In the 1860's he invented a combination repeating and single loading rifle and a cartridge greasing machine that found wide use in both the United States and Europe.

ball ammunition

small arms cartridges containing solid bullets.

Ballard

a rifle produced from 1861 to about 1892 that arose out of a breechloading action invented by C. H. Ballard, an American, and patented by him in 1861.

ball cartridge

a term used in the military service applied to a round of small arms ammunition consisting of a cartridge case, a primer, powder, and a solid bullet.

balled shot

the clumping together of some pellets when fired instead of dispersing, a condition that sometimes occurred with soft shot, i.e. drop shot.
See "drop shot"

ballistic *(ba LISS tick)*

having to do with the motions or flight of a projectile.

ballistic coefficient

a term used in the science of ballistics. It is a number that serves as an index to efficiency and indicates the ability of a projectile to overcome air resistance and maintain speed during flight. It is calculated from a formula wherein it equals the sectional density of a projectile divided by the coefficient of form. The larger the ballistic coefficient the more efficient the projectile.

ballistic correction

the adjustments made in firing data to allow for the effect of wind, temperature, etc. on the flight of a projectile.

ballistic curve

the path taken by a projectile in flight, also called the trajectory.

ballistic density

an assumed constant air density having the same total effect on a projectile in flight as the varying air densities actually encountered.

ballistic efficiency

the ability of a projectile to overcome the resistance of air. It depends mainly on the weight, diameter and shape of the projectile.

ballistic pendulum

a heavy free swinging bullet catcher (mounted like a pendulum bob) used to determine the velocity of a bullet at impact. The swing or distance the bullet moves the ballistic pendulum, the weight so moved, the weight of the bullet, and the time of swing are used in a formula to arrive at the velocity. The chronograph is a more accurate instrument for this purpose.

ballistics

the science or study of the motion of projectiles. Interior ballistics is the study of the motion of projectiles within the bore of a gun to ascertain the effect of the factors acting upon it, such as weight, size, shape, rifling, etc. Exterior ballistics is the study of the flight of projectiles after leaving the muzzle of a gun and the factors acting upon it such as the effect of air density, wind, velocity, etc.

ballistic table

a table of figures for the various factors involved in the flight of a given projectile, such as range, angle of departure, time of flight, angle of fall, muzzle velocity, remaining velocity, height and location of summit of trajectory, and remaining energy. Ammunition manufacturers publish such tables for the products they make.

ballistic wave

the air wave or disturbance caused by the compression of the air ahead of a projectile in flight. Also called bow wave or shell wave.

ballistic wind

as in the case of ballistic density it is an assumed constant wind that would have the same total effect on a projectile in flight as the varying winds actually encountered.

ballistite *(BAL i STITE)*

a former trademark applied to smokeless powder of the type made of nitrocellulose dissolved in nitroglycerin. First made in 1888 and used in small arms and mortar ammunition. Credited to Alfred B. Nobel the famous Swedish chemist and engineer.

Ball-Powder

first manufactured by Western Cartridge Co., in 1933. It is produced by a process in which nitrocellulose is dissolved and under specific conditions agitated to form small balls, — from which it takes its name. It is noted for its minimum corrosive effect on gun barrels.

ball screw

a screw secured at the end of a ramrod to permit a lead ball to be removed from a muzzleloading gun.

ball starter

See "bullet starter" and "false muzzle"

Ball & Williams

the name associated with a single shot rifle, firing a rim cartridge made by the company of that name, used in the Civil War.

band of fire

a military term for fire from one or more automatic guns that gives a cone of dispersion so dense as to make it impossible for a man to penetrate the area covered without being hit.

bandoleer, bandolier

a cloth belt divided into pockets to hold cartridges or clips of cartridges for small arms. It is usually carried over the shoulder and across the chest by a shoulder strap. See also "cartridge belt".

bands

the strips of metal that encircle the barrel and stock of a gun to hold them together.

BAR *(B.A.R.)*

abbreviation for Browning automatic rifle.

bar

in a top break firearm it is that portion of the frame that projects forward beneath the barrel and into which the rear portion of the barrel normally rests. The barrel is hinged at the forward end of the bar.

bar pistol

an antique oddity formed with two or more chambers in a rectangular solid metal bar, so designed to lie flat in the hand or in a pocket and thus be hidden from sight. Sometimes called a book pistol because of its flat shape. Produced mainly in the period 1900 — 1910.

barrage *(bah RAZH)*

concentrated artillery or machine gun fire.

barrel

the hollow cylinder or tube of a gun from which

a projectile is fired. In built up guns the inner part of the barrel is called the tube. See "smooth-bore" and "rifling". The hollow portion is called the bore, the end of the bore into which the cartridge is seated, the breech, and the end from which the projectile emerges is called the muzzle.

barrel assembly

the barrel of a gun with the parts necessary to attach it to the rest of the gun. A rifle barrel is usually threaded to the receiver or action of the gun.
See "barrel shank"

barrel blank

a forged steel rod used for barrel making. Though generally rough drilled from end-to-end, barrel suppliers offer blanks in all degrees of finish, including rifled or, rifled and chambered, or, rifled, chambered and threaded and, at times, contoured.

barrel diameter

refers to the outside diameter of a barrel.

barrel erosion

the wear on the bore, i.e. the interior of the barrel, caused by the chemical action of the powder gases and the friction between the projectiles and the wall of the barrel. The effect of erosion is to cause a loss of muzzle velocity.

barrel extension

a metal projection fixed at the rear of the barrel of certain automatic guns. It extends rearward and holds the breech locked against the gas pressure in the chamber when the gun is fired.

barrelled action

the receiver mechanism of a firearm fitted with a barrel.

barrel length

the distance between the muzzle and the rear face (breech) of the barrel where it abuts the breech bolt or bolt thus including the chamber. Revolver barrel lengths do not include the

chamber, chambers being in the cylinder. The design of a barrel length takes into account the burning rate of the propellent powder to be used and the projectile to be fired.

barrelling rasp

a cylindrical file-like device having teeth set for various degrees of coarseness from rough to fine so that simple rotation of the head will offer the desired cut. Used to rough cut the barrel channel in bedding a barrelled action to a wooden stock.

barrel manufacture

since the 15th century and prior to the latter part of the 19th century when the art of deep hole drilling of metals was developed, barrels for hand carried firearms were made from tubes formed around a mandrel. Strips of iron rods or wires were twisted about the mandrel and forge welded together. Subsequently the resulting tube was reamed and finished. In this manner Damascus barrels were made. Later strips of iron were wrapped around a mandrel or otherwise fashioned about it and forge welded to form a tube. Until the appearance of smokeless powder, soft iron made a satisfactory barrel for use with low heat and pressures of black powder and soft lead bullets.

barrel obstructions

foreign materials that occupy the bore of a gun barrel. Such obstructions cause powder gas pressure to build up and if beyond the safe limit for the gun will rupture the barrel or cause a ring bulge.

barrel reflector

an instrument for examining the bore and chamber of a gun. It consists generally of a mirror mounted on a frame and a tube that may be inserted in the chamber to give a view of the bore. Placing a piece of white paper or cardboard at the breech, holding the gun to obtain light on the paper and sighting through the muzzle end of the bore, produces a similar but less efficient effect.

barrel shank

that portion of a barrel that is threaded and encircled by the receiver. Generally contains the cartridge feeding cone and the cartridge head portions of the chamber.

barrel step

that portion of a barrel where taper starts immediately in front of the chamber area.

barrel time

the time it takes for a bullet to travel from the instant it starts from its seat to the instant it leaves the barrel of a gun.

barrel vents

1. vent holes drilled in the receiver in close proximity to the chamber of the barrel. As an added safety measure, these are designed to release gases when excess pressures flow back into the breech mechanism. Common to military rifles.

2. Ports cut into a barrel near the muzzle to siphon off gases before the bullet clears the barrel. These are designed to reduce recoil and muzzle jump but frequently create uncomfortable muzzle blasts.

barrel vibration

barrel motion as the result of firing the gun, a vibratory motion shared by the other parts of the gun.

barrel whip

the vertical whipping action of the muzzle end of a barrel upon releasing a projectile. Though unseen by the shooter, high speed cameras have dramatically illustrated barrel whip, which is particularly evident in lightweight barrels firing high velocity shells and in barrels that are severely tapered.

Because of barrel whip, lasting accuracy is largely dependent upon the quality and fit of the wooden forestock which must seek to return the barrel to precisely the same position from shot-to-shot. To minimize the effects of barrel whip, target shooters use heavyweight barrels with little or no taper.

bar sight

the rear sight of a firearm consisting of a movable bar generally provided with an open notch.

base

1. referring to the basic wad of a shotgun shell it is its base filler of solid paper or other material to fill up the space in the shell not occupied by the propellent powder.

2. that portion of a rifle or pistol cartridge which contains the primer. More frequently called the case "head".

base of trajectory

an imaginary straight horizontal line drawn from the center of the muzzle of a gun to the point, level with the muzzle, and in the downward path of the fired projectile.

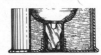

base wad

compressed paper or other material inside a shotgun shell at its base, sometimes referred to as "base", to fill up the space in the shell not occupied by the propellent powder.

batterie

also called frizzen, an upright metal striking plate on the snaphaunce or flintlock upon which the pyrites or flint falls, striking sparks to ignite the priming powder. In the snaphaunce it was not part of the pan cover; in the flintlock it was combined with the pan cover causing it to raise as the batterie was struck.

battery

1. another spelling for batterie.

2. two or more artillery pieces used in combination.

3. the name of an artillery unit.

4. an artillery piece in firing position is said to be in "battery".

battery cup

the receptacle in the head of the case of a center fire cartridge or in the base of a shotgun shell which is adapted to hold the cup or primer.

battle-ax pistol

an oddity. It is the combination of a pistol and a battle-ax, the butt of the pistol being also the handle of the battle-ax. The pistol was either of the wheellock or flintlock type.

battle sight
a rifle rear sight with a large opening or notch set for a convenient range for emergency military use at close range when there is no time for accurate adjustment.

battue *(bah TOO)*
a hunting term referring to the beating of woods and the like, to drive out game, or, to the capturing of such game.

bayonet
a blade attachable to the muzzle end of a rifle for use in military hand combat.

bayonet lug
a projection on a military weapon adapted to engage a slot on a bayonet and thus hold the bayonet as a rigid extension of the weapon.

BB
this is a term that evolved over the years to describe two distinctly different items and, for that reason, often proves troublesome:

1. when referring to a popular size of air rifle or air rifle shot, the term BB relates to a round steel ball which has been lightly coated with copper and which measures .175 of an inch, average diameter. BB caliber air and gas guns have bores that measure between .176 and .177 of an inch in diameter.

2. the term "BB shot" pertains to the lead shot commonly used in shotgun shells. This is usually a dropped shot that measures approximately .181 of an inch in diameter. Obviously, because of the difference in sizes, lead shot of BB size cannot be used in BB caliber air or gas guns.

BB cap
abbreviation for bulleted-breech cap. Essentially a primer or cap, to which a bullet has been added, without a propellent charge other than the fulminate mixture in the cap.

bead
the name given the small knob that is mounted at the muzzle end of a firearm to serve as a front sight.

bead sight
the small knob or "bead" used as the front sight of a firearm.

beaufort scale *(Bo fort)*
internationally used number scale of wind velocities, ranging from 0 for "calm" to 12 for "hurricane".

beavertail forend
a forend of generous width that permits a shooter to hold the weapon without having his fingers touch the barrel.

bedding
1. refers to making close contact between the barrel and the forearm of a firearm by means of bands or screws or other holding means.

2. seating a rifle barrel in a wooden stock in such a way that the wood bears firmly against the barrel at its furthest extremity in order to dampen barrel whip and improve accuracy.
See "Acraglas"
    "bedding control"

bedding control
a device installed in the forend of a rifle stock, about an inch or two from the foremost edge, designed to provide mechanical pressure to the underside of the barrel. In this way it is believed to control barrel whip. Commonly found in target rifles. Often designed with two or more spring loaded plungers that are adjusted by means of screw-like devices set into the wooden forestock and furnished with a battery and light auxiliary unit which indicates when contact is made with the barrel by the plungers.

bedding screws
are adjustable screws in the forend of a stock that apply upward pressure against the underside of the barrel to dampen vibration in an attempt to improve accuracy.

beech *(Genus Fagus)*
a hardwood timber tree whose wood is often used as a substitute for walnut in gun-making, particularly in military firearms. Though strong and durable, beech does not have appealing grain figurations and for that reason is rarely used by sporting arms makers, and then may be found only in inexpensive models.

bell
the outward flare at the muzzle end of a gun barrel, common in antique guns, so named by reason of its bell shape.

bell crank
a bent lever having two arms at an angle to each other and pivoted at the point where the two arms join. Frequently, the two arms are at right angles to each other.

belly gun
a colloquial expression for a weapon concealable in a trousers waistband or one carried in, or on, the belt of the wearer.

belt
the narrow band that encircles some cartridge cases just ahead of the extractor groove and serves to stop the case in the chamber, thus controlling headspace for that type of cartridge.

belted case
a cartridge case having an enlargement in the form of a band or belt just ahead of its extractor groove, to position or seat the cartridge in the chamber of the firearm. Generally employed only on unusually large capacity rifle cartridges of the magnum type.

belt fed
an automatic weapon adapted to be supplied with cartridges from a feed belt.

belt gun
a gun worn in a belt holster.

bench lathe
a machine that may be mounted on a bench and which is equipped to hold and rotate a piece of material being shaped. It is very versatile and finds wide use by gunsmiths for making small precision parts, being adapted not only for turning and boring but, with attachments, for milling, grinding, chasing, cutting and a number of other operations.

bench rest
a firm, heavy table upon which a shooter may rest his elbows and steady his body while he is seated on a chair or stool. A forearm rest for the gun is provided on the top of the table. A bench rest is used for "sighting in" a firearm as well as for accuracy testing. Bench rest target shooting has become a popular sport in recent years.

bend of the stock
See "drop"

Bennett, Epentus A.
an American inventor who, in 1838, with Frederick Haviland, patented a breech loading percussion rifle. Twelve individual blocks, secured together, rotated parallel with the axis of the bore instead of transversely to it.

bent
a notch in which the sear or trigger is held under the pressure of the mainspring until disengaged by movement of the trigger. Such notch is usually in the hammer of the gun.

Berdan, Hiram
a Colonel in the U. S. Ordnance Department and an inventor who in 1870 developed the primer which bears his name and which, for about 20 years, was used in the United States and which is still widely used in Europe.

Berdan primer

a primer developed by Colonel, later General, Berdan in the late 1860's, used in the United States for about 20 years until supplanted by the Boxer primer. The Berdan primer is still used extensively in Europe. It differs from the Boxer primer in that a boss in the cartridge case head serves as an anvil in the primer pocket whereas the Boxer primer contains its own anvil. See "Boxer primer"

Beretta

the name for certain automatic pistols of Italian manufacture. The 9 mm seven shot, semiautomatic pistol was an official weapon of the Italian military from 1934 to about 1955.

Bergmann, Theodore

a German inventor who in 1893 patented the first of a series of unique automatic pistols that became well known in Europe.

Bernardelli

the name for automatic pistols and double barrel shotguns made by the Italian manufacturer of that name.

Berthier

a bolt-action, magazine fed French military rifle used from 1890 through World War II although officially replaced in 1936.

Bessemer, Sir Henry *(1813-1898)*

British engineer and inventor in 1855 of the process for making steel that is known by his name.

big bore cartridge

a term used in the United States that, in the strictest sense, refers only to cartridges of .30 caliber or larger. In recent years, with the advent of high velocity cartridges in the .270 and 7 MM classes, the term is often erroneously used to include these shells under .30 caliber. In England the term big bore refers only to cartridges larger than .450 which are used in hunting large African and Asian game.

binoculars

optical glasses designed to be used simultaneously with both eyes. Binocular field glasses consist of two optically parallel telescopes. It is the practice of binocular manufacturers to indicate optical characteristics of instruments by simple number combinations. The first number of a given combination designates magnification and the second denotes aperture size in millimeters. Consequently the designation 6 x 30 is applied to a binocular with a magnification of 6 and an aperture (objective lens) of 30 millimeters in diameter. By dividing magnification into aperture size, one can determine the size of the exit pupil, i.e. $30 \div 6 = 5$, therefore the exit pupil of a 6 x 30 binocular is 5 millimeters. By the same token, when the sizes of the exit pupil and aperture are known magnification can be determined by dividing the exit pupil dimension into the aperture size: $30 \div 5 = 6$.

bipod

a two legged support for a firearm to carry part of its weight and to permit greater accuracy of fire.

birch *(Genus Befula)*

a tree whose wood is only occasionally used for gunstock work. Though densely grained and ideally suited to gunstocking, it is very plainly grained and resists attempts to beautify it through elaborate staining.

bird shot

a general term referring to small sizes of lead shot, such as that employed in loading shotgun shells. The term "bird shot" may be used to indicate most any given size (from two to nine) and does not relate specifically to one given size. Larger shot sizes are more appropriately called "buckshot" and smaller sizes, "dust shot".

bites

the slots cut into the lugs of a double barrel shotgun which are engaged by the locking bolts when the barrels are secured in a firing attitude. Also called "grips".

biting angle

the smallest angle of impact at which a projectile will penetrate or pierce armor.

black powder

also known as gunpowder, the forerunner of modern powders. Made of a mechanical mixture of about 75 parts of powdered potassium nitrate or sodium nitrate, 15 parts of charcoal and 10 parts of sulphur. Reputed to have been first made by the Chinese in the 13th century. It is a low order explosive used in igniters, primers, fuzes and blank fire charges. Now almost obsolete.

blade

a thin upstanding part used in some firearms as a front sight called a post sight.

blade sight

a flat upstanding metal piece integral with, or adjustably mounted at the muzzle end of a gun to serve as a front sight.

Blanchard, Thomas *(1788-1864)*

the American inventor of the lathe that is named after him. It was the first of its kind, built in 1822 and designed to turn wooden parts of irregular shapes, such as gun stocks. An exact model of the desired finished product is mounted on one side of a frame and serves as a pattern for the wood blank mounted on the opposite side. Transmission of the outline of the rotating model to a cutter applied to the wood blank rotating at the same speed faithfully reproduces the shape of the model.

blank

a cartridge or shell lacking a bullet or projectile, intended to produce a noise when fired in a gun. The explosive charge, generally E.C. smokeless powder, is retained in the case by a wad held in place by crimping the open end of the case. Upon firing, such wad may cause injury to persons immediately in front of the gun.

blank ammunition

is ammunition containing powder but no projectile; used in training, signaling and in firing salutes. Fast burning powder is used in autoloading weapons to compensate for lack of bullet resistance. Blank ammunition cannot be indiscriminately interchanged since what is suitable for one use may not have the proper burning rate for other uses.

blank fire powder

orange or pink explosive powder resembling coarse sand, used as a charge in small arms, blank cartridges, and as a bursting charge in hand grenades. Also called E.C. blankfire or E.C. smokeless powder.

blank firing attachment

generally, an adapter, specifically an attachment mainly employed with autoloading military weapons for training purposes or for simulating combat scenes in the entertainment industry. It serves the purpose of building up pressure or recoil that is normally provided by the resistance of a bullet in being accelerated from a static position to its muzzle velocity. It substitutes for the bullet in blowback and gas operated weapons by restricting the bore; in recoil operated weapons by a restriction on the barrel jacket to build up pressure between the muzzle and the breech face. See "cartridge stop"

blank powder

a powder for use in blank cartridges, which in composition is almost a guncotton and is extremely fast burning. It is dangerous for that reason to load a bullet in front of it since detonation will occur, bursting the gun.

blast

an explosion or violent detonation or violent gust of gases or of wind.
See "muzzle blast"

blind

a camouflaged hunter's shooting stand. Most often employed by migratory bird hunters, in or near waterways. May also be used to refer to places of concealment when hunting dangerous and/or predatory animals.

blind box magazine

an enclosed magazine let into the stock, resembling a mortise in the wood, usually lined on its sides and ends with sheet metal leaving the floor of wood uncovered.

blind hole

a hole extending only part way through a part.

block

that portion of a firearm that serves to lock the cartridge in the chamber and which absorbs the primary recoil thrust. Often called the breech-block, breech bolt or, simply, bolt.

blowback

1. the rearward movement, under pressure, of the gases formed when a projectile is discharged from a gun. This normal rearward pressure is utilized in some types of automatic weapons to cause the breech mechanism to extract and eject the spent case and reload a fresh round in preparation for the next shot.
2. Abnormal blowback is caused by a faulty primer or a broken cartridge case.

blowback action

an automatic or semiautomatic action that utilizes the expanding gases of the propellent powder to drive the breech block action backward. Normally the breechblock holds the breech closed under the force of the recoil spring, no mechanical locking system being employed. The inertia of the movable parts is such that a bullet leaves the muzzle before the breechblock moves backward.

blow forward action

an automatic or semiautomatic action utilizing the expanding gases of the propellent powder to move the barrel forward, away from a standing breech, to open the action and eject the fired case. A spring restores the barrel to firing position and in so doing reloads and cocks the gun. The .32 caliber Austrian Scharzlose (1908) sold in the period 1908-1915 and no longer manufactured is reputed to have been the only pistol with such action to have been commercially marketed.

blowgun

a tube from which a dart or other projectile may be discharged by the force of the breath.

blowhole

a defect in a metal ingot or casting caused by a gas bubble entrapped in the course of manufacture.

blown pattern

a shotgun pattern of erratic distribution usually caused by the escape of gas past the wads into the shot column or by excessive constriction at the choke.

blown primer

a cartridge defect that causes the primer to be dislodged from its seat in the pocket of the case when the cartridge is fired.

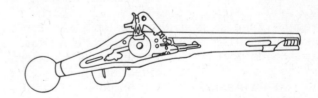

bludgeon pistol (*BLOODGE un*)

an antique oddity designed for use both as a firearm and a club, found in some ignition and percussion type pistols. The barrel serves as a handle for the club shaped butt.

blueing, bluing

the process of creating a gun-blue finish on steel through the application of an acid solution that artificially induces rust. By means of controlled rusting and brushing, the surface of the steel acquires a blue to blueblack finish that minimizes light reflection and secondary rust formations. See "cold blue", "hot blue" and "browning"

blueing tanks

the tanks used by manufacturers and gunsmiths to contain the water and chemical solutions used in the blueing of gun metals.

blue pill

a nickname given to a high pressure test cartridge used for proof firing of small arms.

bluer

any chemical solution designed to induce a blued finish on metal.

blue vitriol *(VI tree all)*

a commercial name for copper sulphate. Other common names are "blue stone" and "blue copperas".

blue whistlers, whistlers

a local term used in some parts for large size buckshot, in that same locality small size buckshot is called "low mold".

blunderbuss

an antique smoothbore flintlock or wheellock gun with a round or oval barrel and a bell shaped muzzle, generally of large bore intended to dis-

charge a number of missiles at close range. In use in the 17th to the first part of the 19th century.

boat-tail

a term meant to define the shape of a bullet. The rear end of a projectile that is tapered or cone shaped instead of cylindrical. Those having a cylindrically shaped base are termed "flat base" or "square base".

bobbing target

a target that is exposed at short intervals for timed practice fire. The target is turned to show only its edge to the shooter between the times it is exposed for fire, or it may be set up so it can be pulled down out of sight of the shooter. Also occasionally called a swiveling target.

Boehler steel

a premium quality gun making steel that is stainless and acid-proof. Manufactured by GEBR. Boehler & Company A.G., Dusseldorf, Germany.

Bofors

a 40 mm anti-aircraft gun known by the name of its manufacturer, Bofors Company of Sweden.

bola

a thong or cord having a round stone or ball attached at one end, adapted to be thrown for the purpose of entangling an animal. It is used by the South American Gaucho.

bolt

the sliding part in a breechloader that pushes a cartridge into position and locks or holds the mechanism to prevent it from opening when the gun is fired. It is also referred to as the breech-block. It usually contains the firing pin and the extractor and takes the back pressure of the discharge. "Bolt mechanism" refers to the assembly that includes the moving parts that insert, fire and extract a round of ammunition. When a "bolt action" gun is referred to it means that a handle projects from the mechanism by which the bolt may be pulled back and forth to eject the spent cartridge, insert a new one, and cock the gun.

bolt action

any firearm that is manually operated by a bolt mechanism. Generally refers to a rotating bolt device that lifts about ¼th of a turn and is pulled rearward to discharge a spent casing, and which is cocked for a second firing upon being returned to its forward-and-down locked position. Rare bolt action rifles were made with a straight-pull action (without rotation) — for example, the Steyr Model 95 military model.

bolt guides

the parallel tracks in the side walls of a receiver that serve to guide the bolt back and forth in line with the chamber.

bolt head

the front half of a bolt or that portion that engages the case head of a shell upon firing.

bolt, altered

a bolt that was primarily designed for military use (when the bolt protrudes straight out at a 90° angle from the vertical line of the pistol grip) and which has been altered, by forging or other means, so as to lie flat against the side of the stock. Most often a bolt is altered so that it will not be interfered with by a mounted scope.

bolt knob

the round or pear-shaped end of a bolt handle that is gripped by the shooter when working the bolt.

bolt lock

the latch, lug or cam that mechanically locks the bolt to maintain the seal of the breech at the moment the gun is fired.

bolt rails

See "bolt guides"

bolt bending jig

a two piece jig mechanism that encloses the main body of a rifle bolt, exposing only the handle which is then heated until it can be bent by hammering.

bolt sleeve *(bolt plug)*

a component part of a number of bolt action rifles such as the Krag and Mauser which serves several purposes in its position at the rear of the bolt.

bolt stop

the projection in the gun in the path of the bolt to stop its rearward motion.

bolt face

that portion of a firearm's bolt which engages the cartridge head and from which the firing pin protrudes when the gun is fired.

bolt throw

the distance that a bolt travels from the fully closed to the fully opened positions.

bomb

a container holding an explosive, or a chemical composition, or both, exploded by contact, time fuzes or a combination of both.

bombard

the name given the earliest type of cannon that hurled stones and other missiles. It also refers to attack by artillery fire such as to "bombard a fortified position", etc.

bombarde

one of the words used in 14th century literature as a name for cannon and hand arms.

booster

an explosive charge added between the primer and the main charge to accelerate the explosion of the main charge. Used in artillery firing.

boot

a leather sheath usually used on the side of a vehicle or saddle to carry and protect a firearm.

bootleg pistol

1. an early type of pistol for dueling and target practice deriving its name from the fact that it was made to carry inside a bootstrap.

2. another type of pistol called a bootleg pistol had its hammer under the barrel and was in vogue before 1850. Also sometimes called a saloon pistol or an under-hammer pistol.

Borchardt, Hugo *(BOOR shard)*

an American gun maker and inventor who in 1890 developed one of the earliest successful autoloading pistols but had to go to Germany to find a manufacturer to undertake its production in 1893. It used a toggle lock system. George Luger an engineer with Ludwig Loewe, the Berlin manufacturer, made improvements which resulted in the production in 1900 of the pistol later to be sold under the trademark Luger in the United States.

bordering tool

a tool used by gun stock checkerers with which to add a decorative edge or border to a checkered pattern.

bore

1. to pierce with a hole.

2. the interior of the barrel of a gun. It is used to refer to the enclosed air space as well as to the inside surface of the barrel, including the surfaces of the rifling if it is a rifled barrel. It is also a term used to indicate caliber. It should not be confused with the gauge of a gun.
See "gauge"

bore brush

a brush used to clean the bore of a gun. Brushes made of brass or plastic bristles are used to clean lead fouling and powder deposits from the bore of a firearm.

bore chamber

See "chamber"

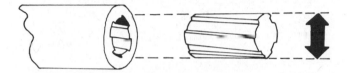

bore diameter

in the case of rifled barrels two diameters are involved. The diameter of the circle on whose circumference lie the surfaces of the grooves and the diameter of the circle on whose circumference lie the surfaces of the lands. It is the land diameter that is used to measure the caliber of a rifled barrel.
See "caliber"

bore leading *(LED ding)*

See "leading"

bore rest

See "clinometer rest"

bore safe

a term applied to artillery fuzes that have an interruption in the explosive train that prevents a projectile from exploding until after it has left the gun. Sometimes the term "detonator safe" is used.

bore sight

1. a device used to visually align the axis of the bore of a gun with an aiming point. It has two

parts, one to be attached to the muzzle of a gun, the other to its breech. By sighting thru these parts the axis of the gun sight and the axis of the bore may be brought in parallel to each other.

2. In small arms a prismatic optical device that enables one to view the length of the bore from a position at right angles to the chamber — designed to permit viewing from the breech to the muzzle on solid breech guns.

bore sighting
sighting through the bore of a gun with or without boresights to align the axis of the bore with the sights of the gun.

boring machines
are of two general classes, — vertical and horizontal. The one built by Smeaton in 1769 was succeeded by the first true boring machine built in 1775 by John Wilkinson, paving the way for the making of gun barrels by other than casting or welding and forging as the Damascus barrels were then made.

boss
1. refers to a raised part or protuberance or the like and such embellishments are found on both wood and metal surfaces of many weapons. Embossing is the act of raising such features on a surface. See also "checkering" as an ornamentive feature for a firearm.

2. the straw backstop used for an archery target.

Boss
Boss & Company of London, England — prominent British manufacturer of high quality side-by-side and over & under shotguns.

bottleneck cartridge
a cartridge whose case tapers to a smaller diameter at the mouth of the case, generally with a pronounced step.

bottoming
1. the term applied to chiselling out the deep recesses and corners of a gun stock in bringing it to the desired final dimensions.

2. the process of cutting screw threads to the bottom of a blind hole — a job that requires the use of a "bottoming" tap.

bound barrel
a barrel that fits so tightly in the receiver of a gun that it has no room to expand when it is heated by the firing of the gun.

bourrelet *(boor LAY)*
a raised band or ring on the forward part of a projectile that centers the projectile in the bore of the gun and makes it fit closely.

Boutet, Nicholas Noel *(1761-1833)*
a famous French gunsmith, maker of fine arms as well as ordinary firearms, known for the artistic decorations with which he ornamented his guns.

bow wave
See "ballistic wave"

Boxer cartridge
a black powder cartridge developed by Colonel Edward M. Boxer of England in the 1860's. It has a coiled brass case with iron head and an anvil type primer. It seats a round nose lead bullet. It was the first center-fire cartridge to be made and used successfully on a large scale.

Boxer, Edward M. *(1823-1898)*
a Colonel (later Major General) in the British Army who, in the 1860's, developed a black-powder cartridge with a round nose lead bullet, anvil type primer and a coiled brass case with iron head with cap chamber. The Boxer primer is still in universal use and is favored in the United States over the Berdan primer.

Boxer primer
a primer in which the anvil is an integral part of the primer assembly. It was developed from the work of Colonel Boxer of the British Army

in the 1860's. Used in the United States almost to the exclusion of the Berdan primer and as a result often called the American primer. It is not generally produced in Europe although British shotgun primers are of this type.

box lock
a 19th century type of lock for rifles, shotguns and pistols characterized by having the hammer inside the lock plate but projecting thru between the stock and the lock plate.
See "side lock"

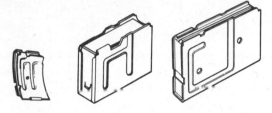

box magazine
a box-like device that holds ammunition and feeds it into the receiver mechanism of certain types of automatic or repeating weapons.

bracket
the space between two shots or series of shots within which the target lies, i.e. the shots straddle the target.

brake
See "muzzle brake"

brass
an alloy principally of copper and zinc in varying proportions, used for the manufacture of cartridge cases and primer cups. Many antique firearms have brass parts.

brass coloring
the color of brass varies widely depending upon its zinc content, but like copper may be given various surface colors by the use of the proper chemical solutions. These colors may among others, be gold, yellow, white, black, green, bronze or gray.

brazing *(BRAY zing)*
a method of joining metal parts together with a melted alloy known as spelter solder or simply spelter having the advantage of producing a joint of superior strength. It is almost the same as hard soldering. Brazing joins by a film of brass, a copper-zinc alloy; hard soldering ordinarily by silver solder, a silver, copper-zinc alloy.

break-action
a term sometimes used to describe a shotgun with a hinged frame.
See "hinged frame"

breech
the end of the barrel into which the cartridge is inserted. It is a term sometimes applied to the mechanism of a breechloader. "Breech face" is the rearmost surface of the barrel or chamber that meets the breechblock or bolt.

breech actions
may, for rifles, be divided into the following classes:

> lever action
> bolt action
> slide action
> automatic action
> falling block action

breechblock
the movable block of metal that closes and seals the breech preparatory to firing the gun. The present day "bolt" is a form of breechblock.

breech bolt
See "bolt"

breech bore sight
a disk with a small aperture in its center fitting snugly in the chamber of a gun. Used with a muzzle bore sight to establish the axis of the bore.
See "bore sight"

breechloader

a firearm in which the cartridge is loaded in the rear or breech end of the barrel as contrasted with the muzzle loader in which loading takes place at the front, or muzzle end of the barrel. First used by the British Army during the American Revolution but the recognized date of the beginning of extended use is 1811.

breech mechanism

the mechanical means for opening and closing the breech of a gun and firing the charge.

breech pin rod

a rod communicating the blow of the hammer to the firing pin in early types of magazine rifles.

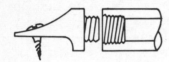

breech plug

a removable metal insert to close and seal the breech end of a muzzleloading gun. It is removed when access to the breech is desired.

breech pressure

See "chamber pressure"

breech support

refers to the ability of the breech block or bolt to back up the head of a cartridge case against the pressure of the discharge.

Bren

a .303 air cooled light machine gun adopted in 1935 by Great Britain for use by its army.

Brenneke

the name of a rifled shotgun slug made in Germany, consisting of a wad and a soft lead plug joined together. Used for big game hunting. The name Brenneke is also known for the development of certain bullet designs popularly used for hunting purposes.

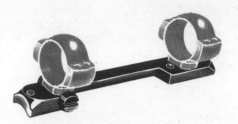

bridge mount

a mount for attaching a telescopic sight to a rifle; a bridge mount has a one piece base that "bridges" the usual two base-and-ring units with a center bar thereby assuring proper alignment of the scope-encircling rings.

bright dip

a quick process for restoring the appearance of a badly tarnished brass piece that consists in dipping it in a series of water and acid baths.

Brinell hardness test

a means of measuring the relative hardness of metals by the application of a specified load upon a hardened steel ball of known diameter resting on the surface of the metal being tested and measuring the resulting area of the indentation.

$$\text{Brinell hardness number} = \frac{\text{load in kilograms}}{\text{surface area of indent in square millimeters}}.$$

brisance *(bree ZAHNS)*

the shattering power of a high explosive.

broaching

the use of one or more broaches to cut away metal to achieve the desired form, size and finish. The broach is a tool having a series of teeth of progressively increasing size or height from the starting end so each tooth takes a light cut. It results in a quick accurate reproduction in the metal of the shape of the final cutting edges on the broach.

bronze

is a metal alloy, largely of copper with tin, zinc and sometimes lead in varying proportions. Bronze for bearings for example might be 82% copper, 16% tin and 2% zinc. Bronze was used in antique weapons for parts and gun barrels and finds use today in instrument manufacture.

Brown Bess

a smooth bore flintlock muzzle loader officially adopted by the British Army in 1690 and used during the American Revolution. Its name arose from the fact that its barrel was brown in color. (the illustration shown is of a replica of a flintlock pistol sold currently under the name "Brown Bess".)

browning

an acid and water oxidation process that was used in the 18th and 19th centuries for coloring steel "brown"; this process was the forerunner of our modern gun-blue finishes.
See "blueing"

Browning

the trademark applied to firearms sold by the Browning Arms Corporation of St. Louis, Missouri.

Browning, John Moses *(1855-1926)*

an American gunsmith said to be the inventor and designer of more successful firearms than any other American. Among the numerous weapons of his design he perhaps is best known for his heavy machine gun and his light automatic rifle, both being military weapons.
John M. Browning also achieved considerable success with his designs for automatic pistols, lever action rifles, slide-action .22 rifles, slide action shotguns, automatic recoil operated shotguns and an over and under shotgun.

Browning, Jonathan *(1805-1879)*

an American gunmaker, father of the renowned John Moses Browning. He is noted for his repeating rifle of the harmonica type and for a breech mechanism that contained a six chambered cylinder resembling that of the revolver of his day.

brushes

a barrel bore cleaning tool generally made of brass or bristle for use in cleaning fouling from the bore.

brush shells *(also called brush-loads)*

a type of shotgun shell developed for use in choke bored guns to provide maximum pattern spread at close range. Also known as a "spreader shell". Generally loaded with number 8 shot, the brush shell is employed by sportsmen who hunt game in dense cover. In this shell, the shot charge is separated into three or four segments by means of horizontal or vertical cardboard dividers.

brush shooting

shooting in heavily wooded terrain.

BT

the abbreviation sometimes used for boat-tail bullets.

buck and ball

a cartridge with a round ball and three buckshot.

buck fever

a condition of excitement brought on by the sight of game which often unnerves a beginner in hunting.

buck lure

a natural or manufactured scent used by hunters to entice deer into shooting range.

buckshot

a small lead bullet or large shot used in hunting large game. Buckshot has been made in many different sizes.

buffer

the means provided in a gun for taking up and checking the recoil action of the gun when it is fired or to absorb the shock of recoil.

buffing wheels

are made from disks of bleached or unbleached cotton or woolen cloth that serve to carry abrasive powders such as tripoli, rouge, etc. bonded with a grease or wax. The metal to be buffed dictates the type of wheel to be used for best results.

bulged barrel

a barrel enlarged at a place along its length

because of the abnormally high pressure built up in the bore by reason of an obstruction that prevents the normal passage of the projectile and following gases out of the barrel.

bullet

a shaped projectile designed to be shot from a firearm.

bullet catcher

a box or other container filled with water, cotton waste or oiled sawdust to serve as a means for trapping a fired bullet without marring its surface.
See "bullet trap"

bullet drop

the normal fall of a bullet during its flight from the gun to the target due to the influence of gravity upon it. A bullet starts to drop immediately upon leaving the muzzle of a firearm under the effect of gravity.
See "gravity, force of"

bullet lubricant

a lubricant used on cast bullets to facilitate loading into a case. Lithium soap greases are satisfactory but special greases having superior qualities are available.

bullet lubricator

a tool used for sizing and lubricating lead bullets. Most often employed in making bullets for pistols or revolvers.

bullet metal

a metal alloy, principally of lead, but mixed with varying amounts of tin or antimony depending upon the degree of hardness desired. Bullet metal, for reloaders, is sold in 3-lb. "billets".

bullet mould, mold

a cavity or series of cavities into which molten lead or a lead alloy may be poured and allowed to harden.

bullet plug

a device used in casting hollow point bullets: that tool which creates the hollow in the bullet nose.

bullet proof glass

a special glass designed to be resistant to the passage of a bullet thru it.

bulletproof vest

a vest made of heavy fabric enclosing hardened steel chain, steel plates, or other impenetrable material. Designed to cover a man's torso, protecting it from small arms fire and shell fragments. In military jargon, often referred to as a "flak-vest".

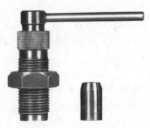

bullet puller

a tool used for removing bullets from "live" rounds. Two types of bullet pullers are currently available: one works on the inertia principle and permits re-use of the bullet; the other is a vise-like tool that is surer and faster but which damages the bullet so that it is not suitable for re-use.

bullet seater

See "bullet starter"

bullet shell

an explosive bullet having a bursting charge in a tube.

bullet starter

an implement used to assist in starting a bullet into the bore of muzzleloading rifles. Usually it consists of one long hardwood dowel and one short hardwood dowel inserted at right angles into a ball handle, the exposed dowel ends being slightly cupped to fit the bullet. The short dowel is used to start the bullet and the longer one to push it still further into the bore after which a ramrod may be used to seat the bullet on the powder charge. Also called a ball starter or bullet seater.

bullet trap

a means for safely absorbing the energy of a bullet in flight and bringing it to a stop in a designated location. To preserve such a bullet for examination in connection with the identification of a firearm the bullet is fired into a sufficient thickness of non-abrasive material, such as cotton waste. Gallery ranges usually employ a steel plate set at an angle to not only absorb the energy of the bullet but to deflect it downward into a pit or receptacle.

bullet wear

the wear in the barrel of a gun caused by the friction of bullets passing thru it. This wear is insignificant compared to the destructive effect of the erosion due to the velocity of the hot gases of the propellent powder produced by each firing of the gun.

bull gun barrel

a type of rifle barrel designed for target shooting. Originally intended for long range (1000 yd) big bore shooting, bull gun barrels are now also popular among small bore and benchrest marksmen. Bull barrels are approximately 26-28 inches in length and are made with little or no taper: average diameter at the breech is 1.25 inches; muzzle diameter is rarely less than .875 inches. Guns equipped with bull barrels range in weight from 13 to 20 pounds.

bull's eye

the center of a target: it also is used to describe a shot that hits the center of a target.

Bull's Eye powder

a type of powder commonly used as a propelling charge in small arms ammunition.

burnishing

1. to make shiny or lustrous by means of polishing. In gunmaking, decorative burnishing is often called "engine-turning" or "jewel-indexing", or "jewelling".

2. to secure a smooth finished surface by compressing the outer layer of a metal by applying highly polished tools or by the use of steel balls which by rolling contact produce smooth surfaces.

Burnside

the name given the breechloading rifle invented by Union General A.F. Burnside which used a special brass cartridge of conical type.

Burnside, Ambrose Everett *(1824-1881)*

a U. S. Military Academy graduate of 1847 best known as a Civil War General. He invented, in 1856, a breechloading percussion rifle and subsequently headed companies manufacturing firearms, the Burnside Arms Company producing Burnside carbines, and Burnside cartridges for the Government.

burnt umber

a brown earth containing deposits of manganese and iron oxides. Valued as a pigment. When burnt, it has a reddish-yellow brown color. In gun making it is often used in mixing stains for gunstocks.

burp gun

the knickname given to submachine guns in general during World War II, originally applied to the German Schmeisser.
See "grease gun"

burr hammer

a hammer having a projection with a knurled top surface to provide a gripping surface for cocking the gun.

burst

refers to a series of shots fired by a single pressure on the trigger of an automatic weapon; it also may refer to the explosion of an artillery projectile either in the air or on impact.

burst center

See "center of burst"

burster

an explosive charge in a chemical projectile, bomb or mine to open it and spread its contents.

bursting charge

the explosive charge in a projectile, grenade, bomb or mine that upon ignition produces the fragmentation, demolition or other desired actions.

burst wave

the wave of compressed air caused by the bursting of a projectile or bomb which generally results in extensive local damage. Also called "detonation wave".

Burton, James Henry *(1823-1894)*

an American gunmaker who spent some time in England in the manufacture of arms and subsequently held a commission as a Lieutenant Colonel in the Confederate Ordnance Department. Best known as the man who perfected the French designed Minie ball.

bushing

a sleeve used to concentrically space two parts. An example is the barrel bushing in the U.S. Pistol caliber .45 Model of 1911.

busted hulls

a local term used in some parts for fired cases.

butt

1. the end of the stock of a small arms weapon. In a hand gun it is the bottom of the grip in a shoulder gun the surface that bears against the shoulder of the shooter.

2. the shortened name for target butt which is a retaining wall placed on the side of a target pit nearest the firing point, with an earth cover facing the shooter.

butt figure

a gunmaker's term used to refer to the graining in the butt end of a stock.

button lock

said to be the first improved version of the matchlock. The cock or serpentine after being drawn back was held by sear under spring pressure. By pressing a button the cock was released to bring the lighted match to the priming. Arriving on the scene about 1500 it continued in use until about 1520 when superseded in the line of development by the pressure lock.

butt plate

a covering of metal, rubber or other material for the end of the stock of a small arms weapon.

butt plate screws

screws to secure the butt plate to the stock of a firearm.

buttstock

the rearmost section of a gunstock — that portion which engages the shoulder when the gun is held in a firing attitude — or, the shoulder section of a two-piece stock assembly.

C

caisson *(KAY sun)*
a two wheeled vehicle used for carrying artillery ammunition.

cal.
abbreviation for "caliber"

caliber, calibre
1. the diameter of the bore of a gun, which in rifled bores is the diameter of the land surfaces. It is expressed in decimals of an inch or in millimeters. American gun makers have not always produced guns having the exact caliber by which they are designated by the makers.

2. the diameter of a projectile although ballistically it may be used to express comparative dimensions. Thus a bullet of "three calibers" has a length three times its diameter.

3. the length of a cannon bore is also expressed in calibers, the caliber being the length of the bore from muzzle to breechblock, divided by the diameter of the bore. Thus a cannon 20 feet long with a 6" bore diameter is said to be 40 calibers long and would be referred to as a 6"-40 caliber gun.
See "markings"

calibration
the comparison of the scale of a measuring instrument with a standard to determine the accuracy of its readings and make the necessary corrections to the scale to make its readings accurate.

calipers
an instrument consisting essentially of two movable arms having opposing contact points that may be brought to bear on the surfaces whose distance of separation is to be measured.

caliver
a 16th century matchlock, a special form of the arquebus, being lighter in weight and fired without the use of a forked rest.

call the shot
it is the giving of an estimate or opinion of where the bullet strikes a target before the actual location becomes known. A good marksman will be able to do this accurately by his observation of the position of his sights with relation to the target.

cam
a rotating or sliding piece having a contoured surface or projection to bear against another piece for the purpose of imparting a special or eccentric movement to it.

camber
refers to the slight convexity of a member or part.

camera gun
also called an aircraft camera. It is a camera mounted in an aircraft in a machine gun frame and operated by a trigger. Its function is to make a photographic record of each shot, both in aerial target practice and in combat.

Cam Lock
the unofficial name of a single shot breech loading rifle and carbine issued to the U.S. Army after the Civil War and used as late as the Spanish American War. It is characterized by a top hinged breechblock locked by a cam piece at the right rear. This action extracts the fired case and leaves the chamber open for reloading.

camouflage (KAM a FLAHZH)
to disguise a place, person or thing to deceive an observer.

Camp Perry
the Ohio National Guard military reservation bordering Lake Erie at Port Clinton, Ohio. Camp Perry is the site of the annual National Matches.

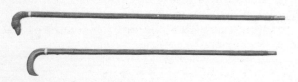

cane gun
a walking stick or cane having a bore from which a projectile may be fired. The handle carries the trigger mechanism, the trigger being concealed in some cane guns. Formerly made in quantity in Belgium, Great Britain and France for gamekeepers, naturalists and poachers.

canister
as used in military arms it is a metal cylinder containing metal fragments that scatter when the cylinder is broken by explosive means.

canister powders
powders made and suitable for a specified purpose and so called because they are generally packed by the manufacturer in tin cans holding one-half or one pound of such powder.

cannelure (KAN a loor)
the name given a circumferential groove in the cartridge case or projectile near its base. When in a cartridge case it is the extractor groove to facilitate the removal of the case from the chamber after firing. When in a bullet it acts as a lubrication groove, a receptacle for metal scraped off in passing through the barrel or as a groove into which the case is crimped to hold the bullet.

cannon
fixed or mobile artillery pieces classified as guns, mortars and howitzers. In general, calibers up to one inch are classified as small arms; 37 mm and greater as cannon. The 20 mm gun, famous as an aircraft cannon, being one of the exceptions.

cannon lock
a hand held or artillery weapon fired by placing a lighted coal, hot iron or hot wire to powder placed in a touch hole located over that portion of the barrel containing the propellent charge.

cant
the sidewise tilting of a gun. The effect is to cause a loss of accuracy which may be considerable at long ranges.

cap
1. in percussion guns a thimble shaped cup holding a small quantity of detonating powder placed

on a hollow steel nipple leading to the propelling charge. Patented for the first time in the U.S. in 1822.

2. a small quantity of high explosive used to set off the explosive charge in a projectile, fuze, mine, etc.

3. the nosepiece on a projectile.

cap and ball
referred to the cap lock percussion system that employed a cup, called a "cap", to hold the detonating powder. The projectile was usually a lead ball and hence the term "cap and ball".

cap lock
a percussion system for muzzle loaders using a cap containing a detonating powder.
See "cap"

capped bullet
a bullet that has a protective cap of harder metal over its nose.

capper
a container or magazine for holding a number of percussion caps and for facilitating the fixing of each upon the firearm nipple as needed.

cap screw
a screw usually inserted into a tapped hole like a machine screw but made in larger sizes and generally used for heavier work.

carbide tipped drills
machinist's high speed drill bits equipped with carbide tips to facilitate drilling in hardened steel.

carbine
a short barrelled musket or rifle whose barrel is generally not longer than 22". It is characterized by its light weight and was primarily intended for use by cavalrymen. Its name is derived from the short rifled firearm carried by the French cavalrymen or "carbinieres".

carbon
a chemical element whose chemical symbol is C. It is known in three forms, namely, diamond, graphite, and amorphous. Charcoal is in the amorphous form. Charcoal with sulphur and saltpeter (potassium nitrate) was used to make the first gunpowder. The amount of carbon in iron determines its qualities and the name by which it is called.

carbon dioxide
a colorless, odorless gas whose symbol is CO_2, not only used to extinguish fires but when compressed in capsules used to propel pellets from a gun.

carbon steel
a term commonly applied to steel containing no alloying metals to distinguish it from alloy steels containing tungsten, nickel, chromium or other metals. Made by refining molten pig iron, distinguished from cast iron by its malleability and lower carbon content. High grade carbon steels, such as those used in gunmaking, contain only about 1% carbon.

Carborondum
the registered trademark of The Carborundum Company for silicon carbide and other abrasives made by it.
See "trademarks"

carburizing
See "case harden"

Carcano
also known as the Mannlicher-Carcano, an official Italian Army rifle from 1891 to 1945, the first Italian smokeless powder rifle, caliber 6.5 mm, six shot repeater.

carnauba wax
a wax obtained from the Brazilian wax palm; used in making varnish, candles, etc. May be used in a mixture of turpentine and boiled linseed oil to make a finishing oil for gunstocks.

carreau *(kaa ROE)*

a type of "bolt", a huge spear-like projectile fired from early cannons. They were also used in launchers like the "espringale". Also known as a "garrot".
See "espringale"

carriage

a fixed or mobile support for a cannon. Frequently the word is applied to the carriage inclusive of the elevating and traversing mechanisms.

carrier

that part employed in repeating firearms having self contained magazines, that moves the cartridge from the magazine to a position directly in line with the chamber.

carrying strap

a strap made from leather, webbing, or other similar material and fastened to a rifle or shotgun for carrying purposes. A sling (see "sling strap") differs from a carrying strap in that it is made with a number of adjusting features that serve its function as a shooting aid. Slings are used by riflemen to steady their hold and aim; carrying straps are not particularly suited to this purpose.

cartridge

the complete assembly of a round of ammunition consisting of the primer, case, propellent powder and bullet. In the United States it is used in referring to such rounds used in small arms other than shotguns. Assembled rounds for shotguns are called "shells". In Great Britain the word is used to cover shotgun rounds as well as other assembled small arms rounds.

cartridge bag

a bag containing a propelling charge for use in certain cannon in which separate loading ammunition is used.
See "separate loading ammunition"

cartridge belt

a belt for wear on the person and having loops or pockets for carrying cartridges or clips of cartridges.

cartridge block

a block of wood or other material having recesses in its top surface in which cartridges may be placed to be readily available to a shooter for loading. Sometimes mounted on a small bore rifle to enable quick loading without disturbing the firing position or requiring undue movement by the shooter.

cartridge box

a box or pouch suspended from a belt, sling or harness in which to carry cartridges, usually in holes in a wooden block within the box. Used from the early days of firearms until displaced by improved carriers such as the cartridge belt.

cartridge brass

a sheet brass having the composition, 68 to 71% copper, and a maximum of .07% lead, .05% iron, .15% other materials and with zinc the remainder, according to A.S.T.M. specifications B19-29. Used for manufacturing cartridge cases. Each case manufacturer usually has slightly different specifications to meet a desired degree of toughness, hardness and other qualities.

cartridge case

the container that holds the propelling charge, and, in fixed ammunition (i.e. assembled rounds) it also holds the projectile and a primer. In addition to its accommodation of projectile, powder and primer it serves to act as a gas seal to prevent the rearward escape of powder gas. Made of copper, brass, steel, paper or plastic depending upon use, availability of materials and cost.

cartridge clip

in the strictest sense, a clip is a mechanical device that is designed to facilitate the loading of a number of shells into a magazine. The military frequently call this device a "stripper clip" — in Great Britain it is known as a "charger" or "charger clip". A cartridge-feeding device that contains a spring and follower is more correctly called a "magazine". However, over the years the more familiar term "clip" has attained a broader meaning, now encompassing all detachable cartridge feeding mechanisms.

cartridge stop

a device used in the feedway of certain belt fed weapons when blank cartridges are being used. It serves to hold the shorter blank cartridge in the proper position for feeding and also prevents the use of live ammunition. Used in conjunction with blank firing attachments.
See "blank firing attachment"

case

shortened term for cartridge case.
See "cartridge case"

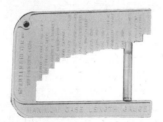

case gage, gauge

a jig-like tool that is used to check cartridge casings for length or diameter, or both. Manufacturers inspect newly made cases with such a device. The practice of reloading fired casings makes this tool especially important to handloading enthusiastics because brass casings tend to stretch under repeated firing and re-sizing. Handloaders check case lengths after each firing to determine when they must be shortened at the

neck. Failure to keep casings within specified minimum-maximum dimensions can lead to dangerous operating pressures. Small bore target shooters often use a special form of case gage designed to measure only the head diameter and rim-thickness of the .22 Long Rifle cartridge. By matching cartridges with like dimensions, from the same "lot" (see "lot number") of ammunition, they minimize variables and are reasonably assured of a consistent standard of performance from shot-to-shot.

case harden

(sometimes referred to as "case-carburizing", "carburizing" or "cementation").

the formation of a very hard carbon-steel "skin", "shell" or "case" to the outer surface of wrought iron, malleable iron or carbon steel by treatment with a carbon-rich medium under high temperatures. The depth of the resultant "skin" or "case" generally varies between .005" to .007". In gun making the carbon-rich medium, called a carbonizing agent, most often consists of a form of animal charcoal, such as, bone-dust, charred horn, or charred leather. Case-hardening is generally used only on gun parts that are vulnerable to surface wear.
See "Carbonizing agent"

case head

the head or base of a cartridge case; that portion of the casing into which the primer is fitted.

case life

refers to the number of firings a given case can be subjected to if repeatedly reloaded. When a brass casing is worked hard it tends to thin and elongate rapidly, at the same time acquiring an undesirable degree of hardness which leads to cracking or splitting.
To prolong case life the reloader tries to minimize re-sizing operations, working the case only as much as absolutely necessary to stay within prescribed dimensional limits. Case life can also be prolonged by timely annealing of the case neck which is subject to the most pronounced dimensional change.

case shot
a container holding a number of small projectiles.

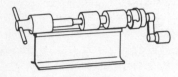

case trimmer
a tool used for cutting back the necks of cartridge cases that have been lengthened beyond prescribed dimensions through repeated firing and reloading.

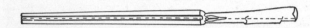

cast
1. the offset of the butt of a gun from the longitudinal center line of the gun. When the offset is to the right, for right hand shooters it is called cast-off. When to the left for left hand shooters it is called cast on.

2. to form a substance by pouring it into a mold and removing it after it has hardened such as forming a bullet by pouring liquified lead into a mold and removing it after it has cooled.

cast bullets
bullets made by casting a lead alloy in a mold. The lead used is often melted with small amounts of tin or antimony depending upon the degree of hardness desired. Cast bullets are used in low velocity weapons because the heat and pressures generated by high velocity cartridges tends to melt or deform them before they clear the barrel. A hard alloy cup, called a gas check, fitted to the base of a lead bullet, tends to protect it from heat and pressure and permits some increase in powder charge and resultant velocity. However, these pressures and velocities are still far below those employed in propelling fully jacketed bullets. Cast bullets are most often sized and lubricated after casting.

casting
may refer to the process of making a part by pouring or forcing molten metal into a mold or die, or to a part so made.

cast iron
an iron containing so much carbon that it is not malleable at any temperature. It may contain from 2% to 5% of carbon but commercial cast iron usually has from 3% to 4% of carbon. Cast iron cannot be tempered.

cast-off
a term applied to the shape of shotgun stocks. It is the slight offset of ¼″ or more of the butt to the right of the center line of the gun to accommodate a right handed shooter. When it is offset to the left it is called "cast-on".

cast-on
a term applied to the shape of shotgun stocks. It is the slight offset of the butt to the left of the center line of the gun to accommodate a left handed shooter. When it is offset to the right it is called "cast-off".

catapult
in ancient days a machine for hurling stones, etc. horizontally. Today it refers to a device for launching planes from the deck of a ship using compressed air or gunpowder as the force to give flying speed to a plane.

catch, safety
See "safety catch"

cavity
1. a hollow place in shaped charges of high explosives.

2. the interior of a projectile filled with high explosive.

3. the open nose of hollow point bullets.

4. the recess or recesses in a mold in which the desired product is cast.

CB cap

a .22 caliber rimfire cartridge similar to the BB cap and Flobert cartridge but made with a conical bullet. In CB cap cartridges the bullet is propelled either by a light powder charge or by the priming mixture alone.

cease firing, cease fire

the command or signal to stop shooting.

cement

a substance used in a soft state to adhere to bodies afterwards becoming hard to unite them. Cements for uniting metal, wood, and other materials are commercially available and find use in the manufacture and repair of certain firearms parts and accessories.

cementation

See "case harden"

center-fire

refers to a center-fire cartridge whose primer is located in the center of the base of the case, as distinguished from rimfire.

center of dispersion

it is the theoretical center of all the hits that would be made by firing an unlimited number of shots with the same firing data. Actually it is the center of impact of all shots already fired.

center of gravity

the point in a body at which it is assumed that gravity acts as a single force on the body. The location of the center of gravity of a gun effects its carrying, mounting and behavior when fired.

center of impact

the center of a shot pattern in a target made by a series of rounds fired with the same firing data or from a machine rest.

centigrade

pertaining to a thermometer, is one on which the temperature range between the freezing and boiling points of water is divided into 100 equal degrees. Freezing temperature of zero degrees on a centigrade thermometer is equivalent to 32 degrees on the Fahrenheit thermometer. The centigrade thermometer is used throughout the world for scientific work. The abbreviation for Centigrade is "C".

centimeter, centimetre

a unit of measure in the metric system, being one hundredth of a meter and equal to .3937 inches. One centimeter equals ten millimeters.

Cerrolow

a trademark for an alloy of bismuth, lead, tin, cadmium and indium having a melting point of 117°F. It has a negligible growth and shrinkage factor and has been used to make barrel casts from the muzzle end of rifles and pistols and from the breech on revolvers.

C.F.

abbreviation for center fire cartridge.

chain shot

a pair of projectiles, round or half round, joined by a short length of chain. Used in sea warfare in the days of sail and wooden ships.

challenge

the privilege given a competitive shooter to protest against what he feels are errors or rule infractions. A challenge calls for an impartial ruling by a person, or persons in authority. Most frequently employed in questioning the scoring of a given shot that is critically placed between two scoring values.

chamber

the enlarged part of the bore of a gun in which the charge is placed. In a revolver it is each of the openings in the cylinder; in most rifles and automatic weapons it is the rearmost part of the bore; in a cannon it is part of the breech.

chamber piece

the forerunner of the cartridge, employed in matchlock weapons to facilitate quick loading. It was a steel case holding powder, wad and ball, inserted at the breech.

chamber pressure

the pressure exerted in the chamber of a gun by the force of the expanding gases of the propellent powder. Sometimes improperly called breech pressure.

chamber reamer

a cutting tool used to form the chamber area of a barrel bore. This is usually a two-step operation calling for the use of a rough reamer and a finishing reamer.

chamfer

1. to bevel.

2. a bevelled surface as between the chamber and the bullet throat in a pistol or revolver.

charcoal

is the chemical element carbon in amorphous form. It was combined with sulphur and potassium nitrate (saltpeter) to make the first gunpowder.

charge

the explosive used to give propelling or bursting effect to a projectile. A "propelling charge" discharges the projectile from a gun; a "bursting charge" within the projectile causes it to fly apart to produce demolition, fragmentation, or chemical action.

charger

the term used in Great Britain for a cartridge clip.

Chassepot, Antoine Alphonse *(1833-1905)*

a French gunmaker and inventor. Best known as inventor of the Chassepot needle gun, a bolt action, breechloading rifle adopted by the French Army in 1866.

Chassepot rifle

an 11 mm needle fire percussion lock rifle brought out by the French in 1866 based on the Dreyse Needle Gun design, but characterized by having an obturator of India rubber on the forward face of the bolt and the primer in the head of the paper cartridge.

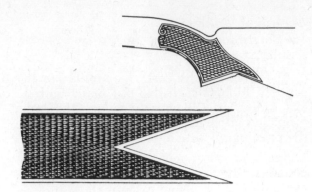

checkering

the roughened gripping surfaces of a wooden stock that serve ornamental as well as functional purposes. Checkering is made by filing the wood into diamond-like pointed pyramids within a specifically bordered pattern. The number of lines-to-the-inch determines the density of the pattern: the more lines to the inch, the finer and more desirable is the pattern. Many other forms of grip decoration are often used, such as, stippling, flat veining, etc., and these are sometimes erroneously referred to as "checkering" as well.

checkering cradle

a frame having vertical end supports between which a gun stock may be held while its gripping surfaces are being checkered.

checkering tools

the hand tools used for filing checkering patterns in wooden stocks.

cheek, cheekpiece

that part of the stock of a long gun designed to support the face of the shooter in proper aiming position.

chemical analysis

the determination of the constituent elements of a substance. If only the elements are identified it is called a qualitative analysis, if the percentage of each element is also determined it is called a quantitative analysis. For example if an analysis of brass in a cartridge case shows the presence of copper and zinc it is a qualitative analysis; if it shows that it contains 70 per cent of copper and 30 per cent of zinc it is a quantitative analysis.

cherry

1. a milling cutter for making circular or spherical impressions in dies. Used by manufacturers in making bullet molds.

2. a timber tree, sometimes known as a black cherry tree, (genus Padus serotina). Cherry wood is highly valued in the manufacture of furniture and is occasionally used in making gun stocks.

chilled shot

also called "high antimony shot" made of lead with antimony added to harden the pellets. It has replaced the drop shot made of lead only.

chisel, wood

a metal tool having a cutting edge at the end of a blade for shaping wood. Wood chisels come in many forms, those in greatest use by gunmakers are the corner, butt, firmer, carving, gouge and bottoming chisels.

choke

the muzzle constriction in the bore of a shotgun barrel that serves to condense the shot pattern.

For purposes of identification various degrees of constriction are given choke ratings, as follows:

AMERICAN CHOKES	DEGREE OF CONSTRICTION IN POINTS*	EUROPEAN EQUIVALENTS	TYPICAL EUROPEAN BARREL MARKS
cylinder bore	(no constriction)	cylinder bore	(CL)
improved-cylinder	5 to 10	¼ choke	(****)
modified	20	½ choke	(***)
improved modified	30	3/4 choke	(**)
full choke	40	Full	(*)

one point is equivalent to one-thousandth of an inch.

This table gives *approximate* choke values because there are no hard and fast rules for bore and choke sizes. The result is that slight variations will be found from one manufacturer to another and often from one gun to another within a given model. This is especially true where skeet chokes are concerned; the terms Skeet #1 and Skeet #2 may denote any degree of constriction between cylinder bore and improved cylinder.

Length of choke (taking into consideration the cone and parallel sections) also varies according to the taste of the individual manufacturer. The following table generally applies:

CHOKE	LENGTH
full	2½ inches
improved modified	1⅞ inches
modified	1¼ inches
improved-cylinder	⅝ th inches
skeet	⅝ th inches
cylinder	0

chokebore
the bore of a shotgun provided with a choke. See "choke"

choke, cut
See "cut choke"

choke, jug
See "jug choke"

choke reamer
a cutting tool, not unlike a drill bit, with long tapered cutting edges of a size to cut metal from the choke portion of shotgun bore.

choke, swaged
See "swaged choke"

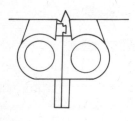

chopper lump
an English term for a barrel-making technique that forms the locking lugs (for a double barrel shotgun) as an integral part of the barrels. Generally, side by side shotgun barrels are made with a lug assembly that is brazed or soldered to the underside of the barrels. Chopper lump construction is believed to be stronger.

chord
a straight line joining two points that lie on a curve. Thus the straight line that forms the base of the curved path of a projectile is a chord.

chrome molybdenum steel
   (mo LIB da num)
an alloy steel containing chromium and molybdenum, used in the manufacture of better grade gun barrels. Chrome molybdenum steel has a very high melting point and is particularly desirable for barrels that are to be subjected to soldering (as when fitting ribs, etc.) Familiarly referred to as "chrome-molly".

chrome plating
depositing by electroplating, a protective and ornamental coating of the metallic element chrome on a metal surface. The coating produced is almost as hard as diamond and highly resistant to corrosion. The bores of some gun barrels and other gun parts subject to extreme wear have been plated to secure those qualities.

chrome steel
a high carbon steel alloyed with chromium, also called chromium steel. The chromium increases the hardness of steel making it useful for both armor and armor piercing projectiles.

chromium
is a steel gray, very hard but brittle corrosion resistant metal element whose chemical symbol is Cr. Alloyed with steel it imparts hardness and toughness to it, causing it to be used for armor plate and other ordnance and weapons manufacture where those qualities are desired. To prolong barrel life, chrome plating of the bore has been resorted to.

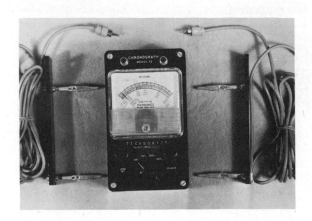

chronograph
an electronic instrument used to measure the velocities of projectiles. It measures and records small intervals of time. The first chronograph was invented by Captain Paul le Boulenge of the Belgium Army.

chronograph grid
See "chronograph screen"

chronographing
measuring the velocity of a projectile by the use of a chronograph.

chronograph screen

or grid, the circuit-completing wire cords or plates which, wired to the chronograph, are placed at precisely measured distances in the bullets path. A chronograph employs two screens: when the first is penetrated the chronograph starts the timing sequence; when the same bullet penetrates the second screen (which is positioned a specific distance behind the first) timing stops and the operator can then calculate the speed of that particular shot. New screens are required for each shot.

classification of guns

guns are classified in numerous ways to distinguish them by period of development, size, ignition systems, loading methods, uses, etc.

clay target

a circular disc of frangible material, such as hardened clay, scaled through the air by a launching device called a "trap", to provide a flying target as used in skeet or trap shooting. Regulation targets must measure no more than four and five-sixteenths (4 5/16th) inches in diameter nor more than one and one-eighth (1⅛) inches in height, and must weigh 3.5 ounces, however a variation of up to 5% is allowable in weight. First clay pigeon target patented in 1880 in the U. S. by George Likowsky. First trap shooting clay pigeons June 12, 1900 in the U. S. in Queens, New York.

clean

a colloquialism employed by target shooters to denote a perfect score.

cleaning bolt

a cleaning device usually employed only for .22 caliber match rifles. Made of metal or hardwood it fits into the receiver in place of the regular bolt, extending into the chamber up to the neck of the chamber in the case of center fire rifles and only to the barrel breech in the case of rim fire rifles. A hole having the same diameter as the bore of the rifle and coaxial with it, extends

the length of the bolt. Purpose of the cleaning bolt is to permit a cleaning rod to pass thru it and the bore of the barrel without rubbing the bore just ahead of the chamber.
See "muzzle guard"

cleaning brush

a brush or pad on a rod, cable or string, used to clean the bore of a firearm.

cleaning patches

square or round pieces of absorbent material (usually flannel) of appropriate size and weight of material for use with cleaning rods to clean the bore of a gun.

cleaning rod

a rod having a brush, cloth or other attachment at one end, for cleaning the bore of a gun barrel. A one piece stainless steel rod at least 6" longer than the combined length of the barrel and receiver and having a rotatable handle is considered ideal as a cleaning rod for rifles and handguns. For shotguns of 20 gauge and larger a wooden rod is considered satisfactory.

clear

to make certain no ammunition remains in a gun or to remove stoppages that interfere with the firing of a gun.

clearance

in the manufacture of a firearm is the space allowed between the moving parts of a gun as for example between the bore of a gun and the cartridge. It may also refer to the elevation of a gun at such an angle that when fired its projectile will not strike an obstacle between the muzzle and the target.
See "angle of clearance"

clearing block

a wooden block placed between the bolt and the rear of the barrel of an automatic weapon to prevent closing of the action and to show that the gun is unloaded.

clinometer

an instrument for accurately measuring vertical angles such as the angle of elevation of a gun.

clip

See "cartridge clip"

clip guides

slots let into the sides, barrel extension, or receiver to permit the insertion of the edges of a cartridge clip and firmly engage it for loading. Sometimes called "ears" in gunsmith's jargon.

clip loading machine

a machine for loading cartridges into a clip.

clock-face method

See "clock method"

clock method

a method for designating direction from a central point that uses an imaginary clock face as a reference. Thus to call a shot the center of the target is considered the center of an imaginary clock face and the hit, if directly above is at 12 o'clock, if directly to the right, at 3 o'clock. To refer to wind direction the observer is at the center of the imaginary clock, so that if the wind comes from the right it is called a 3 o'clock wind. It is also called the clock-face method or the clock system.

clock system

See "clock method"

closed-breech action

in a firearm is one in which the bolt or breech-block is closed with a cartridge seated in the chamber immediately ahead of it. The M14 and M16 rifles are examples of firearms having such an action.

cm

abbreviation for centimeter.

CO_2

the chemical symbol for carbon dioxide.

coach

an instructor or one to whom an instructor in firearms has delegated certain duties in target shooting.
See "coach and pupil method"

coach and pupil method

a method of training in the use of firearms whereby pupils are paired off with each one of a pair alternating in teaching the other or in performing some observations as may be prescribed by the instructor.

coarse sight

an adjustment of the sight of a gun so that a part of the front sight is visible through the notch in the rear sight. This is in contrast with a fine sight or a full sight.

coated lens

an optical glass lens coated with a material that enhances light transmission qualities.
See "lens coating"

coated shot

lead shot that has been coated with copper by electroplating to make it harder and less likely to lead the bore.

Cochran

a breech loading rifle considered an oddity, having a turret type revolving cylinder usually with 7 or 8 chambers for feeding paper cartridges to the receiver. Invented by John W. Cochran and made by the firm of Allen and Cochran in the mid 19th century.

cock

the condition of a gun when it is ready to fire, or, the act of putting it into such condition. Thus in a gun having a hammer, it is in a pulled back position, ready to fire. A half-cock position is one in which the hammer is mechanically held in a less than full cock position and unable to fire. In early days it referred to the predecessor of the hammer.

cocking indicator

a pin projecting from certain rifles, shotguns, combination rifle-shotguns, and semiautomatic pistols to indicate by sight and touch that the hammer is cocked. Also called a signal pin.

cocking lever

a mechanical part of the firing mechanism of certain guns that moves the firing pin back into firing position preparatory to firing the gun.

cocking piece

the rearward extension of a striker or firing pin that, in some guns, extends from the rear face of the receiver or barrel extension, external of the gun so it may be grasped and pulled back to cock the gun.

cocobolo

a colorful South American wood that is frequently used in making decorative forend tips and pistol grip caps for gunstocks.

coefficient

in general is a number by which some other number is multiplied and in physics is a number that expresses the amount of change or effect under certain conditions of length, temperature, etc.
See "coefficient of expansion"

coefficient of expansion

in the case of linear expansion it is the number that represents the amount of expansion per unit of length due to each increase of one degree in temperature. The coefficient of cubical or volumetric expansion is the number that represents the amount of expansion per unit of volume for each degree of increase in temperature. In each case if given the coefficient of expansion it must be known if it is based on the Centigrade or the Fahrenheit temperature scale.
See "expansion"

coefficient of form

a term used in the science of ballistics. It is a number that serves as an index to the shape of the point of a given projectile. Generally, the sharper the point, that is its shape from point to maximum diameter, the more efficient it is.
See "ballistic coefficient"

coffee mill carbine

a Sharp's carbine provided with a coffee mill, with a detachable handle in its butt, assembled during the Civil War at the U.S. Arsenal in St. Louis. It was intended that one be issued in each company of soldiers. Relatively few were so altered.

cold drawing

the process of drawing cold metal bars of round, square or hexagonal cross section through dies to improve the physical properties of their surfaces and produce bars of accurate dimensions.

cold forging

a process by which a metal block is squeezed down to the desired shape. Used in making odd shaped metal gun parts.

cold rolled steel

steel that has been passed through rolling mills while cold, resulting among other advantages in producing a so-called "bright" finish as contrasted with the oxide scale formed when steel is rolled hot.

cold weather lubricant

See "lubricant, cold weather"

collar

a band or ring used as a spacer or to limit motion.

Collier, Elisha H.

an American gunmaker and inventor who had to take his flintlock rifle, chambered like a revolver, to England to obtain recognition. He was granted a British patent in 1818. His action was also used in shotguns and in pistols and later made in caplock and pill lock.

collimate *(COL i mate)*

to bring the line of sight of a gun parallel with the axis of the gun barrel. In the case of binoculars it means bringing the two telescopes into optically parallel relationship.

collimation

the state of having the line of sight of a gun parallel with the axis of the gun barrel or in having two telescopes or binoculars optically parallel.

collimator

an optical device used to aline the sights of a gun with the vertical plane through the axis of the bore. It can be moved in elevation independently of the gun, so that it can be kept sighted on an aiming point.

color case hardening

a process for the surface hardening of steel that results in a decorative mottled-color finish. This finish is attained by packing the component into a steel box together with a generous amount of charred bone, then heating the entire unit to a temperature of approximately 1400°F for two hours or more. Upon removal from the heating ovens the part is quenched quickly in cool, soft water. A marbleized red-yellow-blue color results. See "case harden"

Colt

the trademark of Colt's Inc. for its firearms, the first having been the single action revolver invented by Samuel Colt.

Colt, Samuel *(1814-1862)*

an American designer and manufacturer of firearms. Best known for his revolver design, the original having been patented in the U. S. in 1836, in England in 1835. It was the first practical gun with a cylinder that was revolved and locked by the action of cocking the hammer.

comb

the crest or topmost ridge portion of the stock of a rifle or shotgun. That portion of a gun stock upon which the shooter's cheek rests.

combat arm

1. a branch of military service whose basic function is to engage in actual fighting with an enemy.

2. a firearm designed specifically for military or police combat purposes.

combat course

1. a military infantry training course given to simulate combat conditions.

2. a particular course of fire practiced by law enforcement personnel.

combination gun

a firearm made to handle more than one size of ammunition. Generally accomplished in an over-and-under styling with two barrels of different caliber. In Europe, combination guns are popular when made with one rifle barrel in conjunction with one or two shotgun barrels. In the latter instance, a three-barrelled gun is the result and this is called a "Drilling" gun.

combustible

capable of combustion.

combustion

the chemical union of oxygen with other elements and compounds usually at such a rate that flame and heat are produced. When it is extremely rapid it is called an explosion; when the union is slow it is called oxidation.

commence firing
the command or signal to begin shooting at once.

comparison microscope
an arrangement in one assembly of two microscopes with an optical bridge between them so one-half of the field seen by a viewer comes from one microscope, the other half from the other microscope. First used in firearms identification procedures in April of 1925.

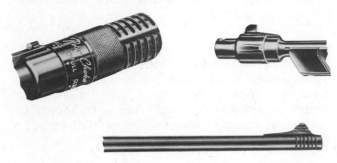

compensator
a muzzle brake commonly used on cannon, now often used on some types of shotguns and automatic weapons to reduce the upward jump of the muzzle as well as recoil. It consists of a metal tube of bore slightly larger than the bullet or shot charge, screwed to the muzzle. Its wall has a series of openings at right angles to the bore, of selected patterns, designed to cause the muzzle blast to exert forward force in opposition to the backward recoil movement of the gun when it is fired. The Cutts Compensator is an example.

complete round
all of the ammunition components, such as the primer, the propelling charge, the cartridge case and the projectile, required to fire the gun once. When assembled as one unit it is termed a "fixed round"; "fixed ammunition"; "shot shell"; or "metallic ammunition". When loaded into a gun separately it is termed "separate loading ammunition".

component
an essential part of the whole, such as the trigger in a gun or any one of the numerous parts that make up a firearm.

concussion
the sudden and violent disturbance of the air caused by an explosion.

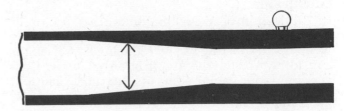

cone
1. the sloping portion of the rear of the choke at the muzzle of a shotgun.

2. the forcing cone in a shotgun barrel is sometimes merely called "cone".

cone of dispersion
the coneshaped pattern formed by the paths of a group of shots fired from a gun with the same sight setting. This pattern is caused by the variable factors such as, ammunition, wind changes, gun vibration, etc. Also called "cone of fire" and "sheaf of fire".

cone of fire
See "cone of dispersion"

conoidal bullet
a bullet that is cone shaped.

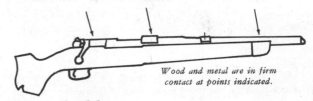

Wood and metal are in firm contact at points indicated.

contact bedding
(as opposed to "free floating") the practice of bedding a rifle in a stock so that a pressure contact is made between the wood and specific areas of the metal components. In bolt action rifles three specific points of the barrel and receiver assembly require this form of contact if the weapon is to function accurately. These are, 1 — the rearmost portion of the receiver, 2 — the point at which the barrel joins the receiver (including the area of the recoil lug) and, probably most important, 3 — the area of the forend tip. In "free floating" a barrel, only the receiver assembly makes firm contact with the wood.

continuous fire
fire conducted at a normal rate without interruption for adjustment corrections or other reasons.

conversion

the alteration of a gun to some other use or in method of operation. Conversion of military weapons to sporting use by reducing barrel length and alteration of the stock is an example. Conversion from percussion to cartridge ignition, another.
See "adapter"

conversion table

a chart or tabulation of figures that shows for one system of measurements the equivalents in another system of measurements. For example the metric equivalents of "inches" such as shown in the appendix of this book.

cook-off

a cartridge said to "cook-off" is one that is fired by the heat of the gun, a condition usually encountered with rapid firing military automatic weapons when the barrel is seriously overheated.

Cookson

a type of repeating flintlock that used a repeating system credited to a Florentine gunmaker in the mid 17th century, Michele Lorenzoni. A John Cookson made such a gun in England about 1670 — 1680 and a John Cookson, relationship unknown, made such guns in the American Colonies around 1756.

copper

a soft, ductile metal element whose chemical symbol is Cu, prized for its immunity to corrosion in the atmosphere and high electrical conductivity. It alloys freely with other metals, particularly zinc to form brass and, tin to form bronze. By suitable treatment it may be made very strong or very tough and malleable. Brass, an alloy of copper and zinc, is extensively used for cartridge cases and primer cups. Copper has been used to plate lead bullets of small caliber to prevent bore leading.

copper clad steel

a steel surface coated with copper by either alloying the copper to the steel by applying the copper in a molten state or by welding to the surface by applying in a plastic state.

copper hardening

as practiced by the ancients, consisted of cold

working the metal by hand hammering. Today in addition to the cold working method a second method exists, that of alloying the copper with any one of a number of other metals.

copper jacketed

a bullet made with a full copper jacket (occasionally having an exposed lead tip when made for hunting purposes).

copper sulfate

also called blue vitriol or bluestone, whose chemical symbol is $CuSO_4 \cdot 5H_2O$ is in the form of blue crystals soluble in water. It may be used for coppering objects (i.e. applying a thin coat or "wash" of copper) and in copper plating solutions.

cordite

a double base smokeless powder, slow burning, made of guncotton, nitroglycerin and mineral jelly, developed in Great Britain by following the footsteps of Alfred Noble's patented propellent "Ballistite". Originally made in a cord-like shape from which it got its name. Still used in modified form in Great Britain.

cord wick

a cord made from hemp and treated with slow burning chemicals used as the igniter on matchlock weapons.

core

the central part of a bullet, generally an alloy of lead.

corned powder

the early name given to gunpowder made of saltpeter, charcoal and sulphur, ground wet and formed into grains. This type followed the dust-like powder previously ground dry and called serpentine powder.

corrected azimuth

a term in usage with artillery fire: It is the azimuth from the gun to the target after making allowances for winds, condition of the gun, and other variable factors. Also called "corrected deflection".

corrected deflection

See "corrected azimuth"

corrected range

a term used in artillery firing. It is the actual range after allowances have been made for weather conditions, ammunition variation and other factors that cause departure from standard conditions. It is the range at which the projectile is calculated to hit the target.

correction

any changes made that depart from what are considered standard or ideal conditions to compensate for variable factors such as wind, temperature, wear, etc.

corrode

to eat away gradually such as by chemical action induced by humidity, presence of acids, etc. Modern ammunition with its noncorrosive primers and propellent powders has practically elimi nated corrosion from that source.
See "corrosion"

corrosion

the effect of corroding or corrosive agents. Moisture on metal parts of steel will cause rust to form and when rust is permitted to form, pits will develop causing a roughened surface. In the bore of a gun the passage of a bullet will be impeded, the shape of the bullet slightly deformed and fouling will increase. Companion evils are abrasion, erosion, fouling and leading.

corrosion resisting steels

are steels having in common a chromium content and corrosion resistant characteristics, commonly referred to as stainless steels.

corundum

an aluminum oxide found in nature in many variations, the gems ruby and sapphire being of the transparent variety while impure-granular and massive forms are known as emery. Corundum, as the term is generally used is neither, since it does not have the impurities found in emery and it possesses a larger percentage of crystalline alumina which gives cutting quality.

coslettizing

a process for rustproofing iron or steel in which the subject material is immersed in a bath of near-boiling phosphoric acid in which iron or zinc filings have been dissolved. The thickness of the protective coating thus provided depends upon the length of time the work remains immersed and may range from thirty minutes to three hours.

Cosmoline

the registered trademark of E. F. Houghton & Company for a liquid rust preventative cleaner and fingerprint neutralizer for use in protection of steel parts between processings on machine operations. Sometimes the term is improperly applied to a heavy grease used to coat firearms when prolonged storage is anticipated.

counterrecoil

the forward motion of a gun to return it to firing position after having moved backward due to recoil.

counterrecoil mechanism

the mechanical, hydraulic, or pneumatic system that returns a gun to proper firing position after recoil. Also called "recuperator" or "recuperator mechanism".

covered primer

a primer widely used in Europe in which the outer cup or face of the primer completely encloses the inner cup instead of leaving it exposed as in the American type. Generally refers to shotshell primers.

crack shot

a common expression for a proficient shooter.

cradle

a supporting framework for a gun of weight or size for which a tripod or bipod would be inadequate.
See "bipod" and "tripod"

cradle, gunstocker's

a device designed to hold a gunstock in a manner permitting rotational adjustment. Like a lathe in principle, most gunstocker's cradles are made with a center point that engages the leading surface of the forend and a clamping device that secures the butt. In this way the stock may be rotated a full 360° and, since it may be locked in any given position, the stockmaker has easy access to all stock surfaces.

crane

or yoke, being that part of a revolver having a swing-out-cylinder which is pivoted to the frame and upon which the cylinder and ejector rod are mounted.

crank

in some automatic pistols, a bent arm that, when the breech mechanism recoils, acts as a lever to compress the recoil spring housed in the grip. After the expanding propellent gases have lost their force the spring restores the action in its forward position and loads and locks the gun. Sometimes called a "bell crank".

crease

a line or mark made in the skin by a projectile, bomb, or shell fragment in flight, similar to that made by folding a pliable piece of material. Used to describe a slight wound.

creep

any small movement caused by looseness, wear or vibration in movable parts. This is a term especially applied to such a movement in the trigger of a gun.

crimp

the inward bend or lip of the mouth of a cartridge case to grip the bullet and hold it in place. In the case of a shotshell to hold the top wad

and thus the shot, in place, or to hold the base wad in position. A rolled crimp is one in which the mouth of the case is turned inward around its entire circumference. A star crimp or indent crimp is one in which a number of indents are formed in the circumference of the encircling mouth, or in the case of primers, the edge of the primer pocket.

crimped primer

(a misnomer) a term frequently used to describe a cartridge case having a crimped primer pocket. This crimp is stamped into the lip of the primer pocket when the primer is seated, the purpose being to lock the primer in place and facilitate water sealing. Found almost exclusively in military cartridges, this feature was recently discontinued by U.S. arsenals when it was found that lacquer sealing was adequate and that there was no real need to lock-fit primers.

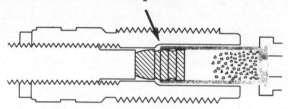

crimping chamber

that part of a cartridge loading die that serves to crimp the neck of the case around the bullet. This practice is often important to loading operations for pistol or revolver cartridges. Few rifle cartridges require bullet crimping — generally only those that are intended for use in tubular magazine guns where there exists some possibility that, under recoil, a cartridge will recess the bullet of the shell behind it.

crimping groove

the groove around an artillery projectile for crimping the cartridge case to the projectile. It is analogous to the cannelure in the jacket of a bullet.

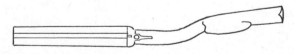

cripple stock

a stock offset to the right from the axis of the bore to permit a shooter to fire from his right shoulder while aiming with his left eye, or vice versa.

Crosman

Crosman Arms Co., Inc., manufacturers of CO_2 (gas) rifles and pistols, located in Fairport, New York.

crossbolt

a form of shotgun lock originally conceived by the W. W. Greener Company of London, England. A Greener type lock is identified by a top extension that protrudes from the chamber area of the barrels into a fitted recess in the face of the breech. The top lever of the action actuates a crossbolt that slides to the left (at right angles to the axis of the bore) and passes thru a hole or slot in the top extension. Some crossbolts are shaped like cylindrical pins while others are more or less bar-shaped. A properly fitted cross bolt does much to strengthen the locking mechanism of break open type firearms, however, too many cross bolts are not properly fitted — do not really engage the top extension — and are therefore really only ornamental.

cross-cut file

a file having one round edge with sides tapered toward the opposite edge and being single cut, that is single rows of parallel teeth extending across the face at an angle of from 65 to 85 degrees with the axis of the file. Used to file saw teeth and similar surfaces.

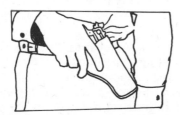

cross draw

the practice of using the opposite side hand in drawing a handgun from a holster, i.e. drawing a revolver holstered on the left hip with the right hand, or vice-versa.

cross fire

intersecting fire from two or more positions.

cross hairs

the crossed lines that a viewer sees in looking through a sighting telescope and which, centered on a target, establishes the line of sight. Cross-hairs have been made of hair, spider webs, fine platinum wire or other finely drawn material, almost invisible to the naked eye, mounted in the telescopic instrument on a ring called the reticle.

crossing target

a moving target that crosses the line of sight at any angle. A shooter must aim ahead of, or lead, the target so that the paths of the target and bullet will meet.

cross level

to level a weapon such as a mortar at right angles to the line of sight.

cross split bullet

a metal cased bullet having two slits in the jacket that criss cross the nose of the bullet for the purpose of improving its ability to expand on impact.

crosswind

a wind blowing at right angles to the intended flight line of a bullet: a three o'clock or nine o'clock wind direction. The most difficult wind direction for a shooter to cope with.

cross wires

See "cross hairs"

crotch figure

the generally outstanding, irregular, grain pattern common to a stock blank cut from the crotch of a tree.

crown

the bevelled edge common to the muzzle of a barrel.

crowning

the act of bevelling the edge of a barrel muzzle; a task that requires considerable care. A carelessly executed crowning job can ruin the performance of a rifle. By the same token, some rifles that give poor accuracy for inexplicable reasons, can often be corrected by simple cutting and re-crowning of the muzzle.

crusher gage

a mechanical means for holding a cylinder of copper or lead in juxtaposition to the chamber or bore of a gun to expose it to the gas pressure generated by a fired cartridge. The gas pressure compresses or crushes the cylinder and the cylinder being of known dimensions and composition the pressure can be computed from the amount the cylinder is compressed. Two types are in general use. In the United States the "radial" system; in England, the "oil case" system.

culverin

a two man hand cannon of the early 15th century (about 1430 to 1460) measuring about five or six feet in length of bore and firing only a .70 or .80 caliber ball. It was supported on the back or shoulder of one man called the collineator, or aimer, and fired by the incendiarius, or firer.

cup primer

an early primer that required a blunt nosed hammer to crush the rim of the cartridge where the priming mixture was contained. In limited use in the mid 19th century.

cupronickel *(COO pro NICK ell)*

a copper-nickel alloy and in the proportions of about 60 per cent copper and 40 per cent nickel formerly extensively used for bullet jackets. Largely replaced by gilding metal in the 1920's. Being white in appearance it was often called "German silver".

curvature

the condition or state of being curved such as the curvature of the trajectory of a projectile in flight.

curved barrel

a design for a military rifle perfected by the German Army in World War II for shooting around corners.

cut choke

a choke formed during manufacture of the barrel of a shotgun by a reamer during the final ream of the interior of the barrel.

cutlass pistol

a rare antique pistol made by Morrill & Blair and called Elgin's Patent Percussion Cutlass Pistol, having a 3-inch barrel, 12 inches overall length, and a 7-inch knife blade 1″ in width mounted beneath the barrel. The rear end of the blade serves as a trigger guard. The term is sometimes applied to any pistol having an attached knife.

cut-off

1. in the military sense, a mechanical device incorporated in certain automatic weapons to restrict them to semiautomatic or single-loader operation.

2. in the sporting sense, a mechanical device that is employed in tubular magazine guns so that only one shell will feed onto the carrier (or lifter) with each cycle of the breech mechanism.

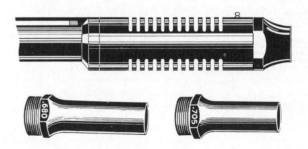

Cutts compensator

a muzzle attachment for shotguns made with a ventilated sleeve and designed to accept choking sleeves of various sizes interchangeably. In addition to providing the shooter with a selection of chokes for one barrel or gun, the Cutts compensator also serves as a recoil reducer. It is particularly popular among skeet shooters. Originally developed by Colonel Richard M. Cutts (USMC Ret.) as a muzzle depressor for the Browning Automatic Rifle and the Thompson Machine Gun. Manufacturing rights were acquired by the Lyman Gun Sight Company of Middlefield, Connecticut in 1929. The Lyman company has since manufactured and distributed the Cutts compensator for shotguns without interruption.

cyanide hardening

a very effective, quick, process for the hardening of small parts. Components are heated until red, dipped in powdered potassium cyanide, and quenched in clear water. For added hardness the part may be heated and dipped repeatedly before quenching. Potassium cyanide is a very deadly poison and cannot be allowed to enter the eyes, mouth or a break in the skin.

cycle

an interval of time in which a sequence of events is completed, such sequence reoccuring regularly. In automatic fire the sequence of events that make up one cycle are those which load, fire, extract and eject the empty case.

cyclic rate

the rate of automatic fire expressed in terms of shots per minute. The maximum rate of fire of an automatic weapon.

cyclic rate mechanism

also known as cyclic change mechanism. A device on an automatic gun, such as the Browning automatic rifle, by which the rate of fire can be controlled, to reduce or increase it.

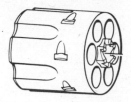

cylinder

the rotatable part of a revolver that chambers its cartridges and as it rotates, presents in succession, each of the cartridges for firing.

cylinder stop

the recesses in the outer, rear, surface of a revolver cylinder into which a lever, housed in this frame, is engaged to stop the rotation of the cylinder so that it is properly aligned with one chamber behind the barrel.

D

DA
abbreviation for double action.

dag
an old name for a short pistol, especially a wheel-lock. It was in use in England and Scotland in the 16th and 17th centuries being eventually displaced by the word "pistol".

dagger pistol
another name for a knife pistol.

damascene, damaskeen
is the finish given iron, steel or bronze by making furrows in the surface and then hammering a wire, usually gold, into them to form a decorative scroll or design. The term is often confused with "Damascus barrel" and with "Damascus steel", terms to which it bears no relationship.

Damascus barrel
also known as a "laminated" or "twist" barrel. Made of two or more rods or wires of iron and steel, called skelp, welded together, then rolled to form a ribbon and twisted about a mandrel with the abutting edges of the ribbon welded together. After withdrawing the mandrel the welded tube was finished inside and out to form the finished barrel. This method of making gun barrels appears to have started in the 16th century in the Near East.

Damascus steel
is characterized by having surface patterns of wavy parallel stripes or mottled patterns attributed to irregularly disposed carbon in the metal. It was produced in India and Persia and exported to Europe in the Middle Ages. Once thought to be the result of welding together rods or wires of dissimilar steels, as was done in the making of Damascus barrels.

danger flag
a bright red flag flown on firing ranges as a danger warning when firing is going on.

danger space
1. the space in which the trajectory of a small arms bullet does not rise above the average height of a man.

2. the space around the bursting point of a shell hazardous to personnel.

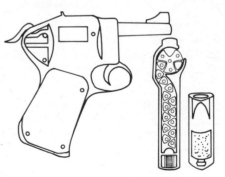

Dardick
the name of a unique cartridge and weapons system named for its inventor, David Dardick. Briefly manufactured and marketed in the mid 1950's by the Dardick Corporation of Hamden, Connecticut. The unusual design of the Dardick pistol, combining features common to the revolver and the automatic pistol, had a cylinder containing three compartments (chambers) fed by a 15-shell capacity clip-type magazine. The cartridge was made with a unique triangularly shaped plastic casing. Lack of commercial interest forced the closing of the Dardick plant after but a few years of operation.

An example of current Darne manufacture — a sliding breech shotgun.

Darne (DARN)

the name of Regis and Pierre Darne, French gunmakers and inventors, one of their first inventions being a gas operated, light weight machine gun developed during World War I. Today the name identifies firearms made in France by the Darne firm, in the town of St. Etienne.

datum

the basis for measurement or calculation such as datum plane which is taken as a plane of reference from which elevations are measured. Sea level is often used as such plane of reference.

deactivation

rendering an explosive shell or charge inert by removal of the priming element, such as the fuze or detonator. Also a term applied to the procedure followed in rendering a firearm incapable of performing its intended function.

dead shot

a colloquial expression for a shooter who always, or nearly always, hits what he aims at.

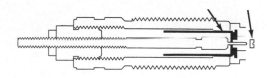

decapper

a tool that is used to remove spent primers from cartridge cases that are to be reloaded.

decibel (DES i bell)

a unit of measure used in evaluating sound levels. Measurement is made by a sound level meter. As an example of some measurements, a purring cat about 25 decibels, a quiet business office about 40 decibels, average street traffic approximately 100 feet away, from 60-70 decibels, a gunshot about 100 decibels, a boiler shop about 130 decibels, just below the limit of the endurance of the human ear.

decoy

a lure or bait designed to entice game into gunshot range. This term is most commonly associated with waterfowl hunting where artificial likenesses of ducks or geese are set out by the hunter to attract the birds. The likenesses are appropriately called "decoys".

definition

See "resolving power"

deflagration

an explosion whose power builds up smoothly and evenly as contrasted with "detonation".

deflection

the distance a hit is off target, to the right or to the left, due to wind, variations in ammunition or movement of gun or target. It also refers to the setting on the scale of a sight that allows for such conditions so that when the sight is aligned with the target the gun is pointed sufficiently far to the right or left of the target to cause it to be hit.

deflocculated graphite

is a lubricant comprising finely divided graphite suspended in water or oil, which prevents rusting of iron or steel.

degreasing

removal of grease, oil or other foreign matter from a firearm through washing in a cleansing agent, such as: boiling water, a solvent, or a 25% solution of hydrochloric acid. Degreasing is the first step in blueing or browning firearms.

degree

1. a unit of angular measure equal to 1/360 of a circle.

2. a unit of measurement for temperature which in the case of a Fahrenheit thermometer is 1/180 of the temperature range between the freezing and the boiling temperature of water. In the case of a Centigrade thermometer it is the unit of measurement for temperature which is 1/100 of such temperature range.

deliberate fire

a rate of fire slower than normal to permit better judgment of its effect and thereby to enable more precise sighting adjustment.

demolition

the act of demolishing or destroying, especially by explosives.

Demondion, Augustus

a French inventor who, in 1830, was granted a patent for a breech loader having a lifting breech block hinged at the front and what is considered to have been the forerunner of the successful pinfire cartridge.

density

of any substance whether solid, liquid or gas is the mass weight of that substance per unit volume. When, as in scientific circles, it is expressed in grams per cubic centimeter, the density will for all practical purposes be equal to the specific gravity.

density of loading

the ratio of the weight of the powder in a cartridge case to the weight of the powder the case can hold if filled to the base of a seated bullet, expressed in percent. There is authority for calculating the density of loading by taking the ratio of the weight of the powder charge to the weight of the amount of distilled water at 39.2 degrees Fahrenheit that would fill the powder chamber.

dent remover

a gunsmithing tool used to remove dents from shotgun barrels.

deplating

the act of removing a plated coating (such as nickel, chrome, or cadmium) from a metal such as steel. Because the removal of plating by polishing is generally slow and frequently results in damaged edges, most gunsmiths use a simple electro-chemical deplating process. This consists of sulphuric acid, distilled water, a glass tank, a storage battery, copper wires and a lead plate designed to act as a cathode. The work to be deplated serves as the anode.

depress

to lower the muzzle of a gun.

depression angle

See "angle of depression"

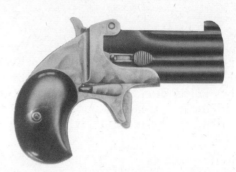

Deringer, Derringer *(DER in jer)*

1. a "Deringer" refers to any one of the guns made by Henry Deringer, Jr., a Philadelphia gunsmith. Originally a single barrel, muzzle loading percussion type pistol.

2. "Derringer", used by competitors of Deringer has come to mean all tip-open pocket pistols of short barrel and large caliber.

Deringer, Henry *(1786-1868)*

an American gunsmith and manufacturer of firearms. Made famous by the short single shot percussion pistol he first made in 1825, but which was never covered by patents issued to him.

descending branch

the path of a projectile in its descent from the highest point in its flight. The path from the muzzle up to the highest point is called the ascending branch.

desert ironwood

common to the American Southwestern desert, this is an extremely hard, durable wood, that is occasionally used in making forend tips and grip caps, etc., for gun stocks. Ironwood is heavy, has a deep brown-black color, and is most difficult to work.

detent

a catch, pawl, dog or similar piece that, generally under spring loading, engages a movable part and holds it in place until disengaged.

determinate error

an error of such a nature that its cause can be determined and appropriate allowance made for its effect.

deterrent

See "inhibitor"

detonate

to explode both suddenly and violently.

detonating agent

an explosive capable of being detonated and used to set off another explosive, also called a detonating charge; fulminate of mercury and tetryl are examples.

detonating explosive

See "high explosive"

detonation

an explosion that is sudden, violent and practically instantaneous. A slower action is called a "deflagration".
See "deflagration"

detonation wave

See "burst wave"

detonator

1. the name given in past years to a gun fired by a percussion cap.

2. a device or charge used to set off the main charge in a projectile, mine, bomb, etc.

deviation

the distance of a hit from the target expressed as an angle or by linear measurement.

diameter

1. any chord passing through the center of a figure or body.

2. the length of a straight line passing through the center of a figure or body.

3. the diameters most often a subject for firearms users are barrel, bore, bullet, lead, neck, rim.

diaphragm

in optics, is a plate having a hole in it, or a ring, placed in an optical instrument to control the amount of light passing through it.

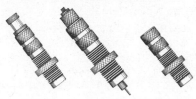

die

a tool used to size or form an object or material. Used in hand loading of ammunition to size cases and bullets, seat bullets, etc.

die casting

is the casting of molten metal under pressure in a metal mold or die.

diffraction

an apparent disturbance or modification in a light's rays caused when passing close to reflective surfaces, opaque bodies, or through narrow slits.

Dimick, Horace E. *(circa 1811-1873)*

an American gunsmith and manufacturer who furnished many firearms used in the winning of the West.

diopter, dioptre

a unit of measure used to indicate the power of a lens. It is equal to the reciprocal of the focal length in meters.

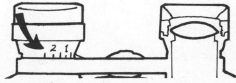

diopter scale

a focusing scale — such as that often found on one of the eyepieces of a binocular — which serves to indicate the degree of convergence or divergence of the light rays emerging from the optical instrument.

diphenylamine test
See "paraffin test"

direct fire
an artillery firing term describing fire in which the sights of a gun are brought in direct line with the target. Also called fire by direct laying.

direct hit
a perfect hit on the target. Also called a "bull's eye".

Director of Civilian Marksmanship
a commissioned officer of the Army or of the Marine Corps detailed by the President of the United States to serve as such under the direction of the Secretary of the Army.

direct pointing
an artillery term akin to "direct firing" describing the pointing of a gun in direction or in both range and direction by means of a sight directed at the target.

disappearing target
a target that is exposed to the view of a shooter for a short, timed, period. A bobbing target is a type of disappearing target.

disarm
1. render a gun or explosive device impotent.

2. take away the weapon of an opponent.

disassemble
to take apart a firearm for cleaning or repair. To "take down" a gun is to disassemble it.

discharge
to cause a weapon to fire.

disconnector
a mechanical feature of an automatic pistol which prevents the gun from being fired unless the action is entirely closed, and prevents the firing of more than one shot for each pull of the trigger.

disc primer
a tiny copper disc containing fulminate exploded by the fall of a hammer to ignite a propellent charge. Invented by Christian Sharps in 1852.

dispersion
a scattered pattern of shots fired from the same gun with the same firing data.

dispersion error
the variation in a series of shots fired from the same gun under firing conditions kept as constant as possible. In practice the dispersion error of a shot is considered the distance to that shot from the center of impact.

dispersion ladder
a tabulation showing the probable distribution of a series of shots made with the same firing data, usually in percentages of shots falling in several zones.

dispersion zone
the area over which shots scatter when fired with the same sight setting.

displode, displosion
to explode or strike apart with violence. Rarely used in reference to weaponry.

distinguished marksman
a soldier who has won three badges or medals for rifle fire in competitions designated by the Department of the Army.

distinguished pistol shot
a soldier who has won three badges or medals for pistol fire in competitions designated by the Department of the Army.

doghead
the vise-like device on a flintlock hammer (i.e. cock) used to hold the flint in place. Also known as "jaws".

dog lock
an improved English lock which had a safety or dog catch to secure the half cock position when the shooter so desired. Many variations have appeared since about 1600 and for about 250 years thereafter.

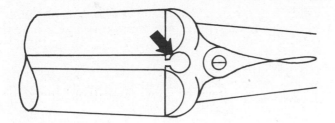

doll's head extension

a form of "top extension" made with a circular tapered knob which fits into a corresponding recess in the top of the action. A very efficient form of lock for double barrel shotguns and other similar hinged barrel weapons.
See "top extension"

dot reticle

a reticle that instead of having visible cross wires has invisible wires that have a visible dot at their intersection to serve as a sight guide. Some riflescope manufacturers combine the dot reticle with the conventional cross wire reticle, in which case the cross wires are visible. Dot reticles of specific "minute-value" in size may be used for range estimation purposes.

double, doubles

1. in target shooting two bullet holes that overlap and appear to be but one bullet hole.

2. in trap or skeet shooting, when two targets are thrown simultaneously.

3. a malfunction in a double barrel or over and under gun that results in both barrels firing at precisely the same time.
See "doubling"

double action

that type of firing action whereby a single squeeze of the trigger both cocks and fires the weapon. It is employed in revolvers and old types of rifles and shotguns. It contrasts with single action which requires the hammer to be cocked by hand prior to firing by a squeeze of the trigger.
See "single action"

double barrel

a firearm having two barrels; generally used in referring to side by side twin barrelled shotguns but could also appropriately refer to any two-barrelled gun, regardless of barrel positions, such as an over & under gun.

double base powder

produced by dissolving nitrocellulose (gun-cotton) in nitroglycerin and forming the resulting colloid into granules, flakes or cylinders. Also called nitroglycerin powder. Used as a propellent powder. It derives its name from the use of both nitrocellulose and nitroglycerin. Single base powder has only nitrocellulose as its base.

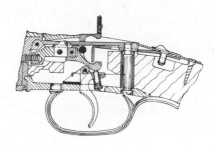

double pull trigger

so called because the design requires slack to be taken up in squeezing the trigger before the firing stage is reached. Used mainly on military rifles for reasons of safety.

double recoil

1. is produced when both barrels of a double barrelled shotgun are fired simultaneously.

2. normally a single shot produces two recoils in succession. The first is the initial recoil that occurs before the bullet or shot charge leaves the gun and moves the gun very slightly to the rear. The second occurs just after the bullet or shot charge leaves the muzzle and produces the violent effect on the shooter.

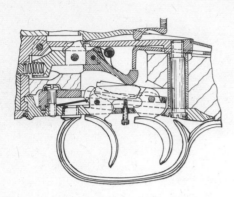

double set trigger

two triggers mounted together in such a fashion that pressure on one trigger will so engage the sear that a slight touch on the second trigger will fire the gun. This is a trigger system that has long been popular in Europe and has just recently started to gain acceptance in the U.S. Double set triggers are ideally suited to shooting at moving targets where precisely timed trigger let-off is essential. Generally, the rear trigger is the "setting trigger", and the front trigger the "firing trigger".

doubling

a term applied in shotgun shooting when inadvertently the shooter pulls the trigger a second time immediately after the first shot or simultaneously pulls both triggers of a double barrel gun equipped with two triggers. Also applicable in the case of a semiautomatic weapon that fires two or more shots with only one continuing pressure on the trigger, a condition arising when the disconnector fails to function properly.

doughnut pattern

a shotgun pattern distributed around a hole in its center usually caused by interference of the top wad of the fired shotshell. Common to roll crimped shotshells which are now almost entirely phased out of commercial production.

dovetail

a milled, tapered slot cut into metal to facilitate the fastening of a second member. For example, the dovetail slot found at the muzzle of some rifles, into which the front sight is anchored.

dowel

a pin fitting into a matching hole in an abutting piece to prevent motion or slipping.

downwind

the direction toward which the wind is blowing, the leeward.

drag

the resistance offered by air to movement of an object through it. Rarely used in describing air resistance to the flight of a projectile.

dragoon

an obsolete word for a short musket, sometimes spelled "dragon". More popularly used as a name for a cavalryman armed with a short musket.

drams equivalent

an expression that is used to equate the ballistics of a certain charge of smokeless powder to a certain weighed charge of black powder. Before smokeless powder came into being shotgun shells were loaded with black powder. At that time, manufacturers developed a system for labelling boxes of shells to show the weight of the powder charge together with the weight and size of the shot charge. Thus, a box marked "3¼ - 1⅛ - 8" would contain shells loaded with 3¼ drams of black powder and 1⅛ ounces of lead shot, size 8. In spite of the fact that black powder is now obsolete, this labelling procedure is still employed because shotgunners use it to determine the effectiveness of a particular shell. Today, shotshells are loaded with smokeless powder and boxes are marked to show what a given smokeless charge is EQUIVALENT TO in the old dram rating. It must be remembered that smokeless powder is measured in GRAINS and that a very small amount is equal to a much heavier charge of black powder. To load a shell with 3¼ drams of smokeless powder could prove disastrous.

draw

to pull a handgun from its holster.

draw mark

a straight scratch running lengthwise on a cartridge case caused by a foreign substance in the drawing dies.

Dreyse, Johann Nickolaus von,
(DRY zeh)(1787-1867)
a German gunmaker and inventor who developed
the famous Dreyse Needle Gun.

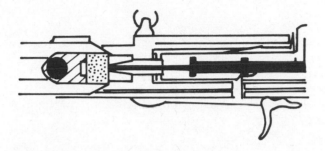

Dreyse needle gun *(DRY zeh)*
a single shot percussion lock rifle having a breech
loading action called the "slide system" but actually by today's standards a bolt system. Developed by Nicholas Dreyse, its bolt contained a long
needle that, when activated, penetrated the paper
cartridge, passed thru the propellent powder,
and detonated the primer which was attached
to the base of the bullet. In 1840 the .607 caliber
Dreyse, called the Zundnadelgewehr was adopted
by the Prussian Army. Its successor models remained standards in that army until after the
Franco-Prussian War.

drift
the amount of shift of a projectile to one side
or the other due to its rotation in flight or air
resistance. If the bore of a rifle is rifled with a
right hand twist the drift is slightly to the right.
If rifled with a left hand twist the drift is slightly
to the left.

drift slide
the movable piece within the frame of a leaf
sight that is pierced and notched to constitute
the rear sight of a rifle and which, when raised
to a position opposite the desired range grada-
tion on the scale of the sight, moves not only
upward but slightly sideward to compensate for
drift at such range.

drill ammunition
dummy ammunition used in practice and in drill.

Drilling
a three-barrelled gun popular in Europe in which
a combination of smoothbore and rifled barrels
is used. The most common form of Drilling gun
is made with two shotgun barrels of 16 gauge
over a single rifle barrel of 8 MM caliber. The
rifle barrel is positioned directly beneath the
connecting rib of the shot barrels.

drilling jig
a tool used by gunsmiths to locate the holes to
be drilled and tapped in a firearm for the purpose of installing a sight or scope mount.

drill press
of the bench or floor type basically consists of
a motor, base, movable head and an adjustable
table. It is used for drilling or sanding wood
and other materials, for inletting rifle and shotgun stocks, drilling receivers for micrometer
sights and a number of other operations required
in gunsmithing.

drills, carbide tipped
machinist's high speed drill bits equipped with
carbide tips to facilitate drilling in hardened steel.

driving fit
is a fit obtained by driving one part, such as a
shaft, into another part having a hole or opening,
to retain them in fixed position relative to each
other.
See "forced fit"
    "shrinking fit"

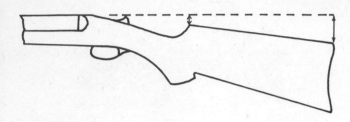

drop

otherwise known as the bend of the stock — is the distance from an imaginary line extending along the top surface of the barrel to points over the top surface of the buttstock. The distance between this line and the foremost edge of the stock-comb is called "drop at comb". The distance from this line to the rearmost top edge of the stock (the heel) is called "drop at heel". These dimensions vary according to the use for which a given firearm is intended and (in custom-made firearms) to the dimensions of the shooter.

drop forging

the shaping of metal by a falling hammer which forces heated metal into a die.

drop of bullet

the vertical distance a bullet has fallen under the influence of gravity, during its flight. At any point in its path of flight it is the distance from that point to the line of departure, i.e. the imaginary line that is the continuation of the axis of the bore the instant the gun is fired.

drop shot

shot pellets made of lead by pouring molten lead thru a collander to drop from a height of from 100 to 200 feet or so into water. As the lead droplets hit the water they solidify into the spherical form of shot in various sizes. By screening, the sizes are segregated. Also called soft shot. See "shot manufacture"

dross, drossing

the scum that forms on molten metal is called dross and is caused by oxidation of the metal when exposed to air. It is encountered when casting bullets of lead and lead alloys. It is held to a minimum by casting at the lowest possible temperature.

drum

a cylindrical magazine containing cartridges and adapted to feed certain types of weapons.

dry firing

practice by aiming, cocking, and squeezing the trigger of an unloaded firearm.

DT

abbreviation for double trigger.

duck foot pistol

an oddity from the past. A multibarrel pistol with barrels radiating outward from the handle bearing some resemblance to the toes of a duck's foot.

dud

a projectile that has failed to explode.

dueling

in a formal manner is a combat between two antagonists fought with deadly weapons, by agreement, and under prescribed conditions and in the presence of witnesses. In the United States the first state to prohibit dueling by law was Tennessee, on November 10, 1801.

dueling pistol

a pistol generally flintlock or percussion sold in matched pairs, designed to be reliable in action and accurate at ranges up to 30 yards. Pistols of this type were introduced between 1770 and 1780.

dum dum

a term generally applied to a soft nose or expanding bullet. It is reputed that the name is derived from the British arsenal at Dum Dum, India where, during the British campaigns in India, in the final years of the 19th century, fully jacketed .303 Lee-Enfield bullets were made expanding by grinding off the nose of the jacket.

dummy

a shell or cartridge having no primer or explosive charge. A shortened term for "dummy ammunition".

dummy ammunition

ammunition without an explosive charge used in training and practice and to function-test magazines and feeding mechanisms. The case has holes, grooves or other means to readily distinguish it by touch, from loaded rounds.

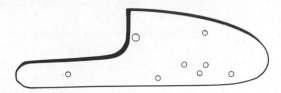

dummy side plate

blank side plates fitted to a box lock shotgun to give the appearance of the more desirable side lock action.

dunnite

See "explosive D"

dusted target

a clay target which reveals only a puff of dust when hit and which is scored as a miss.

dust shot

very small sizes of lead shot, approximately size twelve, generally employed in making shot cartridges for small calibers such as the .22 long rifle.

dynamite

an explosive highly sensitive to shock but less powerful than TNT (trinitrotoluene). Basically it is nitroglycerin absorbed in porous earth. Invented by Alfred Nobel of Sweden in 1866.

E

ear plugs
substances or devices inserted in the ears to mute sound. Ranging from common cotton tufts and manufactured rubber plugs to elaborate mechanical valve devices, ear plugs are used by shooters to deaden harsh shooting noises — particularly when shooting in confined places.

ears
See "clip guides"

ebony
a black African wood that is frequently used for decorative purposes in the manufacture of high grade gunstocks. Ebony has an extremely hard and dense grain. It is difficult to work with but unusually attractive when professionally shaped and finished.

E. C. blank fire
orange or pink explosive powder resembling coarse sand, used as a charge in blank cartridges, small arms and as a bursting charge in hand grenades. Also called "blank fire powder" or "E.C. smokeless powder".

eccentric
describes something not having a common center, thus being descriptive of something not concentric. Mechanical parts are so made and arranged to provide other than a true circular path when turned on their axis.

E. C. smokeless powder
See "E. C. blank fire"

effective range
the distance at which accuracy of fire may be expected.
See "appendix"

eject
to throw out; the function performed in a firearm by an ejector to expel empty casings. While an empty case usually is thrown out within 90° of the axis of the bore, in some instances empty cases have been thrown back as much as 180° from the axis of the bore.

ejector
1. the mechanism in small arms and rapid fire guns which automatically throws out an empty cartridge case or unfired cartridge from the breech. It should not be confused with the extractor which merely pulls the empty cartridge case or unfired cartridge from the chamber.

2. (automatic and selective automatic): terms applied to the shell removing devices in break-open type guns, of which the side-by-side and over and under shotguns are the most classic examples. Automatic ejectors expel the shells from both barrels when the gun is opened, regardless of whether either or both have actually been fired. Selective automatic ejectors expel only the fired, empty casings when the gun is opened. The device in double guns that only partially removes the casings is not an ejector but an extractor.

ejector rod
the ejector actuating push-rod, located under the barrel (or barrels) that is fastened to the ejector at the chamber end and which engages the swiveling forend-iron at the other.

elastic limit
the amount of stress placed upon a material that will deform it to just such degree that the material will not return to its original shape or dimensions. This limit is below that of the tensile strength of a material. Thus while a gun steel might have a tensile strength of 90,000 pounds per square inch its elastic limit might be in the neighborhood of 50,000 pounds per square inch.

electric bedder
See "bedding control"

electric soldering

consists in clamping together the pieces to be joined and after passing a heavy electric current through them, applying solder to the joint where it will melt and flow in and around the joint. It differs from resistance welding in that the metal of the pieces is not melted and therefore does not flow together.

electric welding

See "welding"

electro-etching

is accomplished by the use of the electroplating process and relies upon the fact that only from exposed metal surfaces on the anode will metal be removed and only on exposed metal surfaces of the cathode will it be deposited. By coating either anode or cathode with wax, varnish or other material unaffected by the electrolyte and then making designs on them as desired, the removal or deposit of metal can be directed from and to the surfaces as desired.
See "electroplating"

electrolysis

corrosion of metal in the earth or structures due to stray currents of electricity passing through them and in effect, conducting a slow acting "deplating" process.

electrolyte

a conducting medium in which the flow of electricity is accomplished by the movement of matter. The liquids in a storage battery and in an electroplating bath are electrolytes.

electroplating

consists in making electrolytic deposits of one metal upon another by suspending both in an electrolyte and passing an electric current from the plating metal to the metal to be plated. Cadmium, chromium, copper, nickel and zinc have been used in varying degrees as coatings. Color plating is also accomplished by this basic process.

element

in chemistry it is a substance that cannot be separated from itself by ordinary chemical means. For example, aluminum, copper, iron, lead, nickel and zinc are elements while brass, bronze and steel are not.

elephant rifle

a term applied to any rifle suited for hunting elephants and not to one of particular make, weight or caliber. Formerly old black powder English rifles were often referred to (using the "gauge" measuring system) as 4, 8 or 10 bore elephant rifles which in inches were respectively .935, .835, and .775 inches in diameter.

elevate

to raise the muzzle of a gun to increase the angle of elevation.

elevation

See "angle of elevation"

elevation knob

the rotatable knob built into the adjusting mechanism of an iron sight or telescopic sight and which is used to raise or lower the elevation setting of the instrument. Generally made with click stops and reference scale.

elevation table

a tabulation of ranges with corresponding elevation settings to be applied to a gun.

Elgin cutlass pistol

a single shot percussion pistol with a pointed cutting blade attached to the underside of the barrel, so the weapon could be used both as a firearm and a cutlass. Patented in 1837 by George Elgin of the United States. The U. S. Navy purchased some about that time but it failed to sell commercially and soon faded from the scene.

emboss

to decorate by raising the surface to form designs, patterns, etc. A form of art formerly extensively employed on both barrels and stocks of sporting firearms.
See "checkering" as a form of embossing
See "engrave" as the opposite of "emboss"

emery

an abrasive found in nature as an impure form of aluminum oxide, the constituent that gives it sufficient hardness to cut metals. At one time all grinding wheels were made of emery but artificial abrasives with superior qualities are now used.

empirical

something that is based solely on experience, observation or experiment and not in reliance upon scientific principles.

emplace

to fix a gun in a prepared position from which it may be fired. A term common to artillery pieces.

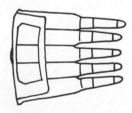

en bloc clip *(ON BLOCK CLIP)*

a clip designed to be inserted together with its load of cartridges into the magazine of certain rifles such as the M-1 Garand.

energy, foot pounds

energy is the capacity to do work and in the English system of measurement is expressed in foot pounds. The energy of a bullet in flight may be determined for any range by use of the formula

$$E = \frac{WV^2}{32.174}$$

where W is the weight of the bullet in pounds and V is the velocity in feet per second.

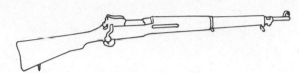

Enfield

the name associated with numerous military rifle and carbine models produced by the Royal Enfield Manufactory of Great Britain from 1853 on, and to a .38 caliber, six chambered revolver, the official arm of the British Army from 1936 to 1957.

Enfield American

name in popular use for the U.S. rifle, caliber .30, Model 1917. It is a bolt type, breech loading 6 shot magazine rifle, being a modification of the British Enfield to permit use of the U.S. standard rimless cartridge, as in the Springfield, with the regular U.S. service 5 cartridge clip for loading the magazine. By such modification it permitted the use of production facilities that had been engaged by the British in the United States, prior to the latter's entry into World War I. The Pattern 14 Enfield originally produced for the British was made in .303 caliber.

Enfield rifling

rifling having square cornered grooves and lands, generally four or six grooves in number. Most modern United States manufactured rifles use this type. A five groove, left-twist rifling of such shape was adopted in 1895 for the British .303 Lee-Enfield rifle.

engine turning

the practice of decorating a steel surface by polishing it with overlapping circular patterns. In engine turning the subject material is placed in an indexable jig on the work surface of a drill press. An abrasive-impregnated rubber bit is then placed in the drill chuck and brought into contact with the work until a circular pattern results. The work is then indexed in such a way that each subsequent application of the polishing bit will overlap the preceding pattern.

English forend

a term describing the small, slim wooden forend common to lightweight English double guns.

English lock

a firing mechanism that made its appearance in the first quarter of the 17th century. It was an improvement on the Snaphaunce in that it made the battery and pan cover in a single hinged piece, so that striking the battery not only produced a spark but caused the pan cover to rise to expose the priming powder in the pan. In addition it added to the Snaphaunce a half cock position. A further improvement became known as a dog lock.

English stock

(also known as straight grip stock)
a type of shotgun stock, common to double barrel guns, for which English gun makers are famous. Designed to keep overall gun weight to the minimum, this style of stock is made with a very straight, slim hand grip.

engrave

to cut, carve or etch designs, patterns, etc. in a surface. Used to decorate or identify firearms on both metal and wood surfaces.
See "emboss" as the opposite

epoxy

1. a chemical prefix denoting the presence of oxygen attached to two different atoms of a chain.

2. shortened popular term for "epoxy resin" which is a polyether resin of recent development. Its excellent chemical resistance and adhesive qualities make it an ideal finishing agent for gunstocks as well as an excellent adhesive for many varied substances including wood and metal.

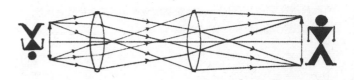

erecting system

the lens assembly in an optical instrument that inverts the upside-down image taken by the objective lens so that it will appear right-side-up to the viewer at the eyepiece.

Erma

a 9 mm German machine pistol used in World War II by German police and SS, and to some extent by the French. The name is also used as a trademark for small arms sold commercially.

erosion

the wear on the bore of a gun caused by the action of the hot gases of the exploded propellent powder on the surface of the metal.

error

the distance by which a shot misses the target.

escutcheon

the part of a weapon, usually metal, on which the name, trademark or other distinguishing feature of the manufacturer is displayed.

espignolle

a muzzle loader repeater that achieved repeated fire by loading bullets and powder charges atop each other. After the foremost charge fired, a powder train in a longitudinal groove of the next bullet transmitted ignition to its powder charge, and so on. The principle was known as far back as 1580 and used to some extent until about 1870.

espringle

an ancient mechanical launcher of the mechanical type which hurled a spear-like bolt of the type known as a "garrot" or "carreau".

etch

to engrave by causing the lines of the design, pattern, or etc. to be eaten away from the surface of a metal by treatment with acid. Used to decorate or identify firearms on their metal surfaces. Acids found to work satisfactorily are, — for iron

and steel: full strength hydrochloric acid
brass: nitric acid
copper: mix of 2 parts nitric and 1 part sulphuric acid
lead: nitric acid
aluminum: 10 percent solution of caustic soda or potash

Various substances including paraffin are used to provide resistance to an acid when etching. The substance used must provide a thin "resist" that will cling to the metal, prevent under cutting by the acid and enable fine lines to be drawn through it without tearing or crumbling.

European walnut

wood from the English walnut tree which is commonly found throughout Europe. The terms Circassian walnut, French walnut, Italian walnut, etc., are misleading since all these woods are from the English walnut tree, which incidentally, originated in China. The differences in the coloring and graining of walnut are caused by varying growth conditions. European walnut is a fine stockmaker's wood because it is hard, densely grained, and very durable.

evening gun

in the military service the firing of a gun as a signal for the lowering of the national emblem at retreat. It is fired after the sounding of the last note of the bugle call at retreat. Also called "retreat gun".

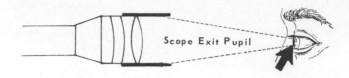

Scope Exit Pupil

exit pupil

the bright spot of light in the eyepiece of a telescope made by the emerging pencil of light when the telescope is pointed toward light and held a short distance in front of the observer's eye. It is the point at which an optical instrument focusses its light rays and it is the point at which the viewer positions his eye.

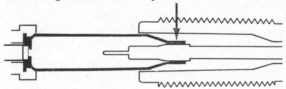

expander button

a device that sizes the inside diameter of a cartridge case neck to a dimension slightly smaller than that of the bullet for which the case is intended. Usually this may be found mounted on the inner stem of a modern sizing die.

expanding point

any bullet made with a point that is designed to expand upon impact. An exposed lead tip, split tip, flat tip or hollow tip bullet may be called an "expanding point" bullet.

expansion

1. the increase in the dimensions of a substance when heated. Expansion of a solid body in length is termed linear expansion; expansion in volume, volumetric expansion.

2. the overall enlargement of a cartridge case as the result of having been fired.
See "coefficient of expansion"

Expert

1. in the United States military service the highest classification given for skill in the use of small arms. It is also the name given to the individual who holds such classification. Next in order are the classifications "Sharpshooter" and "Marksman".

2. In civilian terms (set by the National Rifle Association) "Expert" is the second highest classification for a shooter. In diminishing order the NRA sequence is "Master", "Expert", "Sharpshooter" and "Marksman".

explode

to cause to burst noisily and violently.

explosion

a violent bursting caused by the sudden production of great gas pressure, a very rapid or almost instantaneous combustion. Instantaneous explosion is called "detonation". Slower explosion is called "deflagration".

explosive

any chemical compound or mixture which burns so rapidly that an explosion results. A high explosive is used as a bursting charge in bombs or projectiles; a low explosive is used as a propelling charge in guns.

explosive D

ammonium picrate, a high explosive charge relatively stable in handling and transporting, used as a burster in armor-piercing projectiles. Also called dunnite.

explosive train

the arrangement of explosives in an explosive device whereby an initial fire from a primer is transmitted and intensified and the final step is the setting off of the train charge.

express cartridge

a cartridge loaded with a light, hollow point bullet giving muzzle velocity greater than a comparably loaded cartridge having a heavy bullet. Name is derived from the Express Train cartridges developed in England about 1885.

express rifle

a term formerly applied to a rifle with a long range and relatively flat trajectory.

exterior ballistics

the study of the flight of projectiles after they leave the muzzle of a gun.

exterior ballistic table

a table that for a specific type of gun and projectile gives data on the flight of the projectile after it leaves the muzzle of the gun.

extractor

a device for withdrawing an empty cartridge case or an unfired cartridge from the chamber of a gun. In certain types of automatic weapons it withdraws a cartridge from the feed belt.
See "ejector"

extreme range

the greatest distance a gun will shoot. In the case of small arms a weapon held upward at an angle of about 30° when fired will produce its extreme range. If there were no air to offer resistance an angle of 45° would produce the extreme range.

extrude, extrusion

to force out, such as in forming plastic fibers or in forming the spaghetti-like cords of smokeless powder which are cut into suitable lengths to make powder grains. Metals are also formed by heating and extruding through dies under high pressure. Lead bullets may be made in such a manner.

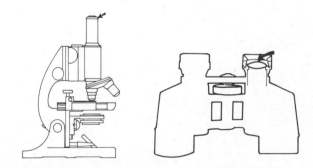

eyepiece

the lens or lenses nearest to the eye of the viewer looking through a telescope, microscope, binoculars or other optical instrument.

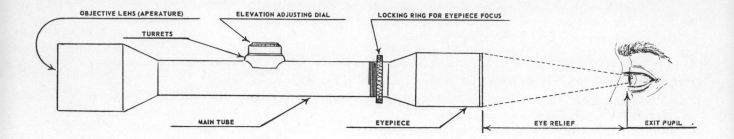

OBJECTIVE LENS (APERATURE)   ELEVATION ADJUSTING DIAL   LOCKING RING FOR EYEPIECE FOCUS

TURRETS

MAIN TUBE   EYEPIECE   EYE RELIEF   EXIT PUPIL

eye-relief

the distance from the eyepiece end of a telescopic sight to the location of the exit pupil. The point at which the exit pupil is focused is where the shooter's eye is normally positioned. While eye-relief is relatively unimportant to scopes intended for .22 caliber rifles, it becomes critical to scopes destined for use on high caliber weapons. If eye-relief is inadequate, scope-mounted weapons having long recoil can cause serious injury to a shooter. Generally, scopes for .22 caliber rifles should have eye-reliefs of about 2 inches. Scopes intended for use on medium to large calibers should never have eye-reliefs of less than three inches and, preferably, four to five inches when intended for use on rifles of the heavier calibers.

See "exit pupil"

F

Fabrique Nationale d'Armes de Guerre, The
famous Belgium firearms manufacturer located at Herstal, Liege, Belgium. Its letters "FN" identify many of its products and models. Better known to Americans as the manufacturers of the Browning line of firearms.

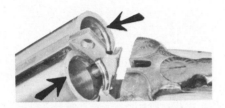

face of breech
the rear surface of the chamber or barrel that contacts the bolt or breechblock

factor of safety
extra strength built into a firearm beyond that required for normally expected loads.

Fahrenheit
the name of the thermometer on which the scale reads 32 degrees at the freezing point of water and 212 degrees at the boiling point of water with each degree being 1/180 of that temperature range. The Fahrenheit thermometer is most commonly used by the English speaking peoples of the world. The abbreviation for Fahrenheit is F.

falling block
a type of single shot rifle action designed with a vertically moving breech block. The block is operated by a lever which is often incorporated in the trigger guard and which extends from the underside of the action. When the lever is actuated the breech block slides down, into the receiver well, exposing the chamber of the barrel.

fall off
the disengagement of the sear with the hammer notch that occurs through the action of force other than the normal one produced by squeezing the trigger, such as vibration, shock, etc.

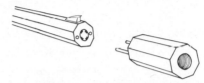

false muzzle
a loading accessory common to muzzle loading guns. At one time barrels for high grade muzzle-loaders were made overly long so that a portion of each barrel (about one to three inches in length) would be left over when the barrel was cut to finished size. These short lengths, each fitted with two or more small pins located to coincide with holes drilled into the barrel muzzle, were then taper-reamed in the bore. Perfectly mated to a given barrel, the false muzzle would facilitate the loading of a solid lead ball and would prevent damage to the rifling at its most critical point — the muzzle. It was removed after each loading and replaced for each succeeding loading.

false ogive
a streamlined cover or windshield covering the nose of a projectile to reduce its resistance to the air in its flight.

fanning the hammer
a rapid fire method of firing a single action revolver which consists in holding the gun in one hand with the trigger held back, tied back or removed entirely, and the hammer slapped or fanned back with the lower part of the palm of the other hand.

Fast Draw

the sport of drawing a single-action revolver from a belt holster in a race against time. Only blank shells or primed, empty casings loaded with wax bullets are permitted in fast draw competition. (Use of live ammunition is strictly forbidden).

Several forms of fast draw competition are regularly practiced:

1. Standing Reaction Event — upon a given signal the competitor draws and fires while a split-second timing device records his reaction time.

2. Walk & Draw Event — two competitors simultaneously walk a prescribed path toward inanimate targets, drawing and firing upon a given signal. In this event wax bullets are used in primed but powderless cases so that accuracy may be considered as well as speed.

3. Balloon Events — variation of "Standing Reaction" and "Walk and Draw" events in which balloons are employed as targets.

Fast Draw rules strictly specify the type of equipment that may be used in competition. While there is no national Fast Draw organization, a number of regional associations are currently in operation; these include: The Texas State FD Assoc., Western States FD Assoc., and Mid-West FD Assoc.

Fast Draw Timer

a timing device that measures reaction time in 100ths of a second. Chrondek Electronics Inc., 2125 "D" Street, LaVerne, California is one of several manufacturers of such devices.

fast swing

starting to aim behind a moving target and then swinging up behind it and overtaking it until the proper lead is reached and then firing.

fatigue

a condition that sometimes occurs in parts that are subject to repeated shocks and stresses, causing rupture of the part.

Federal Firearms Act

repealed as of December 15, 1968 by the "Omnibus Crime Control and Safe Streets Act of 1968", enacted June 19, 1968.

Federal Firearms License

a license issued under the Federal Firearms Act or, since December 16, 1968 one issued under the Gun Control Act of 1968, that authorizes a person to engage in the business of importing, manufacturing or dealing in firearms or ammunition in conformity with the law.

feed

1. the movement of ammunition to a gun.
2. the mechanism by which ammunition is fed to a gun.

feed belt

See "ammunition belt"

feed guides

means for guiding cartridges as for example the lips at the top of a magazine to guide a cartridge into the chamber and the shaped surfaces within the receiver above the magazine well to guide a cartridge into the chamber as it leaves the magazine.

feeding

the operation of successively passing cartridges by mechanical means from the magazine of a gun into its chamber.

feed mechanism

a device on an automatic or self-loading weapon that furnishes fresh cartridges or shells as fast as the used ones are ejected.

feet per second

the term used in the English system of measurement to express velocity or speed of a projectile. Abbreviated as FPS, fps, f.p.s., ft/sec or fs.

Ferguson, Patrick *(1744-1780)*

a Scotsman, firearms enthusiast and a British officer who was killed at the battle of Kings Mountain while serving His Majesty in the American Revolutionary War. He developed and in 1776 patented an improved breech loading rifle which became the first breech loader used by the military.

ferrule
a short bushing or tube.

field of fire
the area effectively covered by the fire of a weapon.

field of view
the extent of an area visible through the lens of an optical instrument. For example: a 2½ power rifle scope rated to yield a field of view of forty-three feet will show the viewer an area forty-three feet in diameter at a distance of one-hundred yards. Field increases at distance to the subject increases: rifle scopes, however, are generally rated in accordance with performance at 100 yards. There is a relationship between magnification and field of view in instruments of comparable size — the higher the magnification, the smaller will be the field of view.

field piece
a field artillery gun or howitzer.

field strip
to take apart the major assemblies of a gun for cleaning or minor repairs.

fine sight
aiming of a gun, or the adjustment of the sight of a gun, so only the tip or top edge of the front sight is seen through the rear sight. This is in contrast with a full sight or a coarse sight.

finish
1. the final step in completing the appearance of the exterior surface of a firearm.

2. the coating placed on the exterior surface of a firearm. Examples of finishes for metal parts are, — blueing or browning.

fire
to shoot or discharge a gun.

fire adjustment
improving the accuracy of fire by moving the gun in elevation and/or windage, or, in the case of an explosive projectile to regulate the time of its explosion.

firearm
any weapon from which a projectile is discharged by explosive means. Definitions with respect to legal obligations and liabilities vary with the laws covering this subject. While all sizes of such weapons fall under this definition, it is the rifle, shotgun, hand gun and other weapon of size conveniently carried by a man that is popularly referred to as a firearm. Its predecessor was a flame throwing tube used long before powder was used to hurl a projectile.

firearms principles, early applications of
begins with the compounding of gunpowder, believed to have occurred early in the 13th century. Its early use to hurl a projectile out of a tube began the series of improvements in guns, propellents, projectiles and other features that eventually attained the degree of perfection known in modern times. That hundreds of years were required to accomplish this was not due to lack of ingenuity on the part of man, — it was lack of suitable materials, metal working tools and precision measuring instruments. Examples of early anticipation of some modern features are found in crude but workable:

multi-barrelled cannon	14th century
front and rear sights on matchlock	1475
rifling	1498
interchangeable barrels	early 16th century
repeaters	early 16th century
3 barrel matchlock	early 16th century
single action lock (pressure)	1521
paper cartridges	1575
revolver, snaphaunce	1650
automatic pistol	1664
6 chambered revolver, hand turned & locked	1700
breechloaders	1730
grenade launcher (flintlock)	1760
7 barrel successive fire	1790

fire at will
command to fire independently of others on the firing line — comparable to saying, "fire when ready".

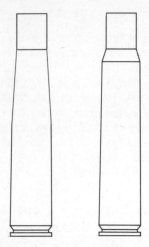

fire-forming

the process of changing the shape of a cartridge case in order to increase its powder capacity, by firing it in a gun having a larger chamber. In fire-forming to create wildcat cases from conventional factory brass, two dimensions must be constant between old and new: these are head-diameter and headspace length. Only the taper, shoulder and neck areas can be safely altered by fire-forming. In forming, the case is loaded with a light charge and fitted with a bullet mated to the new barrel bore. Upon firing, this case will be "blown out" (expanded) to assume the dimensions of the new chamber size. Often two or more firings are necessary to attain desired finished size. Fire-forming should only be attempted by experienced reloaders using tried and proven fire-forming data.

firelock

sometimes used in referring to a matchlock. In Great Britain it means a flintlock.

fire position

the location of an individual or gun from which the gun is fired. Also called firing position. Posture of the body is referred to as "prone position", "offhand position," etc.

firing elevation

the vertical angle at which a gun is held or set for firing with respect to the horizontal.

firing line

in target practice the line along which the shooters are placed for firing at the target.

firing mechanism

those parts of a gun that cooperate to cause the propelling charge to fire. Also called the "gun lock" or just the "lock".

firing pin

that part of the firing mechanism of a gun, basically a plunger, that is adapted to strike the primer and thus cause the propelling charge to fire.

firing point

the place from which a gun is fired.

firing range

the distance from the gun to the target.

firing squad

1. a military detachment designated to fire three volleys of blank cartridges at the burial of a person accorded military honors.

2. a detachment of riflemen designated to carry out a sentence of death by shooting.

firing table

a tabulation or chart which furnishes all of the necessary data for accurately firing a gun under standard conditions together with the corrections required to meet special conditions such as wind, etc.

fishtail wind

a wind that is constantly changing direction back and forth.

fixed ammunition

a round of ammunition assembled as one unit, that is, cartridge case, primer, propellent powder and projectile, and so loaded into a gun. "Separate-loading" ammunition is placed in a gun in parts and is utilized in cannon of large calibers.

fixed round

See "fixed ammunition"

fixed target

a stationary target.

flame staining

the practice of enhancing a plain stock by scorching its surface with a blowtorch, thereby creating irregular lines which resemble natural figuring.

flammable

has the same meaning as inflammable, i.e. capable of being easily ignited. Its use is preferred to inflammable because of the possible ambiguity of the prefix "in" which as a prefix technically means "not" or "non".

flareback

a burst of flame from the breech of a gun. It is caused by gases that remain in the barrel and when the breech is opened, pass to the rear where they ignite when mixed with air.

flare pistol

a pistol for discharging a flame for signalling or illuminating purposes.

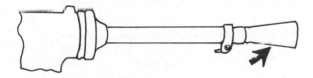

flash hider

a muzzle attachment for a gun to conceal the flame when it is fired at night.

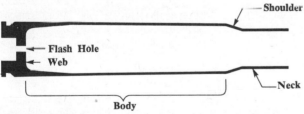

flash hole

the hole in the primer pocket through which the primer flash passes to enter the powder charge. Its function is similar to that of the touchhole in the flintlocks.

flash in the pan

the flash produced in the pan of a flintlock by igniting the small powder charge in the pan with the sparks produced by the flint striking the steel frizzen. The flash if it passed through the touchhole ignited the propellent powder charge

in the bore. Failure to do so resulted only in a pyrotechnic display without results giving rise to the use of the expression for other unsuccessful efforts.

flashless-nonhygroscopic powder

smokeless powder that does not readily absorb or hold moisture and does not produce a flash upon explosion. Used mainly as a propelling charge for projectiles.

flash pan

See "pan"

flash point

with respect to oils is the lowest temperature at which the vapor produced by heating the oil will flash up without setting the oil on fire. The fire or burning point is the lowest temperature at which the oil will burn. The flash points of mineral lubricating oils with few exceptions lie between 300 and 600 degrees Fahrenheit. Heating to the flash point decomposes the oil as a lubricant; heating to the burning point causes the risk of fire.

flask

a small flattened container with a narrow neck used to carry powder or shot for muzzleloading firearms.

flat fire

another term for "flat trajectory fire"

flat nose bullet

a bullet whose shape is characterized by having a flattened end instead of a rounded nose, i.e., it curves from its maximum diameter to a flat end instead of a rounded end or point. Commonly employed in cartridges intended for tubular magazine rifles.

flats

common to double barrel shotguns and most weapons having barrels that swivel about a hinge pin. The "flats" are the broad, flat surfaces that project forward from the face of the breech and that engage corresponding flats on the underside of the barrels, in the vicinity of the lugs, when the barrels are locked in firing position.

flat trajectory

a trajectory with little vertical curvature. This is a characteristic of projectiles with a high muzzle velocity fired from long guns and of projectiles fired at short ranges.

flat trajectory fire

fire at such a range or elevation setting that the projectile in flight describes a path that is almost flat, rather than curved. Also termed "flat fire".

flat trajectory weapon

a gun firing projectiles at such velocity that the path is almost flat rather than curved. At battle ranges a machine gun and a rifle are such weapons.

fleeting target

a target that is exposed for so short a time that deliberate aim is difficult.

fleschette (FLAY shet)

a small dart with a fluted shaft or a vane, adapted to be dropped from an aircraft or propelled by an explosive.

flexible gun

gun on a movable mount that permits it to swing in all directions.

flight

the act of flying such as the flight of a projectile from gun to target.

flinch

the involuntary movement of a shooter at the instant of firing causing the weapon to be jerked from its aimed position.

flint

an extremely hard stone, of the quartz family, usually gray, brown or black in color, that produces sparks when struck against steel. Used in flintlocks to produce the ignition required to set off the priming powder.

flintlock

a firearm ignition system, the highest state of development of a system that ignited priming powder by striking a spark. It is credited to Marin le Bourgeoys of France around the year 1615. The anvil is a hinged steel pan cover which, when struck a glancing blow by the cock, not only produces sparks but rises to expose the priming powder in the pan causing it to ignite. Other features gave it advantages not possessed by the snaphaunce. The flintlock reigned supreme for 200 years. In 1690 it became the official British arm, called the Brown Bess because of the color of the barrel.

flintlock arms

many arms using the flintlock system were developed beginning in 1615. Various features of modern arms were found in them, such as sights, multi-barrels, revolving barrels and cylinders, repeating fire and even breechloading. During the first part of the 19th century the flintlock era came to a close.

floating barrel

a rifle barrel that is not contact-bedded to the stock but left to float freely as opposed to a barrel that is closely fitted to the stock and pressure-bedded at the forend. A controversy exists among target shooters over which of the two methods is most conducive to accuracy.

Flobert, Nicolas *(1819-1894)*

noted French gunmaker who shaped a percussion cap to give it a rim, provided it with a lead bullet, and used only the priming mixture as a propellent. The present day BB Cap is almost identical to it. Flobert produced an early rim fire cartridge in 1847 and is credited with being the first to initiate its development.

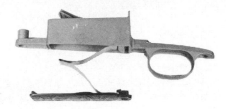

floorplate

that portion of a self-contained box magazine, in a rifle, that acts as a base plate for the follower spring.

flux

a substance used to clean and prevent the oxidation of surfaces to be joined by soldering, brazing or welding. Examples are powdered resin for soldering tin, muriatic-acid for zinc surfaces, borax for brazing, sal-ammoniac (ammonium chloride) for steel, iron, gun metal, copper and brass.

flying firing pin

a firing pin shorter than the length of its travel in the breechblock, a coil spring holding it away from the primer until the falling hammer drives it against the force of the spring and onto the primer.

FMJ

in referring to a bullet it is the abbreviation for "full metal jacketed".

FN

abbreviation for The Fabrique Nationale d'Armes de Guerre, a Belgium firearms manufacturer.

FNH powder

abbreviation for "flashless-nonhygroscopic powder".

focal length

the point some distance behind an optical lens at which parallel light rays passing through the lens are converged and focussed.

focal ratio

the number obtained by dividing the focal length of a lens by its aperture. In this way the "strength" of a given lens is ascertained: the lower the focal ratio, the stronger the lens.

folded crimp

See "star crimp"

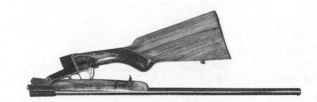

folding gun

a type of hinged gun (usually a single barrel) that permits the barrel to swing in an arc approximately 180° so that it folds snugly against the stock portion for easy transportability.
The term "folding gun" has been used somewhat erroneously in recent years in referring to conventional break-open type side-by-side and over & under guns. These types "fold" open in arcs of about 30° to 40° and are not true folding guns.

folding sight

a hinged open rear sight that is used in the upright position but which may be folded down, out of the way, so as not to interfere with a mounted scope or "peep" sight. Generally intended for use only as an auxiliary sight.

folding trigger

1. a hinged trigger that when folded forward lies close to the under side of the frame. Commonly found in antique pocket pistols and "hide-away" guns.

2. in some fine quality large bore weapons, having two barrels and double triggers, the forward trigger is often hinged so that it folds forward. This is done when heavy recoil is anticipated to prevent bruising of the trigger finger when the rear trigger is pulled.

follower

a spring loaded metal plate in a clip or magazine that presses upward against the cartridges resting upon it to urge them into alignment with the chamber of the gun at the proper angle.

foot-pound

a unit of measure of work. It is the work required to raise one pound a height of one foot, where the accelerator of gravity is equal to 32.174 ft/sec/sec. 33,000 foot pounds is equal to one horsepower.

foot-pounds of energy

a British system of measurement used in the U.S. for measuring the amount of work or energy stored up in a moving projectile.

A foot-pound is the work or energy required to lift one pound to a height of one foot. Or more appropriately, it is the work that can be done by a one pound weight when dropped from a height of one foot.

The foot-pounds of energy developed by a bullet are determined by multiplying one-half the square of the velocity in feet-per-second by the mass of the bullet.

force

any cause tending to produce or modify motion; strength that causes the acceleration of the movement of material bodies. Thus the force of the explosion of a propellent powder imparts motion to a projectile.

forced fit

also known as a pressed fit, applied to a shaft, pin or other cylindrical part that is forced under considerable pressure into a hole of slightly smaller diameter. A forced fit has a larger allowance than a driving fit and requires greater pressure.
See "driving fit" and "shrinkage fit"

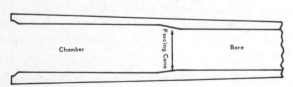

forcing cone

a cone formed in a shotgun barrel between the chamber and bore to ease the passage of the shot from the shell into the bore.

forearm

the heat insulating material of wood or plastic beneath the front portion of the barrel of a rifle or shotgun to afford a means for grasping it and to protect the shooter from the heat of the barrel.

forend

another term for "forearm".

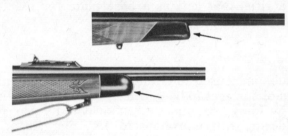

forend tip

the foremost end of a forend (or forearm), towards the muzzle. Generally used only in referring to a decorative forend tip which differs in composition from the wood of the basic forend.

forensic ballistics

the science of ballistics as it relates to crime, specifically the identification of firearms. In the 1920's scientific methods were first applied to the identification of firearms used in the commission of crimes. Colonel Calvin Goddard coined the term and publicized it.

foresight

See "front sight"

forge

to form or shape generally in the manufacture of firearms by heating and hammering.

forge welding

See "welding"

Forsyth, Rev. Alexander John *(1768-1843)*

a Scottish Presbyterian minister, with an interest in chemistry, mechanics and shooting who developed the fulminate of mercury composition from which stemmed the percussion caps, pellets and primers that later proved so successful. It was in 1805 that he began to develop the first percussion lock. In 1807 he finished his design of what came to be known as his scent bottle lock because its magazine was shaped like a scent bottle, replacing the priming pan. He first began experimenting with detonating compositions in 1793.

fouling

the residue of the gases and scrapings from a projectile remaining in the bore of a gun after firing. The gas residue is called "powder fouling" and the scrapings from the projectile are called "metal fouling". The latter is rare with modern copper or gilding metal jacketed bullets.

fouling shot

a preliminary shot from a firearm to carry away oil or other removable, non obstructing matter from the bore of the gun.

fowling

the hunting of wild fowl.

fowling piece

(archaic) a shotgun used to hunt wild fowl.

Fox

the trade name for assorted double barrel shotguns manufactured by the Savage Arms Corporation of Westfield, Massachusetts.

FPS, fps, fs, ft/sec

abbreviation for feet per second, the term by which in the English system of measurement the velocity of a projectile is expressed.

fragmentation

the breaking and flying in all directions of the pieces of a projectile, grenade or bomb.

frame

the basic structure and principal component of a firearm.

Franchi

the trademark for firearms manufactured by the firm of Luigi Franchi s.p.a. of Brescia, Italy. The Franchi firm is represented in the U.S. by Stoeger Arms Corporation of South Hackensack, New Jersey.

Frankford Arsenal

a U. S. Army manufacturing arsenal established near Philadelphia, Pennsylvania by Act of Congress in 1815, the first land being purchased for its use in 1816. It became the technical and production center for small arms ammunition, artillery ammunition components, fire control and related instruments.

free-bore

a form of "leade" or "throat" cut with parallel walls instead of tapered walls.
See "leade" and "throat"

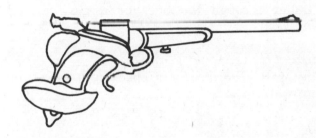

free pistol

a .22 calibre target pistol having minimum established requirements to qualify for use in International Shooting Union (ISU) and some NRA competitions.

free rifle

a type of target used in International shooting that falls within a certain category, the word "free" signifying a minimum of restrictions as to weight, stock, etc.

French checkering

a pattern of checkering for stocks in which, at regular intervals, lines are omitted. Also called skip-line checkering.

French polish

a finishing technique for gunstocks that results in a very high gloss (although somewhat fragile) finish. The basic French polish formula consists of boiled linseed oil, shellac and alcohol. A cotton tuft is first moistened in alcohol and then wrapped inside a piece of lint-free cloth to form a ball. The finisher then alternately dips this into the linseed oil and shellac, rubbing the mixture onto the surface of the wood in smooth circular motions.

freshening-out

the restoration of a worn or rough bore of a barrel to good condition by slightly deepening the grooves and smoothing the tops of the lands.

friction

the resistance of the movement of one body with respect to another body with which it is in contact. Thus there is resistance to the passage of a bullet through the bore of a gun causing some wear.

frieze *(freeze)*

a decorative border for a checkered, carved or engraved pattern.

frizzen

the upright portion of the flintlock firing mechanism consisting of a steel or iron plate against which the flint strikes to produce the sparks for igniting the charge.
See "battery"

frizzen pick

a short pointed metal pick carried as an accessory and used to clean out clogged flash holes of flintlocks or primer holes of percussion type firearms. In the latter case they were termed nipple picks.

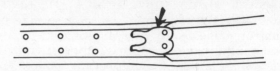

frog

the double-toothed metal hook used on a rifle sling to permit adjustment for length.

frog mount

the popular European type of detachable scope mount consisting of scope rings equipped with twin hooks which engage recessed bases.

front loading

the term applied to early percussion revolvers because they were loaded into the chambers of the cylinder from the front.

front sight

a fixed or detachable, and sometimes adjustable, projection above the barrel near its muzzle that when placed in line with the target, the rear sight and the shooter's eye establishes the line of sight from the gun to the target. Also called "foresight" or "muzzle sight".

fugee

a corruption of the term "fusil".

full automatic

an automatic weapon that gives continuous fire as long as the trigger is held back.

full jacketed

refers to a lead or lead alloy bullet that, except for its base, is completely encased by a thin wall of harder metal.

full length sizing

the practice of restoring a cartridge case to its original dimensions. In reloading, the fired, expanded case is forced into a die that restores it to original factory size. Full length sizing is particularly important to shooters who load for semi-automatic, lever action or slide action firearms.

full patch

a now archaic term for a fully jacketed bullet, a term that probably traces its origin to the muzzle loading era.

full service round

a complete round with the maximum military service charge. Each smaller charge counts as a certain percentage of a full service round.

full sight

aiming a gun with all of the front sight seen through the rear sight. This is in contrast with a fine sight or a coarse sight.

fulminate

any highly explosive powder that detonates. Fulminate of mercury is an example.

fulminate of mercury

See "mercury fulminate"

fulminating powder

means any highly explosive powder but usually refers to a mercuric fulminate powder.

fume, fumes

smoke or vapor.

fusee *(FEW zee)*

a friction match or colored flare designed to continue burning in a wind.

fusil *(FEW sill)*

a light flintlock musket. The word is of French origin meaning steel for striking sparks. This term is used interchangeably with "fusee".

fuze, fuse

a device, mechanical or electrical, as part of a projectile, bomb, mine or grenade, that causes it to explode at a fixed time or on impact. The word also applies to a train of powder connected to an explosive, that causes ignition when the train of powder is consumed by burning.

G

Gabilondo

manufacturers of the "Llama" and "Ruby" lines of automatic pistols and revolvers: Gabilondo y Cia, Vittoria, Spain. Represented in the U.S. by Stoeger Arms Corporation of South Hackensack, New Jersey.

gage

a measuring instrument or device for accurately testing the dimensions of a manufactured object. The advances in the art of making gages made possible the introduction of mass production methods in industry. Mechanical, electrical and air gages are types commonly in use today.

gage blocks

are small blocks of precise dimension in thickness (within a four millionths of an inch) used to check or establish accurate measurements in shops and laboratories. A complete set might total as many as 85 blocks.

gain twist

a type of rifling that increases the number of turns it makes as it curves from the breech end of the bore to the muzzle, instead of having a uniform helical curve thruout.

Gallagher

the breech loading rifle invented by Mahlon I. Gallagher characterized by a trigger guard lever that moved the barrel ahead and down for loading with a paper cartridge. It was a contemporary weapon of the Civil War.

Gallagher, Mahlon, J.

American inventor of a trigger-guard-lever operated breeching system (1860) which swung the barrel ahead and down for loading. A number were purchased for use by the Federal Government in the Civil War. Also patented, in 1857, a self priming gunlock.

gallery

an enclosed or partially enclosed range for target practice with small arms.

gallery practice

small arms practice in an enclosed or partially enclosed range.

gallery practice ammunition

small caliber ammunition or reduced charge ammunition used in gallery practice.

gallery practice cartridge

a small caliber cartridge or a cartridge with a reduced charge, used in gallery practice.

gallery range

an indoor target range generally suitable to .22 calibre firing usually providing a distance of at least 50-feet between the firing line and targets.

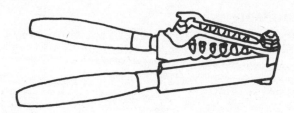

gang mold

a mold form having multiple cavities for forming a number of castings with a single pour.

Garand, John C. *(1888-   )*

a Canadian born American citizen who moved to the U.S. at the age of 10 and became an outstanding ordnance engineer, best known for his work at Springfield Armory in designing the semiautomatic weapon adopted by the U.S. Army in 1936, officially the cal. 30, M1, but popularly known as the Garand rifle.

Garand rifle

the U.S. Rifle, Caliber .30,M1. A semiautomatic gas-operated, clip-fed rifle weighing 8.56 pounds.

garrot

1. a spear-like "bolt" shown in old illustrations of the firing of a cannon, believed to be the earliest illustration of the use of gun powder (1326 A.D.). Also known as a carreau.

2. an ancient term for the lever used to wind a cross bow.

before sizing on bullets   after sizing on bullets

gas check

1. a device in a gun that prevents the escape of gas through the breech, such as the gas escape hole which diverts gas entering the bolt through the striker hole.

2. a cup of copper or other metal on the base of a lead bullet to protect it from hot powder gases.

gas check bullet

a lead bullet designed specifically for use with a gas check.

gas cutting

the more rapid erosion caused when the propellent gases escape through small openings such as the corners of the grooves at or shortly beyond the bullet seat, before the bullet has expanded to cut off gas escape. "Erosion" is the term applied when larger areas are worn by the gases. See "erosion"

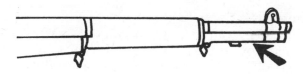

gas cylinder

a tube having a piston, connected to the barrel of a gas-operated automatic weapon, whose function is to operate the cartridge extracting and cartridge reloading mechanisms.

gas filled

a term that is sometimes used in referring to gas-filled rifle scopes. Most often nitrogen is used for this purpose and the most commonly used description is "nitrogen-filled".
Gas-filling is employed to prevent fogging when the instrument is subjected to radical changes in temperature.

gas gun

the term usually applied to guns using liquefied carbon dioxide (CO_2) as a propellent. In 1834 use of such gas was experimented with in a gun by Peder Rasmussen of Denmark. The term applies to guns using other gases (except air) as propellents.

gas leak

See "primer leak"

gas operated

a self-loading firearm that utilizes the expanding force of the propellent powder gases to extract a fired cartridge case and insert a fresh cartridge with gun cocked ready to fire. A small hole or port in the barrel provides the means for a portion of the expanding gases to enter a gas cylinder below the barrel and thus to act on a piston and initiate the several steps required to empty and reload the chamber.

gas piston

the piston-like rod which, powered by the propellent gases that are siphoned from the bore, serves to operate the breech mechanism of the firearm. A device common to automatic and semiautomatic gas-operated weapons.

gas port

1. the small hole in a gas operated rifle that connects the bore with the gas cylinder.

2. a port provided in the wall of a receiver to permit the escape of gas flarebacks harmlessly into the open air. Sometimes called "gas vent".

gas recoil

the rearward pressure exerted by the force of the expanding gases of the exploded propellent powder.

gas sealed

1. in riflescopes, a moisture or fog preventing technique that calls for the filling of the instrument with nitrogen gas and meticulous sealing of all openings to prevent the contamination of interior surfaces by exterior atmosphere.

2. a term occasionally employed when referring to the ability of a breech mechanism to contain the gases created by a fired cartridge.

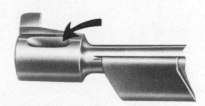

gas vent

1. the vent holes cut in a rifle receiver in the vicinity of the bolt head. Employed as a safety measure to release excess gas pressures when they are inadvertently developed.

2. the slotted vents in a muzzle brake which are designed to divert gas pressure from behind the projectile as it clears the muzzle. Used in this manner, gas vents tend to reduce recoil and minimize muzzle jumps.

gas welding

See "welding"

gat

slang for a handgun, adapted from the name "Gatling gun".

gate

an opening into a passage provided with a closure such as a "loading gate" found in certain revolvers.

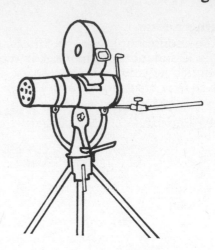

Gatling

The first successful mechanical machine gun, named after Richard J. Gatling, who patented it in 1862. Initially it was hand driven, later motor driven. Characterized by its mounting of a number of barrels. The number of barrels in the initial six guns had six barrels of .58 caliber, rimfire, grouped about a central axis. While it was replaced by the automatic Maxim gun, the multibarrel principle has had modern application.

Gatling, Richard, J. *(1818-1903)*

an American Doctor of Medicine, mechanic and inventor. The first design of his multiple barrel gun was patented in 1862 but his improved model patented in 1865 was the one commercially successful.

gauge

a unit of measure: in a shotgun it refers to the diameter of its bore based on the early measuring system which assigned to the size of the bore the number that was the same as the number of pure lead balls, each of the diameter to fit the bore, that made up one pound in weight. Thus the 12 gauge bore uses a lead ball weighing 1/12 of a pound.

Geiger, Leonard

an American inventor of the first true rolling block lock for which he was granted a U.S. patent in 1863 and which he sold to the Remington Company.

giant powder

an explosive akin to dynamite.

gilding metal

an alloy containing from 90-95 per cent of copper with the balance of the alloy being zinc. Used for bullet jackets and when so used generally a thin coat of tin is applied to prevent tarnishing.

glass bedding

See "bedding"

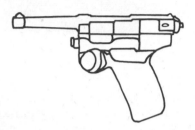

Glisenti

a seven shot 9mm Italian semiautomatic pistol adopted as official Italian military weapon in 1910 and officially designated "Pistola Automatica Model 1910".

globe sight

a type of front sight made for rifles; designed to prevent distorted "sight pictures" by eliminating reflections. In a globe sight, the front sight blade is positioned inside of a hollow tube, the open ends of which are aligned with the receiver sight. Globe sights generally permit the interchanging of a number of assorted sight blade inserts.

glue

a term loosely applied to any number of substances that have adhesive qualities. Good commercially available glues are acceptable for work on gunstocks.

gonne, gunne

the 12th and 13th century forms of spelling "gun".

go off half cocked

the accidental discharge of a miguelet lock, the first to combine the frizzen or battery with the cover of the flash pan. To load the pan the hammer had to be retracted to engagement with a secondary sear, the half cock position, the cover raised, the pan charged and under light spring pressure the cover returned to its normal closed position. In this condition the loaded gun could be carried and when it was to be fired, fully cocked before the trigger was squeezed. When a worn or defective secondary sear let the hammer slip off, the gun discharged. It is a common expression since that time to describe someone who speaks or does something before being fully prepared.

gouge

a form of wood chisel having a concave blade, used by gunmakers in roughing out the concave curve where the barrel of a gun fits into the wood forearm.

grain

1. a unit of weight, there being 7000 grains in an avoirdupois pound. The weight of a powder charge and the weight of a bullet are expressed in grains. It also has other meanings such as a descriptive word for a small hard particle, and frequently is improperly used to describe the granules or pellets of powder.

2. the natural figurations found in wood.

granulation

the size and shape of granules of propellent powder.

grapeshot

a cluster of small iron shot fired from a cannon and intended to spread in flight.

graphite

a mineral essentially of carbon. It clings readily to wood and iron surfaces and is unchanged by heating. Used as a lubricant.

graphite grease

a lubricant containing graphite.

graticule

the English term for "reticle".
See "reticle"

gravity, force of

the force exerted by the attraction of the earth. When it acts upon a free falling body it accelerates the speed or velocity of fall at the uniform rate of 32.174 feet per second per second. Starting with zero velocity at the instant the body is let fall, the velocity at the end of the first second will be 32.174 feet per second, at the end of two seconds 64.348 feet per second. This force acts on a bullet the instant it leaves the muzzle of a gun.

grease

1. a fatty substance.

2. a thick lubricant used on metal parts of guns in preparation for shipment or storage. A mixture of one part of white petroleum jelly and one part of anhydrous lanolin is recommended as a gun grease for prevention of rust.

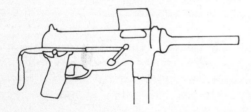

grease gun

the nickname given to the U. S. M3 and M3A1 submachine gun used in World War II and the Korean War.

Greek fire

while many incendiary mixtures were known to have been used in ancient times, even as early as 429 B.C., what is known as Greek fire is said to have been introduced in the 7th century by Callinicus of Heliopolis at Constantinople to set fire to enemy ships. It is believed to have been a mixture containing quicklime which in contact with water developed heat, and together with materials like sulphur or naptha caused spontaneous fire.

Greene, James Durrel

a Colonel in the U. S. Army, inventor of a carbine in which a forward trigger was pulled to unlock

the barrel to permit it to be twisted to the left and slid forward for loading. It was equipped with the Maynard tape primer. Also later the inventor of an oval bored bolt action rifle, patented in 1857.

Greener safety

a pivot-type thumb operated safety produced in 1875 by W. W. Greener, an English gunmaker, for use on his shotguns and rifles. Later employed by many European manufacturers.

grenade

a miniature bomb thrown by hand or discharged from a rifle and detonated by a fuze. Grenade launchers, in the form of mortars, were known prior to 1600.

grinding

1. the removal of material by abrasive means, usually with grinding wheels.

2. the reduction to powder by friction or crushing.

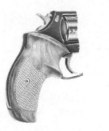 

grip

1. that part of a firearm about which the fingers of the hand may be clasped. On pistols and revolvers it is the handle. On rifles and shotguns the small of the stock immediately behind the breech. The handgun grip has been copied in many hand held devices.

2. the slots cut into the lugs of a double barrel shotgun and which are engaged by the locking bolts when the barrels are secured in a firing attitude. Also called "bites".

grip adapter
a filler placed in back of the trigger guard of a revolver to furnish a lower area of contact between the gun and the shooter's hand.

grip cap
a cap used on pistol grip stocks of rifles and shotguns to protect the lower surface and edges from chipping. Grip caps may also be used to lengthen and enhance the grip itself and are often made from contrasting materials for decorative purposes.

grip marks
insignia or legend on gun grips to indicate manufacturer, usually in the form of an escutcheon.

grip safety
a safety feature found mainly in semiautomatic pistols, incorporated in the grip to prevent the gun from being fired unless the grip is firmly grasped while the trigger is squeezed.

grip stop
an adjustable platform that circumvents the lower edge of a pistol grip for the purpose of supporting the heel of the hand. Widely used on target pistols and occasionally found on target rifles. Sometimes called "hand shelf" or "heel rest".

grip straps
the front strap and backstrap of a handgun grip. The front strap is the curved metal band-like member comprising the leading edge of the frame; the backstrap to the curved metal band-like member comprising the rear edge of the frame.

grommet
a device made of rope, plastic, rubber or metal to protect the rotating band of projectiles.

groove diameter
the diameter of a rifled bore measured from the bottom of one groove to the bottom of the opposite groove.

grooves
the shallow channels that run lengthwise and follow a helical curve in the bore of a rifled barrel, which together with the lands that lie between them, give a projectile passing through the bore a spinning motion that stabilizes it in flight.

ground stone
a pulverized stone, used for lapping, i.e. where a small amount of material is to be removed or a smooth surface is desired.

group
a number of shots fired from a gun by a shooter into a target, usually with one sight setting.

guard

a protective part of a weapon. The trigger guard is a curved metal piece on a firearm surrounding the trigger and serving to protect it and prevent accidental firing. The hand guard, usually of wood, protects the hand from the heat of the barrel.

guard ammunition

ammunition having a reduced charge to reduce its effective and extreme ranges. Used in the military services for guard purposes.

guard screw

one of two or three screws used to secure the trigger guard to the receiver of bolt action firearms.

gun

a weapon discharging a projectile by the force of an explosion, or by compressed air or gas. In the United States it applies to any type of firearm. In England in referring to a firearm it means a shotgun.

gun carriage

a mount for a gun by which it may be moved or fired, or both moved and fired.

guncotton

a nitrocellulose having a very high nitrogen content made by treating cotton with nitric and sulphuric acids. It is used in making certain high grade smokeless powders, is used to carry the flame to the burster in some projectiles, and is also used in electric priming devices.

Gun Control Act of 1968

was enacted on October 22, 1968, effective as of December 16, 1968. It replaces the Federal Firearms Act which was repealed as of December 15, 1968 by the "Omnibus Crime Control and Safe Streets Act of 1968". It extends Government control over the sale, shipment or receipt of firearms and all ammunition in interstate and foreign commerce.

gunfight

a fight in which the principal weapon is a gun.

gunfighter

a term applied in Western frontier days to one skilled in the use of a gun, especially a hand gun, and a veteran of many gun fights.

gunfire

the discharge of cannon or firearms.

gunflint

the flint used in a flintlock firearm.

gun hand

1. the hand customarily used by a shooter in firing a handgun.

2. a slang expression used in stories of the Old West to denote an individual proficient in the use of a handgun and generally one who was hired because of that skill.

gun lathe

a lathe designed for turning and boring cannon of large size and more frequently called turning and boring lathes.

gun lock

1. originally used to refer to the ignition systems used on guns of the type that required a flame or spark to ignite the priming powder. In present day use this term has acquired a broader meaning, one that encompasses all firing mechanisms — specifically referring to that assembly that is comprised of the firing pin, hammer, spring, sear and trigger.

2. the locking system used in sealing the breech of a firearm.

gunmaker

a person, firm or corporation that manufactures guns.

gunman

1. usually refers to a person armed with a gun and suspected of using it unlawfully against others.

2. also refers to a person who makes guns, carries a gun, or is expert in the use of a gun.

gun metal

an alloy of the bronze type formerly used in making cannon, dark gray in color, and containing about 90 per cent of copper and 10 per cent of tin with small percentages of lead, iron and zinc. Sometimes used to describe the dark blue or black finish on the metal surfaces of a gun.

gun moll

a female criminal who carries a gun, or, the female companion of a gangster.

gun mount

a support for a gun, such as carriage, tripod, bipod or other similar gun supporting means.

gunner

1. a person who practices shooting.

2. a naval warrant officer responsible for ordnance on a vessel.

gunnery

the art of handling guns and being familiar with exterior ballistics and the technical problems involved in firing them.

gunning

the sport of shooting or hunting with guns.

gunpaper

a composition for military use made by treating paper with nitric acid so it is similar to guncotton.

gunplay

the serious exchange of shots from firearms, usually with the intent of wounding or killing.

gunpoint

the aim of a gun; at gunpoint meaning in the line of sight of a gun and in close proximity to it.

gunpowder

the term generally applied to black powder. Oldest recorded use as a propellent 1313 A.D.

gun rack

See "arms rack"

gun room

a room in which guns are kept, either for storage or for display.

gunrunning

the smuggling of guns, ammunition and their accessories into another governmental jurisdiction. A gunrunner is one who indulges in such practice.

gunsel

a slang term for a criminal armed with a gun.

gunshot

the firing of a gun; the shot fired from a gun; or the range of a gun.

gun-shy

a human or animal that is unduly frightened by the sound of gun fire.

gun sling

a strap of leather or other material, adjustable for length, attached to a rifle or carbine to make it easier to carry from the shoulder and to steady it when firing.

gunslinger

slang for gunfighter.

gunsmith

a craftsman who makes or repairs firearms, also known as an "armorer".

gunspall

a piece of chert shaped to produce a spark when used in a flintlock. By 1650 it was known as a stone suitable for such purpose.

gunstock

the shaped wood or plastic piece to which the metal parts of a gun are attached and which in rifles, carbines and shotguns also serves to steady the gun against the shoulder of the shooter.

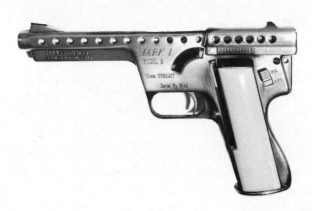

gun-toting
the custom or habit of carrying a handgun with some regularity.

gun wave
the compressed air that fans out from the muzzle of a gun after firing. Also called "muzzle wave", "ballistic wave" or "bow wave".

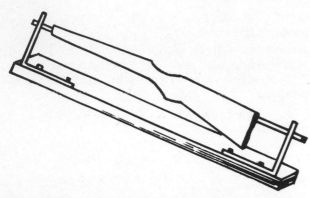

gunstocker's cradle
a wooden device used by gunstock makers to hold a stock in working position. The cradle generally fastens the stock on a point at the butt end and in a clamp at the forend so that it may be swivelled freely and locked in any given working position.

gun-target line
an imaginary straight line from the gun to the target.

Gyrojet gun
a recently developed gun firing a small rocket projectile.

H

hair trigger

a trigger requiring but a light touch to cause it to fire the gun.

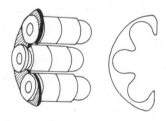

half cock

the position of the hammer of a gun when it is held by a notch in advance of the full cock position. In this position the trigger is locked and the gun relatively safe.

half loaded

the condition of an automatic weapon when the belt or magazine is inserted and receiver charged, but without the first cartridge in the chamber.

half-moon clips

a revolver clip designed to hold the cartridges for one half of the cylinder to facilitate loading; also employed to adapt certain rimless ammunition for use in revolvers which normally accommodate only rimmed cartridges.

Hall, John Harris (*1778-1841*)

an American inventor who in 1811, with William Thornton, patented the breech loading rifle that bore his name. Colonel Hall's rifle is considered to have been the first reasonably successful breech loading gun to be extensively used. He was a pioneer in making parts of his rifle interchangeable.

Hall rifle

a rifle patented in 1811 by Colonel John H. Hall of the U.S., originally a flintlock, later adapted to the percussion system. Considered to be the first fairly successful breech loader. Adapted 1816 in the United States as an experimental arm and used in .54 caliber to a limited extent in the Seminole and Mexican Wars.

hammer

the piece that pivots on an axis to deliver a blow to a firing pin. It may be outwardly visible on a gun, or, concealed within the so-called hammerless guns.

hammerless

a term intended to describe a firearm that does not have an exposed hammer; at times misleading because this does not necessarily mean that a particular gun lacks a hammer — oftentimes the hammer is designed so that it is completely enclosed in the frame or receiver.

Some firearms make use of a spring-activated rod which is appropriately called a "striker". In such instances the striker is employed in place of a hammer.

hammerless gun

a gun with a wholly enclosed hammer and firing mechanism. It does not refer to a gun that uses a striker instead of a hammer.

Hammerli
a Swiss gun-making firm well known for its target rifles and pistols.

hammer pin
a pin that holds a hammer in its designed position in a gun and upon which the hammer turns.

hammer shroud
a detachable cover or protective guard for the hammer of a revolver to prevent the hammer from catching in clothing when the revolver is carried on the person.

hammer spur
in guns having an outwardly visible hammer it is the spur-like rearward projection on the hammer which furnishes a gripping surface and provides the leverage with which to cock the hammer.

hammer strut
a component part of the firing mechanism of a gun that puts pressure on the hammer.

hand
a long, thin steel piece mounted in the lockwork of a revolver to engage the cylinder so that it will rotate the distance of one chamber as the hammer goes to full cock. Also called "pawl".

hand cannon
probably the first one-man portable weapon to enter upon the scene after the introduction of the cannon. Loaded from the muzzle, the powder charge was ignited by applying a torch or red hot iron to a small amount of powder placed over a touchhole that opened into the chamber. With a long hand cannon two men cooperated to fire it. One held the gun on his shoulder and aimed it while the other fired it.

hand guard
a part, usually of wood, surrounding that portion of the barrel of a firearm with which the shooter's hand will come in contact. It prevents the hand from being burned by a hot barrel. Common to military weapons.

handgun
a firearm capable of being carried and used by one hand, such as a pistol and revolver. The first recorded use of the term "hand gun" appears in English records of 1386.

handloading
the practice of loading or reloading a cartridge case manually rather than by production machinery.

hand shelf
the lateral projection from the base of the pistol grip of some rifles, to provide a hand rest for the shooter when the stock is gripped. Sometimes called "heel rest" or "grip stop".

hand-stop
a wood or metal block mounted beneath the forend of a stock against which the hand of a shooter may bear. It may be moved forward or rearward to accommodate the arm length of the shooter and then secured in that position. Mounted immediately behind the forend swivel, the hand stop is most often used on target rifles where a tightly fitted sling is necessary. The hand stop eliminates any possible pinching of the hand under the forward swivel.

hang
to lock the receiver or bolt of gun in open position.

hangfire
a term often misinterpreted by the layman: in the strictest sense, and according to professional ballisticians, the term "hangfire" refers to a minor delay in the ignition of a cartridge after its primer has been struck — a delay of not more than ten milliseconds.

The average shooter will frequently refer to any delay in ignition as a "hangfire", however, if the delay exceeds ten milliseconds it is more properly called a "squib-load" caused by partial contamination of the primer and/or powder charge by fluids such as oil or water. In rare instances squib loads are created by foreign matter blocking, or partially blocking, the flash hole.

On those occasions when a shooter experiences a firing delay he should keep the firearm pointed in a safe direction and wait at least five seconds before opening the breech to investigate or remove the defective round.

hangfire test
the name of a test designed to determine the uniformity and promptness of fire of a type of ammunition.

hardening steel
basically consists in heating the steel to the required temperature and then quenching it suddenly in a cooling medium called a quenching bath.
See "quenching baths"

hardness
of metals is determined by test, the Brinell and Rockwell tests being common standard tests for metals. There is a constant relationship between the tensile strength of steel and its hardness, thus knowing one will enable calculation of the other.
See "Brinell hardness test"
    "Rockwell hardness test"
    "Vickers hardness test"

hard soldering
soldering with silver solder.

harmonica repeating system
a multi-barrel rifle deriving its name from its shape. Also a term applied to a repeating rifle having a rectangular feed block inserted in the breech opening on the side, the block bearing a resemblance to a harmonica. This latter type made its appearance during the first half on the 19th century.

Harpers Ferry
the name of the small-arms manufacturing plant and arsenal established in 1796 by George Washington at Harpers Ferry, West Virginia (then part of Virginia).

Harper's Ferry rifle
the name commonly applied to rifles manufactured at or designed by Harper's Ferry arsenal, such as the U.S. Flintlock Rifle, Model 1803, over 4000 of which were produced at Harper's Ferry between 1804 and 1807, and the U.S. Rifle Model 1841 a percussion lock arm made at the arsenal and by Government contractors between 1846 and 1855.

harpoon gun
a gun adopted to fire a barbed spear or javelin for shooting large fish, whales, etc. The head of the harpoon sometimes filled with an explosive cap and charge.

harquebus *(HARR kway bus)*
same as "arquebus".

harquebusier, *(HARR kway bus EAR)*
same as "arquebusier".

Harrington & Richardson
the name by which pistols and revolvers made by Harrington & Richardson, Inc. of Worcester, Massachusetts, are known.

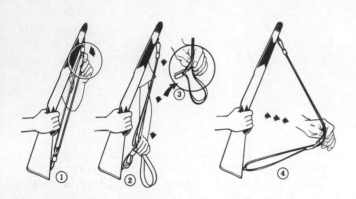

hasty sling adjustment

a quick method of adjusting a gun sling to help steady a rifle while shooting but not as efficient as the "loop sling adjustment". The sling is passed under and behind the left arm.

HE, H.E.

1. abbreviation for "high explosive".

2. abbreviation also for "Hand Ejector" — a specific model of Smith & Wesson Revolver.

head

the small part in a revolver that holds the cylinder on its axis.

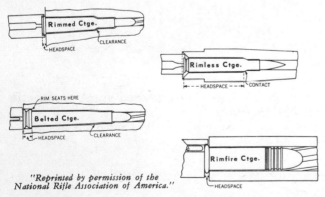

"Reprinted by permission of the National Rifle Association of America."

headspace

1. is the distance between the face of the breech and that part of the chamber against which the cartridge bears.

2. in the case of machine guns it is frequently a term applied to the distance between the base of a cartridge fully seated in the chamber and the face of the bolt.

head wind

a wind direction that blows directly from the targets towards the firing line on a shooting range. This is a desirable wind direction from the rifleman's point of view but a troublesome wind direction to the trap shooter.

heat

heat is transferred because of a temperature difference between bodies and occurs by convection, conduction and radiation. Friction of a bullet passing through a bore and the heat developed by the propellent powder are the principal sources of heat in a firearm.

heat treating

the process of hardening or tempering steel through controlled heating and quenching.

heat waves

refers to the heat waves rising from a barrel that has become heated as a result of prolonged shooting — a condition that is particularly troublesome to the rifle marksman because heat waves tend to distort the sight picture. For this reason some target shooters attempt to divert heat waves from the line of sight by suspending a broad webbed belt over the barrel, stretching the belt from the receiver to the muzzle.

heavy weapon

a weapon such as a heavy machine gun, mortar, howitzer or other cannon.

heel

the upper corner of the butt of a gun stock when the gun is held in firing position.

heel rest

See "hand shelf"

heel-type bullet

a bullet that terminates at its base in a cylindrical portion of smaller diameter than the body portion. It is this smaller portion that is seated in the mouth of a case. The bullet may be either of solid or jacketed type.

height of site

the altitude of a gun above some datum plane such as sea level.

helix

is a curve in three dimensions such as traced by the thread of an ordinary screw. On the other hand a spiral is a curve in one plane, such as traced by a watch spring lying on a flat surface. The twist of the rifling in the bore of a firearm traces a helix but commonly its path is called a spiral.

Henry, Alexander *(1828-1894)*

a Scottish inventor of a system of rifling which when combined with Frederick von Martini's firing mechanism became the Martini-Henry rifle adopted in 1871 for the British Army.

Henry, Benjamin Tyler *(1821-1898)*

an American gunsmith and manufacturer who, in 1858, developed a rimfire cartridge and in 1860 patented certain improvements in the Volcanic rifle. The improved rifle became known as the Henry rifle, and subsequently with minor changes became the first Winchester rifle in 1866.

Henry rifle

a lever operated repeating rifle, .44 caliber, 15 shot tubular magazine designed by Benjamin Tyler Henry that had limited use in the Civil War after 1862. It was the pattern for the successful Winchester models of 1866 and 1873.

Henry, William *(1729-1786)*

an American inventor and manufacturer of firearms, his rifles achieving a reputation for excellence.

high angle fire

fire from a gun that is elevated above the elevation that produces maximum range; as this angle is increased the range of the gun decreases.

high base, high brass

pertaining to the construction of shotgun shells — these two terms are very often misunderstood:

BASE — refers to the height of the base *wad* in a shotgun shell. This is a liner located near the primer aperture at the inner lower portion of the shell. So often referred to as "high base" or "low base" one assumes that manufacturers use two distinct dimensions. This is false — base wads vary greatly in size depending upon the type and quantity of powder to be used and upon the space needed for the wad and shot columns. Because too much wadding can be as detrimental as too little, commercial manufacturers use assorted base wads to compensate for variations in the powder, wad and shot portions of the load. Base height has no real relationship with the height of the brass head of the shell. Although, most frequently, the employment of a heavy powder charge would necessitate a low base wad and a high brass shell head.

In reloading shotshells, one should always gauge the base wad height before selecting the balance of components.

BRASS — refers to the length of the brass sleeve at the external base of a shotshell. This, too, is found in many different dimensions and there are no specific dimensions for "low brass" or "high brass". The manufacturer simply determines a height that is best suited to the performance of a particular shell. Trap and skeet loads are generally loaded with a small brass head, field loads run from small to medium height and express and magnum loads are found in high brass shells.

high explosive

the term applied to a compound such as TNT which detonates rather than explodes. The gases of combustion are given off so rapidly that such explosives cannot be used as propelling charges. Abbreviated as HE or H.E.

high intensity cartridge

a cartridge producing a muzzle velocity of over 2500 feet per second. Between 1925 and 2500 feet per second it is termed a high power cartridge.

Highlander
all metal pistols, mostly flintlocks, of Scottish manufacture that were made from about 1600 until the first part of the 19th century.

high order detonation
a complete and instantaneous explosion.

high power cartridge
a relative term but usually taken to mean a cartridge producing a muzzle velocity of between 1925 and 2500 feet per second. Over 2500 feet per second it is termed a high intensity cartridge.

high pressure test ammunition
ammunition that is loaded with an excess charge of propelling powder. It is used only in proof firing.

high velocity
as defined by the U.S. Army for small arms ammunition is muzzle velocity lying between 3500 and 5000 feet per second.

See "hypervelocity"

Hindustan stone
See "India stone"

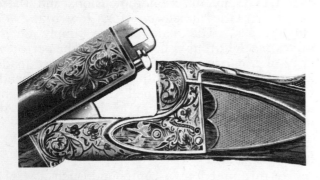

hinged frame
firearm is one in which the barrel or barrels are hinged to the front end of the frame and mechanically locked together to cause the chambers and breech to be in contact when the gun is to be fired. Upon unlocking, the gun may be "broken". In a revolver, the cylinder is a separate segment between the barrel and the standing breech. Hinged on the barrel side the cylinder swings out to the side of the gun for loading or unloading.

hip shooting
shooting with the firearm held in the vicinity of the waistline of the shooter.

Hi Standard
the trade name applied to the products of the High-Standard Manufacturing Company of Hamden, Connecticut, firearms manufacturers.

hit
the impact or point of impact of a projectile on a target.

H-mantle bullet
trade name for a particular type of sectioned bullet, invented and manufactured by the German RWS Munitions Works.

hold
a term relating to a shooter's ability to hold a firearm in a steady aiming attitude.

holding
is continued aiming at the target while applying pressure to the trigger.

hollow ground screwdrivers
screwdrivers that are made with little or no tapered surfaces; designed to minimize the possibility of burring screw heads.

hollow point
a bullet having a cavity in its nose to increase the expansion of the bullet when it hits.

holster
a case of leather or other tough material to hold a handgun such as a pistol or revolver and adapted to be attached to a belt, shoulder strap or saddle.

honing
the process of removing small quantities of material or improving the surface of a piece by use of a fine stone.

hooded sight

a front sight that is equipped with a metal canopy. Designed to eliminate light reflections.

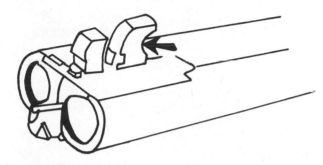

hook of lump

the semicircular cut in the forwardmost lug of a double barrel shotgun (or other similar type of hinged-barrel firearm). It is the "hook" that engages the hinge pin and provides the swiveling action required to open and close the breech.

hook plate

a hook-shaped metal butt plate that is used extensively in target shooting with the rifle. The top-most extension of the hook bears against the upper part of the shoulder while the lower extension (which is generally longer) fits snugly under the arm-pit. Hook plates tend to help the shooter steady the rifle.

Hoppe

a trademark of the Frank A. Hoppe Company of 2310-20 North 8th Street Philadelphia 33, Pennsylvania, well known for their lubricants and cleaning equipment for firearms.

horizon

the line where the sky and the earth appear to meet.

horizontal clock system

a system used in describing the direction of the wind. The firing point is considered the center of a clock dial and the target at 12 o'clock. A 3 o'clock wind is one coming directly from the right; a 9 o'clock wind is one coming directly from the left.

horizontal range

the distance measured on a level line between the gun and a point directly above or below a target.

horse pistol

a large pistol, generally a flintlock of large bore, formerly carried by man on horseback across the pommel of the saddle.

hot blue

a process for blueing steel in which the subject material is sequentially immersed in a boiling degreasing solution, a boiling clear water rinse, and, finally, a boiling acid solution which imparts an overall blue-black finish. Certain steel alloys, particularly those containing chromium or nickel, tend to resist conventional hot blueing formulas. To blue such alloys various other techniques and chemicals must be employed. Some double barrel firearms are made with tin soldered ribs and these cannot be hot blued because the boiling acid solution tends to melt the solder causing separation of the barrels. Tin soldered firearms (sometimes referred to as "soft soldered") must be cold blued. Only rifles, handguns and shotguns having silver soldered components may be hot blued.

Hotchkiss

the first successful gas piston operated automatic machine gun pioneered in 1895. In 1900 it achieved military recognition. Modified from time to time it was used in World War I and formed the basis for the successful .50 caliber machine gun used by the United States in World War II.

Hotchkiss, Benjamin Berkley *(1826-1885)*

an American who, while living in France, developed the rifle that was adopted by the U. S. as its first official bolt action magazine arm. He developed an improved metallic case and in 1875 manufactured a hand operated machine gun in France which outwardly resembled the Gatling gun.

Houiller, B.

a French inventor whose patents in 1847-1850 relate to pin, rim and center fire ignitions with the use of full metal cases.

housing

a frame, support or enclosure for holding a part or parts of a firearm in place.

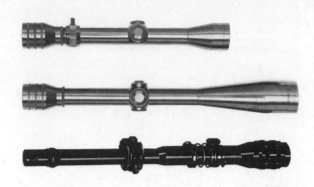

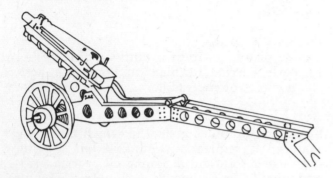

howitzer *(HOW it sir)*

a cannon with a medium length barrel firing shells with a medium muzzle velocity at a high angle of fire capable of reaching targets protected from flat trajectory guns.

HP

abbreviation for hollow point when referring to bullets so made. It is also the abbreviation for horsepower.

hull

a general term used to describe a cartridge casing, usually employed only in referring to shotshell casings.

Hunt, Walter *(1796-1859)*

an American machinist and inventor. One of his inventions was a repeating rifle that formed the basis for the later improvements by others and became the basis for the Winchester rifle.

hunting scope

is distinguished from a target or varmint scope by providing a larger field of view.

Husquarna

a Swedish rifle made by the Husquarna Small Arms Factory in Sweden and commercially available in the United States.

hydrochloric acid

whose chemical symbol is HC1, commonly called muriatic acid, is a solution of hydrogen chloride in water. Among other uses it is employed alone or with other acids as an etching fluid.

hydrometer

an instrument for determining the density or specific gravity of a liquid.

hygrometer

an instrument for measuring the amount of moisture or humidity in the air.

hypervelocity

as defined by the U.S. Army for small arms ammunition is muzzle velocity of 5000 feet per second or more.

See "high velocity"

I

identification of firearms

1. the determination of the make and model of a given firearm, usually only by visual examination of size, shape, markings, material and the characteristics associated with certain firearms.

2. the determination by scientific means of the firearm from which a given bullet or empty case was fired. By microscopic examination and other laboratory techniques the markings on the bullet or case may be compared with the individual characteristics imparted by the manufacturing processes of a firearm.

ignite

to set fire or begin to burn.

igniting charge

in modern ammunition it is in the primer. In former days it was a separatcly loaded charge used to ignite the propelling powder.

ignition

1. in firearms it is the setting on fire of the propellent powder charge.

2. illustrative of the temperatures at which certain substances ignite, —

guncotton	430 degrees F	
nitroglycerin	490	,, ,,
rifle powder	550	,, ,,
charcoal	660	,, ,,
dry pine wood	800	,, ,,
dry oak wood	900	,, ,,

ignition time

the time that elapses between the instant the firing pin strikes the primer and the instant the built up pressure of the propelling gases has caused the bullet to start from its seat.

illumination

in a telescope means the amount of light that reaches the eye through the telescope. The brightness of the image seen depends on the illumination and varies inversely as the square of the magnifying power. Thus, if the magnifying power is doubled the resulting image will be only one-fourth as bright.

image

that which is made visible to the eye through a sighting instrument.

image plane

the collected points of focussed light rays at which the image is formed for viewing, after passing through an optical instrument.

impact

the striking of a bullet or other projectile against a target or other object.

impact, angle of

See "angle of impact"

implode, implosion

to burst inward.

IMR

abbreviation for DuPont's Improved Military Rifle powders.

inactivate

to render a firearm incapable of functioning as such.

incendiary bullet *(in SEN dee er ee)*

a bullet which on impact releases its contained chemical composition. The composition on release generates enough heat to start a fire.

indexing

the practice of rotating a unit of work in a mechanical jig for the purpose of jewel-indexing, engine-turning, etc.

India stone

a natural stone, used with water rather than oil,

to give an initial smoothing and finishing for metal parts, such as sears, ejectors, etc. Also called Hindustan stone.

indicators
pin-like devices that protrude from a firing mechanism when the arm is cocked for firing, and which are recessed when the arm is fired. Indicators permit a shooter to determine by touch, whether or not his gun is in a firing attitude.

inert
a round of ammunition, grenade, bomb or mine containing no explosive or active chemical agent.

inertia
that property of a body by which it will remain at rest, or in uniform motion on the same straight line or direction unless acted upon by some external force.

inertia firing pin
a relatively heavy firing pin that normally lies within its tube. That is, the front end does not contact the primer of the cartridge when the gun is in loaded condition nor does its rear end project so as to bear any pressure from the hammer. Thus, theoretically the loaded gun may be carried with the hammer down. When the hammer is raised the mainspring projects the rear end of the firing pin toward the hammer. When the hammer falls the momentum of the firing pin and its inertia causes it to strike the primer.

inertia lock
See "blowback action"

infinity
in optics, a term used to describe the setting of a scope or camera when adjusted to focus at unlimited distances.

inflammable
capable of being easily set afire.

infra red light
an invisible "light" radiation of frequencies ranging beyond those of visible red. Used in firearms identification to photograph powder combustion deposits on skin and clothing not otherwise detectable.

inhibitor
in chemistry, is a substance capable of stopping or retarding a chemical reaction. Inhibition of corrosion of steel is accomplished by the use of inhibitors, i.e. oxidizing or coating materials of various kinds. In powder manufacture the term "stabilizer" is used to describe a chemical constituent that tends to retard or stop the chemical breakdown of a powder. Sometimes loosely referred to as a deterrent.

initial recoil
recoil before the bullet leaves the muzzle during which a small arm moves a very small fraction of an inch.

initial velocity
same as "muzzle velocity".

initiator
a small quantity of very sensitive and powerful explosive used to start the detonation of a less sensitive explosive. Mercury fulminate is the principal explosive used as an initiator.

inlays
decorative panels or patterns of contrasting materials recessed into wood or metal surfaces.

inletting

the process of recessing metal components in a wooden stock or grip by carving.

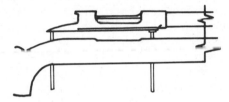

inletting screws

extra long screws that are employed by gunsmiths to facilitate stock inletting work. Temporarily replacing the standard action screws, inletting screws are necessary to align the barrelled action over the trigger guard assembly at the start of rifle inletting operations. The normal action screws are too short for this purpose.

inserts

adapters for shotguns whereby large gauge shotguns may be at will converted to smaller gauges by the insertion of an inner tube.

inserts, sight

interchangeable blades for a front sight that permit selection of a type best suited for given shooting conditions. Commonly employed on target guns.

inside lubricated bullet

a cartridge having a bullet seated within the case deep enough so that the grooves, i.e. cannelures, bearing lubricating grease or wax are inside the mouth of the case.

inside pinfire

a form of cartridge patented in 1869 having a bulb shaped case within which the firing pin lay crosswise, resting at one end against a cup containing fulminate, also lying within the case, and having its other end just inside a blister formed on the outside of the case. When the hammer struck the blister it detonated the powder charge in the case.

instruction firing

practice firing carried out on a practice range under the tutelage of an instructor and sometimes by the "coach-and-pupil" method.

instrumental velocity

the velocity of a projectile measured at a designated point in its trajectory by instrumental means.

interchangeability

1. the ability to exchange similar parts of firearms without impairing their reliability or accuracy. By setting suitable tolerances in the design of a firearm and by proper gaging methods in production, interchangeability has been made possible to a large degree. A system of interchangeable barrels was used as early as the 16th century.

2. the ability to use certain cartridges in place of others without causing malfunction. Tables are available listing cartridges that are completely interchangeable, or interchangeable to a limited degree. Identity of calibers is not alone indicative of interchangeability.

interchangeable manufacture

the manufacture of component parts of an assembled product so that they may be interchanged with similar parts of a like assembled product. Eli Whitney in 1798 laid the foundations for interchangeable manufacture in his production of muskets for the Government. When this system is properly practiced, a rifle, for example, may be assembled from any of the number of parts made for it without the need for reworking the parts used. By contrast see "selective assembly".

interior ballistics
the science that deals with the movement of projectiles within the bore of a gun to ascertain the effect of the various influencing factors, such as size, weight, shape, rifling, etc.

International Free Rifle
a type of rifle used in international target competition. The term "free" stems from the fact that few restrictions are placed on the guns used in such competitions. Other forms of target competition have established limitations for gun weight, trigger weight, sighting instruments, and accessories, etc.

International Shooting Union
founded in 1921 to succeed the original organization, "l'Union Internationale des Federations et Association Nationales de Tir" which existed between 1907 and 1915.
The International Shooting Union promotes and develops international shooting sports, organizes World championships, supervises Olympic competitions and is responsible for the rules governing each of the international shooting sports. Membership is comprised of officially recognized national shooting associations or federations.
The headquarters of the ISU is not fixed at one location but is generally moved, after each election, to the town and country of its new President.
In the United States the ISU is represented by the National Rifle Association, 1600 Rhode Island Avenue NW, Washington, D.C.

interpupillary setting
the millimeter scale on the hinge of a binocular that indicates the separation adjustment of the eyepieces. In focussing a binocular, the user must first set the eyepieces to coincide with the distance between his eyes.

interrupter
a safety device incorporated in a shell fuze to prevent its activation until the projectile has left the muzzle of the gun thus making it "bore safe".

inversion
the act of inverting, or of turning upside down. In shooting, it specifically refers to the image that is picked up by the objective lens element of a scope and inverted. A subsequent lens system, called the erecting lens, then restores the image, rightside up, for viewing.

investment casting
also known as precision casting or lost wax process. A wax or frozen mercury pattern is made for every casting produced by injection molding into metal dies. The pattern or model is placed in a metal flask and the refractory investment material poured around it. After the refractory material has hardened the pattern is melted and subsequently metal is poured into the mold. After hardening the investment is broken away leaving the metal casting in the form of the pattern. Its high cost limits its use to small castings.
See "lost wax process"

iris
an adjustable diaphragm, comprised of a number of movable segments, that enables the user to alter the diameter of the central opening (aperture).
Commonly found in the lens mechanisms of cameras but also used in elaborate metallic sighting instruments.

iris disc
the sighting disc of a receiver or "peep" sight equipped with an iris diaphragm.

iron
a chemical element which is the principal constituent of all commercial iron and steel. Pure iron is silver white, malleable and ductile, melting at 1535°C (2795°F) and weighing 491 pounds per cubic foot.

iron pyrites
See "pyrites"

iron sights
a term that is broadly used to describe metallic sighting instruments, covering common open sights as well as aperture-type receiver sights (as opposed to scope sights).

ISU
abbreviation for International Shooting Union.

Ithaca
a trademark of the Ithaca Gun Company of Ithaca, New York, applied to firearms of their manufacture. The Ithaca Gun Company was founded by the Smith brothers in 1880 and was well known for its fine line of double barrel shotguns until the 1930's. Since World War II they are better known for their Model 37 slide action shotgun, although they also manufacture a number of other models.

Iver Johnson
the trademark for revolvers made by the company of that name, best known for providing a safety feature called "hammer the hammer safety".

ivory grip
grip stocks for an automatic pistol or revolver made from genuine ivory.

J

jacket

the metal casing of copper or steel that forms the outer covering for a lead bullet. Called an "envelope" in Great Britain.

jaeger rifle *(YAY ger)*

a European flintlock hunting rifle popular in the 18th century. Its name in German means "hunter".

jag

a type of cleaning rod tip of cylindrical shape upon which a cleaning patch may be rolled and held in place.

Jager, Jaeger

a German word meaning hunter, applied to a percussion lock, muzzle loading hunting rifle noted for its accuracy. Often called the "1842" it became known in the United States as the Yerger (a corruption of "Jaeger") and the Harpers Ferry rifle.

jam

a stoppage preventing the firing of a gun, usually caused by overheating, faulty ammunition or a broken part.

Janka hardness

a measure of hardness of wood which is taken to be the load in pounds required to imbed a .444 inch diameter ball to one half its diameter in the wood.

Japan drier

a drying agent used in certain stock finishing preparations. Most commonly used in conjunction with boiled linseed oil. Japan drier consists of a solution of mineral spirits containing from one to five percent lead and from two-tenths of one percent to one percent of cobalt or a mixture of manganese and cobalt.

jaws

1. the vise-like device on a flintlock hammer (i.e. cock) used to hold the flint in place. Also known as the "doghead".

2. the gripping plates of a vise.

Jennings, Lewis

an American inventor of a tubular magazine lever action rifle patented in 1849. That was one of the first reasonably successful repeating arms and was a forerunner of the Winchester rifle.

Jessen, Niels Staal *(1797-1880)*

a Danish gunmaker best known for his work on muzzle loaders, his oval gun in 1851 arousing the interest of other gunmakers. The bore was oval in cross section and such section followed a helical curve the length of the barrel, thus constituting in effect two broad grooves to give spin to the elongated ball as it traveled through the bore.

jeweler's rouge

a fine abrasive metal-polishing compound. Generally available in stick form, jeweler's rouge is used to treat cloth polishing wheels before actual polishing operations commence.

jewelling

See "engine turning"

jig

a holding tool or device that simplifies manufacturing operations on a given component. The use of jigs assures manufacturing uniformity and the interchangeability of parts.

Johnson

a semi-automatic rifle having a short recoil system, a rotary bolt locking with eight lugs and unlocking by the rearward movement of the sliding barrel.

Johnson, Cornelius

an English gunsmith who as early as 1521 manufactured pressure lock guns in the Tower of London perhaps from original German designs. The pressure lock is basically the thumb cocked single action as known today.

Johnson, Melvin M.

an American, inventor of the Johnson rotary magazine, semiautomatic recoil-operated rifle just prior to World War II.

Jorgensen, Erik

chief armorer at the Kongsberg Arms Factory in Norway, who cooperated with Ole H. Krag to produce in 1888 the rifle known as the Krag-Jorgensen. Modified, this rifle in 1892 became the U. S. Magazine Rifle, caliber .30, Model 1892, popularly known as the "Krag" or "American Krag".

Joslyn

an American percussion lock breech loading carbine patented in 1855, having a ring above the small of the stock for raising the breechlock for loading.

Journee's Formula

a formula for determining the approximate maximum range for a shotgun, namely that the maximum range in yards is about 2200 times the shot diameter in inches. For example, number one shot being .16 inches in diameter will have a maximum range of .16 x 2200=352 yards.

jug choke

a trial and error method of correcting an inadequately choked shotgun barrel. In "jug-choking" the gunsmith polishes a slight recess in the bore about one inch from the muzzle. This recess tends to let the shot bunch-up before clearing the muzzle and, if done properly, can give the effect of a tighter choke.

A slow and arduous process because the gunsmith must alternate between polishing and test-firing until he achieves a satisfactory shot pattern, or until he determines that a particular barrel simply will not lend itself to jug-choking.

jump

one of the three movements set up in a firearm upon discharge. It occurs while the projectile is still in the gun. It is the turning movement that tends to take place upward and backward about the point of resistance provided by the shooter. See "muzzle jump"

Junior Class shooter

in rifle or pistol competition, a shooter who has not yet reached his (or her) 19th birthday is classified as a "junior". In skeet or trap competition a shooter who has not yet reached his (or her) 18th birthday is classified as a "junior".

K

keeper

a loop that holds straps or cords together such as those used on gun slings.

Kentucky Rifle

an American flintlock rifle that evolved into a pill lock percussion rifle. It was a long barrelled relatively light weight rifle characterized by its short crooked stock and relatively small bore (usually .32 to .50) developed in the 18th century by Pennsylvanians of German descent. Also called Pennsylvania rifle.

Kentucky windage

in shooting, the practice of compensating for differences between the alignment of the sights and the path of the bullet or, of compensating for the effect of wind on the bullet, by aiming to one side of the target rather than directly at it.

key, keyway

a key is ordinarily a piece of metal shaped to fit into a seat or keyway and extends partly in each of two members and when seated prevents rotation of one member with respect to the other. A pulley mounted on a shaft and held by a key and keyway is an example.

keyhole

the elongated hole left in a target by a keyholing bullet.

keyhole shot, keyholing

a shot that makes an elongated hole in a target because the bullet did not strike it straight on but attained a yaw in flight due to insufficient spin. Wear of the bore at the muzzle is a major cause of keyhole shots.

kick

a term used by shooters to describe the effect of the discharge of a gun upon the shooter. It results from the recoil muzzle blast, torque and thrust varying with the shape of the stock. It is not recoil only.

kicker

part of the mechanism on some recoil operated guns that uses the recoil to draw back a rod which in turn forces home the cartridge.

Kiefuss, Johann

an early inventor whom historians credit with having invented the wheel lock in 1517 in either Nurenburg or Vienna.

killing power

the ability of a projectile to kill which depends on a number of factors, such as velocity, shape, sectional density, weight, diameter and material.

"Reprinted by permission of the National Rifle Association of America."

kneeling position

posture of a shooter to give steadiness in firing. For a right handed shooter he kneels on his right knee half facing the right and sits on his right heel. A left handed shooter contrariwise.

knife pistol

an oddity that may in several ways combine a knife with a pistol.

Knocabout

the trade name for a .22 caliber single shot utility pistol produced by the Sheridan Company of Racine, Wisconsin in the 1950's. Now discontinued.

knockdown effect

the ability of a projectile to stop a moving animate object or hurl it backward. So many factors enter into this effect that it is difficult to measure or foretell with any degree of accuracy.

knockout

the ram of a shotshell reloading tool, used to expel the finished shell from the sizing die.

knot

a unit of speed equivalent to one nautical mile (6080.20 feet) per hour. Wind speed is sometimes expressed in knots.

known distance firing

firing over a distance that is known.

known distance range

a range having target positions a known distance from the firing line.

knuckle duster

a hand gun with a metal butt having an opening in the center so it may be grasped with the fingers and used to strike an opponent.

knurling

the scoring or cutting of diamond-like patterns in a metal surface to provide a grip for the hand or finger.

Kollner, Casper or Gasper

a Viennese gunsmith who, in reports of 1498, was credited with producing barrels having straight grooves in the bore.

Krag, American

the popular name given the U. S. Magazine Rifle, caliber .30, Model 1892 which was a modification of the Krag-Jorgensen rifle. It was first issued to troops in October, 1894 and saw service in the Spanish-American War of 1898.

Krag Jorgensen

the 8 mm five shot official military rifle of the Danish Army from 1889 until World War II. Also made as a carbine. Modified, it became the U. S. Magazine Rifle, caliber .30 Model 1892 known familiarly as the Krag. It has a bolt with a single locking lug and a side box loader magazine.

Krag, Ole Herman (1837-1912)

a Norwegian Army officer and gun designer. He invented the rifle that bears his name, the first model being produced in 1868. The one officially adopted by the U. S. in 1892, was produced in 1888 with the aid of Erik Jorgensen and subsequently modified to U. S. military specifications.

Krag-Petersson rifle

the repeating rifle that Ole H. Krag and Axel J. Peterson in 1874 introduced into the Norwegian and Danish navies.

Krupp steel

steel made by the famous German Krupp Works.

L

lacquer

a resinous substance used to give a lustrous surface to polished metal surfaces such as brass, or to wood surfaces. The main constituents are shellac and alcohol plus other substances to give the desired tint. It is sometimes used in gunstock finishing.

ladder

an artillery term for bursts of three rounds each fired in the same direction but aimed to strike at 300-yard intervals; the first round being fired to strike at the greatest range.

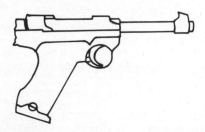

Lahti

the 9 mm, 9 shot semiautomatic pistol adopted in 1935 as a military weapon of Finland and in 1940 by Sweden.

laminated barrel

See "Damascus barrel"

lance

a spear-like weapon once carried by light cavalry, having a long shaft and a sharply pointed steel head.

land diameter

the diameter of a rifled bore measured from the top of one land to the top of the opposite land.

lands

the raised portion between the grooves of a rifled bore.

landscape target

a target displaying the picture of a land scene.

lanolin

a sheep's wool fat derived as a by-product in the preparation of raw wool. It is an excellent rust preventative. A grease made of equal parts of anhydrous lanolin and white petroleum jelly (Vaseline) is used by many gunsmiths.

lanyard (LAN yard)

a strong cord worn about the neck or shoulder and attached to a side arm to prevent it from being lost. It also may refer to a strong cord with a hook at one end, used to fire cannon, pyrotechnic projectors, etc.

lanyard ring

the ring secured to the butt of some revolvers, or to the side of some saddle carbines, to which a lanyard may be attached.

lap

to polish — as to polish the bore of a barrel by means of repeated applications of a fine abrasive.

lapping

the practice of polishing a barrel bore or other metal surface by abrading it.

lapping compound
a fine paste abrasive used in polishing metal.

latch
a movable piece which may enter a notch or opening and hold two objects together. In the case of a revolver with a swing-out cylinder it is the thumbpiece which may be moved to withdraw the locking bolt which holds the cylinder in place, thus enabling it to swing outward.

lateral deflection
the horizontal angle between the axis of the bore and the line along which the gun is sighted. Technically called the lateral deflection angle.

lateral deviation
the distance between the point of impact and the target.

lateral jump
the horizontal angle between the axis of the bore when a gun is fired and the axis of the bore at the instant the projectile leaves the gun. This is the horizontal component of the "angle of jump". The vertical component is called "vertical jump".

lateral lead *(LEED)*
the angle by which the gun is pointed in advance of the target to allow for wind, drift, and travel of the target.

lathe
a machine that is basically designed to hold and rotate a piece of material so work may be done upon it. Lathes are made in many designs and sizes and classified accordingly. For example, bench lathe, turret lathe, chucking lathe, and automatic lathe to name a few.

lay
to direct or adjust the aim of a machine gun or artillery piece. Also means the setting of such a weapon for range, direction, or for both.

laying
the procedure of pointing a gun for range, direction or for both.

lead *(LEED)*
the distance ahead of a moving target that a gun must be aimed in order to hit it.
See "swing-through leading"

LE, L.E.
abbreviation for "low explosive"

lead *(LED)*
a metallic element, softest of the metals in general commercial use. It has a low tensile strength, is very malleable and melts at 621 degrees Fahrenheit. Used in making shot and bullets.

lead azide *(LED)*
a high explosive used in small quantities to set off other high explosives.

lead hammer
See "soft hammers"

leade, lede *(LEED)*
the slightly enlarged and tapered portion of the bore of a gun barrel, just ahead of the chamber, sized to accept the bullet which has a diameter greater than the bore. Also frequently referred to as "throat". The terms "leade", "throat" and "freebore" pertain to the same portion of the bore, however, "leade" or "throat" refers to a taper-cut; free-boring is made with parallel sides rather than tapered.

leading *(LED ing)*
lead deposited in the bore of a firearm upon the passage of lead bullets through it.

leading fire *(LEED ing)*
fire delivered ahead of a moving target to allow for its travel.

lead shot
See "drop shot"
    "shot"
    "chilled shot"
    "coated shot"

lead table *(LEED)*
a tabulation that furnishes the leads required in

order to strike a moving target under various conditions such as range, and speed and direction of travel of the target.

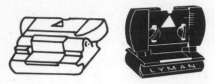

leaf sight

a sight that is hinged at its base so it may normally be laid in a horizontal position but raised to a vertical position when required for sighting. Usually only employed for rear sights.

leather

an animal skin after removal of the hair and tanning. Used for belts, holsters, pouches, rifle boots, etc. The strength and elasticity of leather are much greater in moist air than in dry air.

Lebel rifle

an 8mm, 8 shot tubular magazine military rifle produced in 1886 in France, the first bolt action rifle to use the new smokeless powder and used as a standard by the French until 1936, and as a limited standard through World War II.

LeBourgeoys, Marin *(circa 1550-1634)*

a French gunsmith and inventor. Reputed to have invented, in the years between 1610 and 1615, the first true flintlock, i.e. one having a battery and pan cover in one piece, the blow from the cock opening the pan and striking the spark.

Lee-Enfield

this name was first applied to a .303 caliber, 10 round, bolt action British military rifle adopted as the British service arm in 1895. It used the deep Enfield designed rifling to insure longer barrel accuracy life in the face of the eroding action of cordite. It replaced the shallow Metford grooving of the Lee-Metford rifle which had been adopted as Britain's service rifle in 1888. The name has been associated ever since with the succession of British military models that followed.

Lee, James Paris *(1831-1904)*

a Scottish born U. S. citizen who invented many firearms improvements while living in the United States and whose name is associated with the Lee-Enfield and Lee-Metford rifles, the latter officially adopted by Great Britain in 1888 as the Lee-Metford Magazine Rifle Mark 1. He designed the rifle known as the Lee rifle, made for the U. S. Navy in 1896.

Lee-Metford

the .303 caliber, 8 round, bolt action British military rifle adopted as the British service arm in 1888. It was succeeded as a service arm by the Lee-Enfield in 1895.

leeward

in the direction in which the wind blows. The opposite of windward.

Lefaucheux, M.

a famous Parisian gunsmith who, in 1835, introduced the first truly successful breech loading cartridge and gun. The paper cartridge had a metal expanding base, a cardboard body and projecting brass pin and was termed a pin-fired cartridge. His son, Eugene G. Lefaucheux, patented a revolver in 1845 that became very popular throughout Europe in the 19th century.

Leman, Peter

an American gunsmith who, as early as 1732, was producing rifled arms in the American Colonies along with others of that time.

length of stock

of a shotgun is the distance from the front trigger to the center of the butt; more commonly referred to as length of pull.

lens

a piece of glass ground to concave or convex shape and used singly, or in combination with other lenses, to form an image by changing the direction of light rays.

lens cap

a removable protective covering for a lens.

lens coating

a transparent coating of magnesium flouride, approximately one-quarter of a wave length of light in thickness (5 millionths of an inch), that is applied to optical lenses for the purpose of improving light-transmission properties.
By reducing the amount of light that is normally lost through reflection, lens coating can increase the light-transmission efficiency of an instrument by 30% or more.

Lesmok

the trademark for a blend of black and smokeless powder made by Winchester, consisting of 85 per cent black powder and 15 per cent gun-cotton and loaded into .22 rimfire cartridges.

level

the shortened term for a spirit level, an instrument by which a horizontal line or surface may be determined, used in most types of sighting and fire control equipment. The accuracy of a spirit level depends entirely upon the curvature of the glass tube. In expensive levels this tube is ground on the inside to a barrel shape, the larger the radius of curvature the greater the sensitivity. Nearly filled with ether or similar fluid the tube is hermetically sealed at each end.

level point

the point in the downward curve of the trajectory where the projectile is level with the muzzle of the gun.

lever

a rigid piece that may be turned about a point or axis, called the fulcrum, to transmit force and motion.

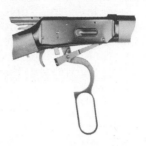

lever action

that type of breechloading action using a lever beneath the grip to open the breech and at the same time extract a cartridge case and then in closing the breech to insert a fresh cartridge in the chamber. Used not only on certain rifles and shotguns but also on pistols.

Lewis

the name of a light air-cooled, gas-operated machine gun with magazine mounted on top of the gun. The first prototype was developed by Colonel I. N. Lewis, U.S.A. in 1911 from a system invented by Samuel McClean. It has the distinction of being the first machine gun to be fired from an airplane, 1912.

Lewis, Isaac Newton (1858-1931)

a U.S. Army Colonel who developed the machine gun (invented by Samuel Neal McClean) used extensively by the British in World War I and many other powers in World War II. Probably best known for his Depression Position Finder.

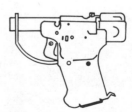

liberator pistol

a cheap single shot .45 caliber pistol weighing less than a pound, produced in the U.S. early in 1942 to the total number of one million for use by allied underground and resistance forces in World War II.

light gathering power

the efficiency of an optical instrument in picking up and transmitting light rays; a factor that is wholly dependent upon the size and quality of the lens systems employed in a given instrument. On clear, sunny days even the poorest grade of instrument will transmit a reasonably good image. Only under poor light conditions will differences in light gathering power become obvious to the user.

light machine gun

the .30 caliber, air cooled machine gun and any machine gun lighter than such gun is so classified by the U. S. military service.

lignum vitae (lig NUMB VY-TEE)

(latin for wood of life) an extremely hard and durable wood from a tropical American tree (*Guaiacum Officinale*) of the bean-caper family. Brown-black in color with yellow-green figuring, lignum vitae is occasionally used in making decorative fittings for gunstocks — such as forend tips and grip caps.

limb work

the crane of a revolver with components, upon which a swing out cylinder swings.

limit of fire

the boundary of the area in which gunfire can be delivered.

linear magnification

the ratio of the size of an image to the object.

line engraving

engraving consisting entirely of fine line or scroll patterns as opposed to engraving that is done in bas-relief.

line in

means to sight a target along the axis of the bore of the gun.

line of bore

the straight line which is the projection of the axis of the bore.

line of departure

the imaginary line which is the continuation of the axis of the bore of the gun the instant the projectile leaves the gun.

line of fall

the tangent to the trajectory of a projectile at that point in its downward curve when the projectile is at the same height as the muzzle of the gun.

line of fire

a straight imaginary horizontal line running from the muzzle of a gun in the same direction as a projectile fired from it.

line of impact

the tangent to the trajectory of a projectile at the point of its impact.

line of sight

the line along which the sights of a gun are set to place them in alignment with the shooter's eye.

line of site

an imaginary straight line extending from a gun or a position-finding instrument to a point, especially a target. Usually called "line of position".

liner

a rifled inner tube for a gun barrel that may be replaced when worn out. For shotguns, to permit use in a smaller gauge, the inserted tube is termed an "insert".

line shot

the hit by a projectile on the imaginary line running from the observer to the target.

line throwing gun

a gun used for rescue operations or in any situation requiring the throwing of a line from point to point. Usually a large caliber smoothbore shoulder gun firing a heavy projectile out of the muzzle and to which a line is secured. A special blank cartridge propels the long projectile.

link

1. a metal unit that connects the cartridges for automatic weapons and with them forms a feed belt.

2. a metal piece in a firearm that flexibly connects two parts.

linkage

a connection of two or more rods or strips to transmit motion in the mechanism of a gun.

link belt

an ammunition feed belt for an automatic weapon formed by links that also hold the cartridges and which disintegrates as it feeds the cartridges to the gun.

linseed oil

a yellowish oil extracted from flaxseed, often used in gunstock finishes. Pure linseed oil does not dry well and must be mixed with a drying agent before it can be used in finishing work. See "Japan drier"

Lin-speed oil

the trademark for a special gunstock finishing oil, having a linseed oil base, that is marketed by the George Bros. Co. of Great Barrington, Massachusetts.

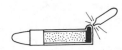

lip fire

an 1860 invention which provided a small lip extending beyond the circumference of the base of a cartridge case and containing the priming charge. In 1865 the Crispin cartridge provided a completely encircling primer ring on the body of the cartridge.

Lippershey, Hans

a Dutch optician who, in October of 1608, applied for a patent on his telescope but the Dutch authorities refused to grant one for "military reasons". He is recognized as the first inventor of the telescope.

liquid oxygen explosive

known as L.O.X, is an explosive found useful in quarrying and mining operations. It is chemically a departure from the conventional type of explosives in that it consists of a mixture of very finely divided carbon, in the form of lampblack or carbon black, with liquid oxygen whose combustion is initiated by a fuse or a detonator. It is considered a safe and stable explosive for commercial use.

lithium soap

a name commonly applied to lithium stearate which is used as a thickener for lubricating greases generally serving an all-purpose use having high water and high temperature resistance as well as good low temperature properties.

live load

a round of ammunition containing an explosive as contrasted with "drill" or "dummy ammunition" which is inert, having no explosive.

load

a single round of ammunition. Also means to place a round in a gun.

loading, density of

See "density of loading"

loading gate

a hinged cover for a magazine or breech to close it except for loading or unloading. In a revolver having a cylinder that does not move away from the breech for loading, it refers to a hinged portion of the standing breech that swings out to expose one of the chambers of the cylinder for loading or unloading.

loading ramp
the platform in a single-shot weapon upon which the cartridge is placed prior to chambering.

loading tray
a hollowed slide which guides the ammunition into the breech of some types of automatic weapons. It also refers to a carrier for heavy projectiles to more readily place them into the breech of a cannon.

load pistol
command to insert a loaded magazine in a pistol.

lock
1. to make a loaded gun safe by setting its safety. It also means the position of the safety mechanism that prevents a loaded gun from being fired.

2. the firing mechanism of a muzzle loader. In a breech loader usually the firing mechanism together with the breech sealing assembly.

3. a device or part for locking two parts together, such as a "locking lug".

lock energy
the energy of the striker blow delivered to the priming mixture.

lock frame
a component of certain firearms used to cushion the shock of recoil of the barrel and bolt assembly before the bolt is unlocked and opened.

locking cam
a movable cam located in the gun to engage mated locking surfaces to seal the breech.

locking lug
a projection from the bolt which locks it to the barrel to seal the breech. Some autoloading firearms have locking lugs on the barrel and slide to lock both together at the instant of firing.

lock plate
a metal plate secured to the stock of a gun for mounting the firing mechanism. Also a plate that is removable to give access, as in a revolver, to the firing mechanism.

lock stock and barrel
the sole components of early hand firearms which constituted a complete gun. It has come to mean completeness of anything to which the phrase is applied.

lock time
the interval of time between the instant the final pressure has been completed to release the trigger and the instant the priming mixture detonates. In that time interval the trigger and sear movements have released the firing pin, the firing pin has been impelled forward striking the primer and the priming mixture has been crushed.

lockwork
See "action"

long fowler
a smooth bore muzzle-loading shoulder gun having an unusually long barrel that, in some cases, reached 6½ feet.

long gun
a term applied to long barrelled firearms to distinguish them from short arms, i.e. pistols and revolvers.

longitudinal deviation
See "range deviation"

long rifle
historically a long-barrelled, relatively lightweight flintlock such as the Kentucky Rifle. In referring to a cartridge, the .22 caliber long rifle cartridge.

loop sling adjustment
a deliberate method of adjusting the sling strap of a rifle on the arm of a shooter to help steady the rifle in shooting. For a right handed shooter the left arm is passed through the loop in the strap and tightened above the elbow to suit the individual.
See "hasty sling adjustment"

loose round

a defective cartridge having a bullet that is loose in the case.

lost

in clay target shooting, a term used to describe a target that has either been missed completely or only "dusted". Scored as a miss.

lost wax process

refers to a method of casting metals believed to have been first used by the Egyptians. It consists in modelling the desired part in wax, surrounding it by spraying or otherwise with a refractory material, then heating to harden the mold and melt the wax. The melted wax is withdrawn leaving a cavity in the mold the exact size and shape of the desired finished product. Various metals in powder form may be blended, melted and poured into the mold. After cooling the mold is broken open and the product removed.
See "investment casting"

lot, lot number

a quantity of ammunition having the same properties as the result of manufacture by the same manufacturer with the same ingredients at the same time under like conditions. Each such lot is assigned a number or other identification called an "ammunition lot number".

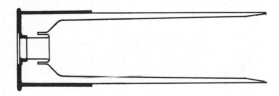

low base

a wad of low height fitted into the base of the paper tube of a shot shell.
See "low brass", "high base, high brass"

low brass

1. a brass shotshell case head that extends but a short distance up the side of the shell. Used with black or bulk smokeless powder in light or moderate loads developing relatively low pressures, and with a wad of low height fitted in the base of the paper tube called a "low base". Contrary to popular belief, the height of the brass head is not directly related to the height of the inner base wad — some low brass cases have high bases and some high brass cases have low bases. Base measurements must be taken from inside the case.
See "high base, high brass"

low explosive

a relatively slow burning explosive, usually set off by heat or friction, employed for propellent charges. Abbreviated as LE or L.E.

low mould, low mold

a local term used in some parts for small size buckshot.

low order detonation

incomplete and comparatively slow explosion of the burster of an explosive projectile.

low power cartridge

a cartridge producing a muzzle velocity of less than 1850 feet per second.

LR

abbreviation for long rifle.

Lubaloy

a trademark of Western Cartridge Company for bullets jacketed with gilding metal (usually 90% copper and 10% zinc) with a small percentage of tin added.

lubricant

a substance such as oil or grease to reduce friction between moving parts like those in the actions of firearms. So called lubricated bullets are those lead bullets lightly coated with grease or those given a copper wash.

lubricant, cold weather

in cold weather the usual oils will congeal and often make the breech mechanism inoperative at low temperatures. For extremely cold weather protection all traces of oil should be removed from the mechanism and finely powdered graphite used as a lubricant.

lug
an earlike projection. Typical is the locking lug on the barrel of a shotgun.

Luger
the registered trademark of Stoeger Arms Corporation for an automatic pistol having a toggle locked breech known in Europe as the Parabellum pistol. From 1908 until 1938 the 9 mm Parabellum was the official military sidearm of Ger-

many. The Swiss Army adopted it as an official sidearm in 1900, in caliber 7.65 mm. When in 1948 it was replaced in the Swiss Army it ended a 48 year period of use as an official military sidearm.

Luger, George *(1848-1922) LEW ger*
a German engineer who, with Ludwig Loewe, a Berlin manufacturing firm, in 1900 patented an automatic toggle locked breech, automatic pistol, (an improved model over the Borchardt design) called the Pistole Parabellum Model 1900 and later sold in the United States under the trademark Luger.

lumps
the British term for "lugs".

Lyman
the trademark for sights, chokes and bullet casting equipment made by The Lyman Gun Sight Corporation.

M

M-1 ammo

ammunition for the M-1 rifle or the M-1 carbine. While both these U. S. military weapons are essentially .30 caliber, there is a great difference between the shells that are used in the M-1 rifle and those used in the M-1 carbine. For this reason it is necessary to differentiate between M-1 rifle and M-1 carbine ammo.

M-1 carbine

a light, small and popular weapon of WWII, the M-1 Carbine is officially designated: "U. S., Caliber .30, M-1, gas-operated semiautomatic carbine". This weapon uses a small .30 caliber cartridge with a bullet that weighs 110 grains (with metal jacket). Muzzle velocity is about 1900 f.p.s.; muzzle energy — approximately 900 foot-pounds. Overall weight of carbine is 5½ lbs. — with sling, oiler and empty magazine.
A later version, called the M-2, was made with some modifications so that it could be used as a fully automatic weapon. A selector lever, located at the top left of the receiver adjusts the weapon for semiautomatic or fully automatic fire.

M-1 rifle

the standard U.S. infantry weapon of W.W. II, otherwise known as the "Garand" rifle.
This model is gas-operated and semiautomatic. Made in caliber .30 U.S. (30/06) it has an 8-round capacity clip-fed magazine. Overall weight is 9¼

lbs. Overall length — 43 inches.
The U.S. Army has since replaced this model with the newer (though somewhat similar) Model M-14 which is made in 7.62 NATO caliber (.308).

machine

1. a combination of parts to transmit force and motion to produce a desired result, thus the term is applied to a continuous firing gun as a machine gun.

2. to do work upon a substance with a machine, such as planing, milling, turning, etc.

machine gun

a firearm of .50 caliber or less in U. S. military service, capable of rapid automatic fire for sustained periods of time; usually fired from a mount. It may have any of the following features: belt fed or magazine fed, water cooled or air cooled, recoil operated or gas operated.

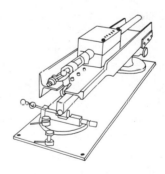

machine rest

a mechanical support for a firearm that holds it steady in a predetermined position even when the trigger is squeezed. Used extensively in firearms testing.

machine tool

a non-portable power driven metal working machine having one or more tool and work holding devices used for the removal of metal. Included in this definition are milling, honing, lapping machines and grinders.

machining
the process of removing metal from a piece by the use of a machine tool.

magazine
1. a container for cartridges which has in it a spring and follower to feed cartridges into the chamber. It may be a separate piece to be inserted into the gun or an integral part of the gun.

2. a place for the storage of powder, ammunition or explosives.

magazine, blind box
See "blind box magazine"

magazine, box
See "box magazine"

magazine catch
the device that holds the magazine in place in a rifle or pistol.

magazine, clip
See "cartridge clip"

magazine, drum
See "drum"

magazine fed
a means of supplying a firearm with ammunition. A magazine containing cartridges is attached to or inserted into a repeating firearm. For example, an automatic rifle is magazine fed.

magazine follower
See "follower"

magazine gun
the name given to a rifle or carbine having a magazine — sometimes called a repeating rifle or carbine.

magazine plug
a wood or metal filler for tubular magazine guns that is used to reduce overall magazine capacity. The Federal Migratory Bird Law requires that repeating shotguns be limited to a total capacity of three shells (counting the one shell in the chamber). For this reason, guns that have larger capacities must be fitted with "magazine plugs".

magazine pocket
a container of leather or other tough material worn on a cartridge belt by which cartridge filled magazines may be carried on the person.

magazine, rotary
See "rotary magazine"

magazine tube
See "tubular magazine"

magazine, tubular
See "tubular magazine"

magazine weapon
a firearm that has a magazine feed. For example the Browning automatic rifle.

"Maggie's drawers"
a slang expression referring to the red target-marker's flag when it is waved back and forth in front of a target to indicate to the shooter that he has missed the target completely.

magna grip
a particular type of Smith & Wesson grip, made for some S & W handguns, that is larger and more handfilling than a conventional grip.

magnifying power

in an optical instrument is the ratio of the apparent size of an object as seen through the instrument to the apparent size of the same object seen without an instrument. In telescopes having a positive eye-piece the magnifying power is equal to the ratio of the focal length of the object glass to the focal length of the eyepiece. While high power increases the apparent size of any object, it decreases illumination and the size of the field and makes focusing more difficult.

magnum

a word of British importation denoting a cartridge of higher than ordinary velocities.

mahogany *(L. Meliaceae)*

hardwood that is yielded by the tropical American or Philippine mahogany tree. Rarely used in stock-making because of its uninteresting grain and heavy weight.

mainspring

the spring that activates hammer or striker and thus the firing pin when the stored up energy in it is released by squeezing the trigger.

malfunction

failure to perform properly. A malfunction may occur in the action of a gun, causing a stoppage, or may occur in ammunition.

mallet

a short heavy hammer of metal or wood. When of wood it is used in gunsmithing as a "soft hammer".

mandrel, mandril

a metal spindle or bar that is inserted into a part or piece to be machined or turned on a lathe.

manganese

is a red tinged, grayish-white, heavy, hard and brittle metal element whose chemical symbol is Mn. It is used in the manufacture of manganese steel and depending on the use the content of manganese in the steel is varied accordingly.

mangonel

a military stone-throwing engine of the 14th century.

Mannlicher

the name under which most of von Mannlicher's firearms designs are known. The most widely known military rifle is the straight pull action of 1895.

Mannlicher, Ferdinand Ritter von *(1848-1903)*

a German born Austrian engineer and inventor whose name is given to a rifle stock extending all the way to the muzzle although he did not develop it. He was a prolific designer of firearms. The name still continues today on certain firearms made in Austria.

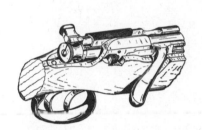 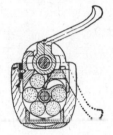

Mannlicher-Schoenauer

the rifle first known by this name was turned out in 1887 with turn bolt lock, spool magazine for single shot or clip loading and with a release for quickly emptying the magazine of cartridges. Sporting models under this name are manufactured in Austria and sold in the United States.

Mann "V" Rest

a machine rest designed by Dr. Franklin W. Mann characterized by having a heavy block of steel having an accurately machined deep "V" slot in its top surface. It is used with a Mann barrel of heavy weight and design, chambered for the cartridge to be tested.

manometer

an instrument for measuring the pressure of gasses or vapors.

Manton, Joseph *(1766-1835)*

an English gunsmith and inventor who with his brother John, were famous London gunsmiths. He patented a percussion pellet lock in 1816 and a tube lock in 1818. His elevated rib for sighting double barrel arms and a patented breech are perhaps his most popular inventions.

man

manual of arms
the prescribed military exercises and drill in the handling of firearms.

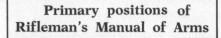

Left Shoulder Arms   **Present Arms**   **Right Shoulder Arms**   **Port Arms**

Sling Arms   **Order Arms**   **Rifle Salute at Order Arms**   **Parade Rest**   **Rifle Salute at Right Shoulder Arms**

marathon shoot

common to skeet and trap shooting—an event that calls for the shooting of from 500 to 1,000 targets in a single day.

Mark, M.

a system of model numbers to identify the design of equipment was adopted in the U. S. military service in 1925, replacing a system of letters and symbols. The number is preceded by the word Mark or simply by the initial M. For example the first Garand rifle of standard issue is designated "U. S. Rifle Caliber .30, M1". A change in the design of the basic model would be shown as "M1, A1"; "M1, A2"; etc.

marker

the individual who marks the targets in target practice. It also means a person, stake or other object that defines a point or boundary line in target practice.

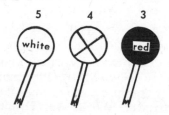

marking disk

a colored disk at the end of a long pole by which an individual in a target pit may indicate to a shooter the location of his hit or value of his score.

marking flag

a flag used to indicate a danger or other point or limit in a target practice area or for other purposes.

marking pennant

a triangular flag used to indicate a danger or other point or limit in a target practice area or for other purposes.

markings

the words and abbreviations found on firearms which may, in addition to designating origin, describe model, material, type of use, etc.

marks, grip

insignia or legend on gun grips to indicate manufacturer.
See "escutcheon"

Marksman

in the U. S. military service the lowest classification given for skill in the use of small arms. It also is the word applied to one who holds such classification.
See "qualification in arms"

marks, proof

See "proof marks"

marksmanship

skill in shooting.

mark target

the order given to a designated individual called a "marker" to mark the shot on the target.

Marlin

a trademark for firearms made by the Marlin Firearms Company (Inc.) founded in 1870. When a machine gun was required by the United States for World War I the company speedily developed one that was also known by the name of Marlin.

Marlin, John Mahlon *(1836-1901)*

an American inventor and firearms manufacturer who founded the predecessor company whose name still is perpetuated in the present day Marlin Firearms Co.

Martin

an early type of centerfire metallic cartridge in which the primer cup was formed as an integral part of the case head.

Martini

the rifle designed by Frederick von Martini for Switzerland was a drastic modification of the Peabody, one feature of special note being an internal firing lock within the breechblock that replaced the high hammer of the flintlocks. England made a modification and used its Henry barrel, thus creating the Martini-Henry rifle officially adopted by the British in 1871.

Martini, Frederick von

Swiss inventor of the now famous Martini firing mechanism, operated by a lever to the rear of the triggerguard. Combined with Alexander Henry's system of rifling it became the Martini-Henry rifle adopted in 1871 for the British Army.

Martini-Henry

a .45 caliber rifle officially adopted in 1871 by the British which combined the Martini firing mechanism and the English Henry system. Modified to .303 caliber was used for Home Guard Service by the British during World War II. The Martini-Henry was replaced by the Lee-Metford in 1891.

master gages

are gages used for verifying inspection gages or for checking questioned parts. Also known as "check" and "reference" gages.

match

1. a slow match is a cord or wick soaked in a solution of saltpeter or of lead acetate and wood ash to enable it to burn at a uniformly slow rate, such as one inch per minute.

2. a quick match is a cord or wick treated with black powder to burn at a rapid rate, such as one foot per minute.

3. the term "match" is also used in referring to target shooting competition.

match-grade ammunition

ammunition made for match use, precision loaded to lower velocity levels than the regular or high speed cartridges ordinarily used in sporting rifles.

matchlock

a firearm ignition system using a slow match in a holder that could be brought to bear on the priming powder to ignite it by the heat of the burning match. Earliest record of use is 1411.

matchlock arms

in addition to being equipped with the matchlock ignition system were produced at various times with other features such as grooves in the bore, both straight and spiral; interchangeable barrels; sights; breech loading; multi-barrels; revolving cylinders; and repeated fire.

matting

the roughing of a metal surface designed to reduce reflections and glare. Matting is commonly found on the top surface of a rib and consists of stipling or a mechanically cut pattern.

Mauser

trademark for rifles and pistols made in Germany. The first successful military bolt action rifle, firing a single metallic cartridge, designed by Peter Paul Mauser was adopted by the German Army in 1871. Subsequently it was converted in 1884 to a tubular magazine repeater and later redesigned for a 5 round box magazine.

Mauser, Peter Paul *(1834-1914) MAUser*

a German gunsmith, inventor of the first successful metallic cartridge bolt action rifle, a patent for which action was taken out first in the United States in 1868. Listed in the patent as co-inventors with him are his brother, Wilhelm, and Samuel Norris, an American. The name Mauser is connected not only with rifles but with pistols and revolvers.

Mauser Werke

the famous German firearms manufacturing plant located in the town of Oberndorf in southern Germany. The huge, mile-long Mauser Works was destroyed after World War II and no longer exists.

Mauser, Wilhelm

a German gunsmith, brother of Peter Paul, and co-inventor with him of the bolt action bearing the name Mauser.

Maxim

the name applied to guns invented by Hiram S. Maxim, known as the father of modern automatic firearms. The basic patent was granted in 1884 by the United States. Maxim guns were first issued to British forces in 1891 and received their combat trials in 1893-94 in Africa. They rapidly replaced the Gatling guns.

Maxim, Hiram Percy *(1869-1936)*

an American son of Hiram Stevens Maxim, but known for his invention of the Maxim silencer, the manufacture of which was discontinued in 1925.

Maxim, Hiram Stevens *(1840-1916)*

a prolific inventor of improvements in firearms, born in the U.S. and, subsequent to going to England in 1882, became a British subject. Brother of Hudson Maxim. Best known as the father of automatic firearms as they are known today. Experiments in 1881 and 1883 produced the first practical method of semiautomatic operation in a rifle. First order for test lot of three machine guns given him by British in 1887.

Maxim, Hudson *(1855-1927)*

an inventor of improvements in explosives. Born in the U. S. but for two years (1886-1888) joined his brother Hiram Stevens Maxim in England.

maximum ordinate

the difference in altitude between the muzzle of a gun and the highest point in the path of its projectile when in flight.

maximum range

the greatest distance a gun with given ammunition can fire.

Maynard

the name for a breech loading rifle invented in 1851 by Edward Maynard, dentist and inventor, that used a percussion cap and a freak brass cartridge case. Its mechanical system later was used when the true metallic cartridge was introduced. The name was also applied to carbines using Maynard's invention.

Maynard, Edward *(1813-1891)*

an American dentist and inventor. In 1845 he patented the tape primer which was in 1855 adopted for official U. S. military weapons. In 1851 he invented an improvement in breech loading rifles which were incorporated in what came to be known as the Maynard rifles and carbines. Other inventions in firearms were also made by him.

Maynard primer

a form of percussion cap having pellets held at spaced intervals between two strips of paper. Also called a "tape primer".

MC

abbreviation for "metal case", in referring to a bullet.

McClean, Samuel Neal

an American gunsmith, inventor of the machine gun made famous by Colonel I. N. Lewis who, after 1910, made improvements in the original design and promoted its manufacture and acceptance by military authorities. The gun is known as the Lewis machine gun.

ME

abbreviation for "muzzle energy".

mean deviation

the average distance by which a group of shots fired from the same gun with the same firing data misses the target.

mean error

the average distance by which a group of shots fired from the same gun with the same firing data lie from the center of impact.

mean radius

the average radius of a group of shots from the center of the group.

mean range

the average distance from the gun reached by a group of shots fired from it with the same firing data.

mean trajectory

the trajectory that passes through the center of impact.

measurements

measurements of firearms parts and cartridges are in the English system normally made to .001". In the metric system to .01 of a millimeter which is the equivalent of .00039".

medium fire

a military term for a moderate rate of fire as for example for a Browning machine gun about 15 bursts of from 6 to 8 rounds each per minute.

meet

a gathering or assembling for a sporting event such as the annual shooting contests held at Camp Perry, Ohio.

mercury

a heavy metallic chemical element in a liquid state at ordinary temperatures, popularly called quicksilver.

mercury fulminate

a sensitive explosive that is set off by friction, impact or heat and burns at a very rapid rate. Used to set off other explosives. Chemically it is mercuric isocyanate, made by treating mercuric nitrate with alcohol.

mercury hardening

the practice of hardening steel tools and parts by heating and quenching in liquid mercury. Although this is a quick and efficient hardening process the high cost of mercury generally limits its application to very small components such as drill bits, taps, etc.

Common Lead Bullet   *Metal Cased Bullet*

metal cased bullet

a lead core encased in a jacket of harder metal, except for its base. The jacket may be of brass, copper, cupro-nickel, gilding metal, steel or other metal harder than the lead of the core. Jacketed bullets give increased penetration and greater uniformity of performance and while particles of the jacket metal may be stripped off, lead fouling is eliminated. To reduce barrel wear or to protect the jacket from corrosion while in storage sometimes the jacket is plated or given a thin metallic wash such as with copper.

metal cased hollow point bullet

a lead core encased in a jacket of harder metal except at the nose. A cavity is formed in the exposed nose of the lead core. The purpose of this construction is to give maximum expansion on impact without shattering the bullet.

metal coating

may be given a metal by electroplating, spraying or oxidizing. Metal spraying is accomplished by spraying atomized molten metal by compressed air upon the surface to be coated.

metal fatigue

See "fatigue"

metal fouling

bits of metal that collect in the bore of a gun, coming from the projectiles passing through it. Seldom encountered today when modern jacketed bullets are used.

metal jacketed bullet

another name for a metal cased bullet.

metallic ammunition

ammunition made up in rounds, mainly for rifles and handguns, the cases being made of brass, copper or mild steel and the projectiles also being made of metal. A term applied to rifle and pistol ammunition by the firearms industry to differentiate between ammo made for rifles and pistols and that which is made for shotguns — the latter consisting largely of cases that are made from paper or plastic. Sometimes referred to merely as "metallics".

metallic sight

a non-optical sighting system for aiming a gun. Frequently referred to as an "iron sight". See "optical sight"
    "sight"

metallurgy

the science that deals with the properties of metals and their separation from their ores. For many years Watertown Arsenal's researchers in metals used in the manufacture of cannon contributed greatly to metallurgical knowledge.

metal patched bullet

generally refers to a metal-jacketed bullet although technically only to a bullet with a cuplike metal jacket extending upward to cover the core, sufficient only to take the rifling of the bore.

metals, melting points of,

See Appendix

metals, properties of

most commonly used in gunsmithing are listed in the Appendix.

meter

an instrument for measuring, especially one to measure the flow of air, gas, water or electricity.

Metford rifling system

a form of rifling having slightly rounded shallow grooves and lands, used extensively in English rifles during the black powder days.

Metford, William Ellis *(1824-1899)*

an English engineer, who in 1865 developed the Metford rifling system of seven grooves which was combined with the bolt action of James P. Lee in the Lee-Metford magazine rifle in 1888. This was the first magazine rifle issued to the British Army (1889) later to be replaced in 1895 by the Lee-Enfield rifle.

metric system

a system of measurement using the meter as the principal unit of length, the liter for capacity, and the gram for weight. All subdivisions and multiples in the system are decimal. The system originated in 1791 in France. Since 1950 the U. S. Army has used millimeters to designate newly developed weapons and ammunition.
See Appendix for equivalents in the English system of measurement.

metro correction

a contraction of "meteorological correction". The adjustment made in the firing data of a gun to allow for wind, air pressure, etc. affecting the flight of a projectile, especially one fired from a cannon.

Mexican rosewood

See "rosewood"

Micro-bed

an epoxy bedding compound used in rifle accurizing work, manufactured and distributed by the Micro Sight Company of Belmont, California.

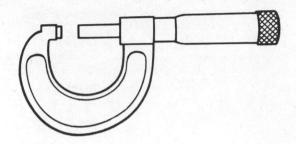

micrometer

an instrument for measuring minute distances.

micrometer caliper

a caliper with a micrometer screw attached, a precision measuring instrument for measuring in thousandths (.001) or ten-thousandths (.0001) of an inch. Generally referred to simply as a "micrometer" or "mike".

micrometer powder measure

a powder measuring tool consisting of a powder storage hopper, an adjustable volumetric measuring reservoir, and a drop tube.
Powder measuring tools of this type measure by *volume*; for safe and accurate handloading purposes powder charges must be determined by *weight*. When used in conjunction with a grain-scale, volumetric powder measures can be adjusted to measure charges with reasonable accuracy and greatly speed-up the handloading process.

micrometer sight

an adjustable aperture type receiver sight equipped with micrometer-like devices to permit fine adjustments, for windage and elevation, in the position of the aperture.

micrometer telescope mount

a form of telescope mount used with fixed-reticle target scopes, that provides external micrometer adjustment devices (in the mount rather than in the scope) for windage and elevation.

micro photograph

a very small photograph or one taken through a microscope such as those taken of bore surfaces, fired bullets, and fired cartridge cases for study.

microscope

an optical instrument for examining minute objects to magnify them for the eye. An essential instrument in the identification of firearms. See "comparison microscope"

middle sight

in the broadest sense a middle sight is any sighting apparatus that is located approximately halfway between the muzzle and the rearmost surface of the receiver. Target shotguns (used for skeet or trap shooting) have — in addition to a bead at the muzzle — a smaller bead (called a middle sight) about 14-inches behind the muzzle sight. In rifles, an open sight located on the barrel, between the front sight and an aperture type receiver sight, would be properly called a middle sight.

mid-range

that point in a trajectory that is half way between the muzzle of a gun and the target.

mil

an angular unit of measure used in the U.S. Army and intended to be an angle that is subtended by one unit of length at a distance of 1000 units of length. Thus a mil subtends 1 foot at a distance of 1000 feet. To precisely do so the mil should be 1/6283 of a circle. The mil formerly used by the infantry was 1/6280 of a circle. The artillery mil now used throughout the Army is 1/6400 of a circle and has the advantage of having a denominator capable of division into whole numbers. For practical purposes it represents 1/1000 of the range. One mil equals 3'22.5" or in fractions, 3.375 minutes. One degree of angle equals 17.8 mils. Civilian firearms users employ minute of angle rather than mils for adjustment of fire.

mile

the English unit of distance, equal to 5280 feet or 1,609.3 meters in the metric system.

mill

to use a rotary cutter to shape and dress a metal surface, a common machining operation in the manufacture of firearms.

millimeter

a unit of measure of length in the metric system equal to .03907 inches. Abbreviated "mm".

mil rule

a ruler that enables an observer to roughly estimate angular distances.

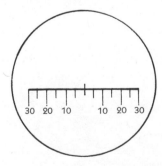

mil scale

the scale consisting of either a horizontal or vertical line, or both, which is divided into mils and used in range finding devices such as a submarine's periscope or a military binocular. Sometimes found in modified form in rifle scopes.

Minie ball

a conical lead bullet having an inverted iron cap in its base adopted to expand the load upon firing, to take the rifling, and acquire the desired spin. Designed by Captain C. E. Minie of the French Army. Later the British in 1852 used a hollow base, then still later, a base with a heavy plug fitted into it. It was extensively used in the muzzle loaders of the Civil War by both North and South.

Minie, Charles Claude Etienne,
MIN i aye (1804-1879)

a Captain in the French Army, famous for his development of the conical lead ball with an iron cup in its base, known as the Minie ball.

Minie rifled musket

a four grooved rifle firing a conical ball, introduced in 1851, became a British service rifle caliber .702, sighted up to 1,000 yards. Some used in Kaffir and Crimean Wars. Replaced in 1853 by the first famous Enfield, a three groove rifle of .577 caliber.

minute, minute of angle

one sixtieth of a degree. A circle has 360 degrees totaling 21,600 minutes. At 100 yards approximately 1 inch of change of point of impact will be caused by a 1 minute change of the rear sight, since 1 minute subtends 1.047 inches at 100 yards. One minute at 200 yards, about 2 inches, at 300 yards about 3 inches, etc. The same relationship exists with the fractions of a minute. For example a ¼ minute adjustment of a sight will move the strike of the bullet ¼ of an inch at 100 yards; a ½ minute adjustment, ½ of an inch at 100 yards. This unit of angular measure is to civilian rifle use as the mil is to military use.

minute gun

in the military service a gun fired at regular intervals as a signal or mark of respect to an individual.

miquelet *(MICK u let)*

a form of flintlock distinguished from the snaphaunce by having a heavy mainspring on the outside of the lock plate. The hammer and pan cover is in one piece, thus when the flint hits the frizzen the pan is uncovered. Named after the inventors, Spanish or Portuguese marauders, known as "miquelites" or "miguelitos" who developed the lock about the year 1600.

mirage

an optical phenomenon. In shooting it is the displacement of the target image due to heat waves and the refraction of light as the light rays are bent in passing thru air layers of different density. The intensity of a mirage varies with a shooter's vision.

misfeed

improper feed of ammunition, especially to a magazine fed or belt-fed automatic gun.

misfire

failure to fire or explode properly and completely. By contrast a hangfire or squib load is delay in the completion of fire or explosion.

miss

failure to hit the target.

missile

an object designed to be thrown or shot, such as a grenade or a bullet.

mitrailleuse *(mee TRI yohz)*

a generic term used by the French for a machine gun although originally it only applied to a multi-barrelled weapon, the first having been invented in 1851, being 37 rifled barrels assembled in a tube.

mm *(m/m)*

abbreviation for millimeter.
See "metric system"

M.O.A.

abbreviation for minute of angle.

mock-up

a scale model of a weapon used to demonstrate the operation of the actual weapon.

model number

when part of the description of a sporting arm it is a number the manufacturer has adopted and ascribed a meaning; when part of the description of U.S. Army ordnance item it has a specified meaning as described under "M".

Mohs hardness

a measure of hardness compared to the hardness of the following substances that are rated from 1 (soft) to 10 (hard):

1. talc
2. sypsum
3. calc spar
4. fluorspar
5. apatite
6. feldspar
7. quartz
8. topaz
9. sapphire
10. diamond

Mosin-Nagant

a 7.62 mm, 5 shot bolt action, magazine fed standard military rifle of Russia from 1891 to about 1946. Designed by Colonel S. I. Mosin and Belgian arms designer E. Nagant it was the first smokeless powder rifle adopted by Russia (1891).

mold, mould

a form adapted to give shape to material applied to it in a plastic or molten condition as for example bullet molds into which molten lead may be poured so that upon cooling bullets of the form of the mold will be produced.

molybdenum *(moh LIB deh num)*

a metallic element whose chemical symbol is Mo is frequently used in making high grade steel alloys for special purposes. Molybdenum is known for its malleability and for its high heat resistance. It has a melting point of 4730°F.

momentum

is the quantity of motion. The linear momentum of a body is the product of its mass and its linear velocity.

monocular

an optical instrument designed for use with one eye, as opposed to binocular, which is designed for both eyes. A rifle scope is monocular.

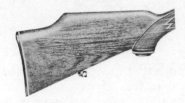

Monte Carlo

a particular type of gunstock design characterized by a pronounced drop in the comb line as it meets the heel of the butt. A Monte Carlo design is often required in order to position the butt properly at the shoulder when the line of sight has made employment of a high comb necessary.

Moorish engraving

a form of art used in firearms decoration which originated with the Moors of North Africa. Moorish style engraving consists entirely of floral and scroll patterns. Because the Moors once invaded and occupied Spain, Spanish engraving and carving often reflects the Moorish influence.

morning gun

in the military service a gun fired at the first note of reveille or at sunrise. Also called "reveille gun".

Morrone

an over and under shotgun manufactured by the Rhode Island Arms Company of Hope Valley, Rhode Island between 1949 and 1953.

Morse

the name of a metallic cartridge patented in 1858. It had a percussion cap which exploded when crushed against a heavy wire anvil attached to the inside of its case.

mortar

a short barreled, short range, high angle fire weapon classified as artillery although employed by infantry troops. Usually smooth bored.

mortar ignition cartridge

a shotgun type shell designed for military use with the firing of mortars, containing a fast burning powder.

mortise

a cavity, hole or opening into which, or through which, another part fits or passes. Combined with a tenon it may form a mortise and tenon joint.

Mossberg

a trademark of the firearms manufacturing firm of O. F. Mossberg & Sons, 7 Grasso Avenue, North Haven, Connecticut.

mottling

a method for obtaining spots, blotches and stain-like appearances on a metal surface in different colors or shades of color. On steel, such colors are obtained by heating to a cherry red heat for several minutes in a cyanide of potassium bath and then while dipping in water moving the piece about vigorously. Used in the decorative treatment of metal surfaces of guns.

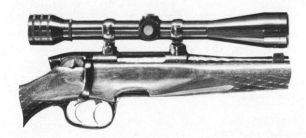

mount

1. a supporting structure or base for a gun.

2. a device used to affix a telescopic sight to a firearm.

mount adapter

a device to make a gun fit properly into a mount.

mouth

an opening into a cavity or tube; the open end of a cartridge case is called the mouth of the case.

mouth pull-down

a cartridge defect caused when the bullet is inserted in the case, pushing the mouth of the case down.

moving target

a target that moves. In international running deer competition it is a facsimile of a deer that is mounted on a moving carriage and exposed to the shooter (at a range of 100 meters) for four seconds as it traverses a 25 yard corridor between protective butts. The deer target travels at about 13 mph.
Flying clay targets, used in skeet and trap shooting, may also be referred to as moving targets — their flight speed is approximately 50 mph as they leave the traps.

mps, m.p.s.

the abbreviation for "meters per second", used in the metric system of measurement to express the velocity of a projectile.

muff pistol

a type of small, single shot pistol, generally not over 3 inches in overall length, of small caliber, made around 1875.

mule ear

a colloquial expression for side hammer.

mullering tool

a wood-carving tool with saw-like teeth used for cutting borders in checkering patterns.

multiple gun

a group of guns emplaced, mounted or adjusted together for firing as a unit.

multiple leaf sight

a type of open rear sight having two or more folding leafs. Each leaf is pre-set for a specific range and this enables the shooter to adjust for the desired range by simply raising the appropriate leaf.

multipurpose gun
a gun suitable for a number of different types of target or game.

munitions
a word that embraces ammunitions, weapons and all other kinds of necessary war materials.

muriatic acid
another name for hydrochloric acid.

mushroom
the effect produced by certain bullets by expanding on or shortly after impact. The word is also used for some soft point or hollow point bullets. See "SP" and "HP"

musket
until about 1750 all shoulder arms of smooth bore were called muskets. The term later was applied indiscriminately to rifled as well as smooth bores. The name originated in the 16th century for a form of arquebus as a "maschetto" in Spanish, "mousget" in French and in England it became in sequence "mousquit", "mouskitt" and eventually "musket".

musketeer
a soldier armed with a musket.

musketry
fire delivered by rifles or other small arms. Also means training in the use of such.

musketoon
a colloquial term for a muzzle-loading firearm of carbine length having a large smooth bore.

muzzle
the front end of a gun barrel from which the bullet emerges.

muzzle blast
the surge of hot air and gases that bursts from the muzzle of a gun as the projectile leaves it. Also called powder blast.

muzzle bore sight
generally a disk with cross hairs that are exactly in the center of the bore when the disk is fitted into the muzzle end of a gun. Used with a "breech bore sight" to establish the axis of the bore. See "bore sight"

muzzle brake
an attachment secured to the muzzle of a gun, which may be a cannon, rifle or shotgun, to utilize some of the muzzle blast to apply a forward force to the barrel at the instant the gun is reacting backward in recoil. Basically it is a tube screwed to the muzzle, having a bore of diameter slightly larger than the bore of the barrel to enable the bullet or shot charge to pass freely through it. The wall of the tube is provided with holes or slits at right angles to the bore or inclined backward and outward at a slight angle to permit a portion of the muzzle blast to thus act against the tube and escape from it.

muzzle cap
a cap for covering the muzzle end of a gun barrel to keep out deleterious matter.

muzzle compensator
a device attached to the muzzle of a gun barrel which utilizes the escaping gases to control the direction and amount of undesireable muzzle movement. It may also reduce the recoil energy of the weapon.

muzzle energy
the energy of a bullet at the instant it leaves the muzzle of a gun, expressed in foot pounds.

muzzle flash
the flash that appears at the muzzle of a gun when it is fired. It is caused by the expanding powder gases that ignite when they and burning powder pieces meet the air at the muzzle of the gun.

muzzle guard

a cap, usually made of brass, to fit over the muzzle of a gun barrel, having a hole in its center concentric with the bore of the barrel. The diameter of the hole is just large enough to admit a cleaning rod. Purpose of the muzzle guard is to prevent wear at the muzzle end of the bore for those rifles cleaned from the muzzle. It is usually employed with .22 caliber match rifles.
See "cleaning bolt"

muzzle jump

refers to the muzzle motion of a gun upon firing. While many factors combine to put a fired gun into motion, "muzzle jump" is essentially caused by the fact that the axis of the bore rests above the mass of the gun. Also, when holding a rifle or shotgun in a shooting attitude, the marksman grips the forend (below the barrel) with one hand while positioning the other hand around the grip and trigger guard which likewise lie below the axis of the bore. As the weapon recoils the muzzle will naturally take the path of least resistance and move in an upward direction.

muzzle loader

a gun loaded with propellent powder and projectile only through the muzzle end of the bore.

muzzle loading

the act of loading a gun through its muzzle end, as in the case of a muzzle loader.

muzzle protector

See "muzzle guard"

muzzle sight

another name for "front sight"

muzzle velocity

the velocity of a projectile at the instant it leaves the muzzle of a gun. Also known as the "initial velocity". Abbreviated as MV.

muzzle wave

the compressed air that fans out from the muzzle of a gun after firing, also called "gun wave".

MV

abbreviation for "muzzle velocity".

N

Nagant

a seven chambered 7.62 mm Russian revolver adopted by Russia and Poland about 1895.

naked bullet

a bullet not encased in a metal jacket or covered by a patch.

Nambu

an 8 mm, 8 shot semiautomatic pistol used by the Japanese Army from 1914 to 1945 although not officially adopted as a standard.

National Bench Rest Shooter's Association

a national organization of those interested in precision shooting, founded 1951 and having headquarters in Minerva, Ohio.

National Board for the Promotion of Rifle Practice

was authorized by Act of Congress in 1903 and consists of from 21 to 25 members appointed by the Secretary of the Army from the Army, Navy, Air Force, Coast Guard, Reserve Officers Association, National Guard Bureau, Selective Service, National Rifle Association and the country at large. The principal mission of this Board is to promote, among United States citizens, practice in the use of military-type small arms, provide arms, ammunition and accessories, and arrange for matches and competitions in their use. Responsibility for conducting the National Matches has been delegated to it by the Secretary of the Army.

National Firearms Act

was signed into law June 26, 1934 and is designed to control so-called gangster weapons such as machine guns, silencers, rifles with barrel lengths of less than 16 inches, shotguns with barrel lengths of less than 18 inches, etc. by imposing a high tax on their importation, manufacture and transfer, and requiring their registration. The "National Firearms Act Amendments of 1968" was enacted into law on October 22, 1968 along with the "Gun Control Act of 1968" as part of a comprehensive program to make firearms laws more stringent. The Secretary of the Treasury administers the law and promulgates regulations to implement it.

National Match Ammunition

National Match ammunition in caliber .30 and caliber .45 was manufactured on an annual basis for the "Camp Perry" matches during the period of 1919 through 1940, discontinued until 1957 when it again was reintroduced under the following designations:

Cartridge, Match, Caliber .30 M72 (National Match) Cartridge, Ball, Match Grade, Caliber .45 M1911 (National Match).

All quantities of the match cartridges, through 1940, and the initial 1957-58 quantities were manufactured at Frankfort Arsenal. Since then all annual requirements of the caliber .30 and caliber .45 Match cartridges were and are produced at other ammunition facilities having greater daily production capacities.

The 7.62 mm Match M118 cartridge was approved for production at Frankfort Arsenal in August of 1964. Subsequent annual requirements are being produced by Lake City Army Ammunition Plant.

Upon reactivation of the "Camp Perry" National Matches in 1953, available stocks of service type caliber .30, Ball M2 and caliber .45, Ball M1911 ammunition were screened, retested and the best qualified lots of each type were selected annually for each year's matches until stocks of the National Match cartridges were made available.

Cartridges designated as "NM" and "Match" are produced to the same specification requirements; however, additional care is exercised in manufacture of the lots specifically intended for Camp Perry which are head stamped "NM" in lieu of "Match".

National Matches

established in 1903 by Act of Congress with participation limited initially to teams from the regular services and state National Guard organizations.

In 1916, upon passage of the National Defense Act, civilian teams were permitted to join in the competition.

Now held annually at Camp Perry, Ohio, the National Matches are comprised of three programs:

1. The Small Arms Firing Schools

2. The National Trophy Matches

3. The National Rifle Association Championships

The National Matches are conducted under the general supervision of the National Board for the Promotion of Rifle Practice.

National Muzzle Loading Rifle Association

a National organization of those interested in black powder shooting, founded in 1937 and most recently having headquarters in Friendship, Indiana.

National Rifle Association, The

a non-profit organization founded in 1871 with headquarters in Washington, D.C. and whose purpose it is to promote the safe, efficient, lawful and rewarding knowledge and use of firearms. It is the largest and best known firearms association in the United States, and numbers hundreds of thousands of members.

National Shooting Sports Foundation

commonly referred to as the "NSSF" this organization is headquartered at 1075 Post Road, Riverside, Connecticut, and was founded as a non-profit organization in 1961 for the purpose of promoting a better understanding of the shooting sports by the American public. Membership is limited to firms that offer a product or service to hunters or shooters. Associate memberships are open to firearms distributors and dealers.

National Skeet Shooting Association

a national organization having its headquarters at 3409 Oak Lawn Avenue, Dallas 19, Texas, the authority in the United States for rules and procedures governing skeet competition and the classification of competitors.

near miss

a projectile or bomb that does not score a direct hit on the target but is close enough to inflict some damage.

neat's foot oil

an animal oil, pale yellow in color and with a peculiar odor, obtained by rendering the hooves of cattle. Used for softening leather slings and for dressing leather belts and holsters, and as a lubricant.

neck

that portion of a bottleneck cartridge case that is of reduced diameter and into which the bullet is seated.

neck crack

a crack in the neck of a metallic cartridge case generally caused by repeated stretching and squeezing of the case in resizing.

neck sizing

the practice of re-shaping, or of restoring to original dimensions, only the neck of a cartridge case when reloading it for re-use in the same weapon that fired it originally.
Neck sizing, as opposed to full length sizing, prolongs case life.

Needham

the name of a needle gun developed in England after the Franco-Prussian War. It was a repeating rifle having a tube below the barrel for a magazine, and a revolving cylinder.

needle file

a very fine, slender, machinist's file for delicate work in confined areas. Needle files come in a large variety of shapes.

needle fire

the means by which the propellent charge in the paper cartridge case used with the Prussian needle gun was ignited. The needle-like extension of what would be a firing pin in a modern gun had to penetrate through the case and its charge before striking the primer which also was contained within the case.

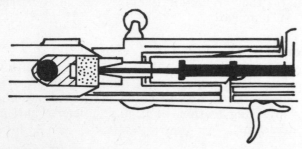

needle gun

a percussion gun adapted for use with a cartridge having a primer located within it. The gun has a needle that can pierce the cartridge and strike the primer, thus setting off the charge. Both muzzle loading and breech loading guns employed this form of ignition system. The Dreyse was the best known needle gun.

negative lens

a lens that causes light rays to diverge, i.e., extend from a common point in different directions.

neoprene

an oil resistant synthetic rubber.

NH powder

See "nonhygroscopic powder"

nickel

is a hard, white, malleable, ductile, rust resistant element whose chemical symbol is Ni. It is extensively used for plating less durable metals and the fiction writer's reference to "nickel plated revolvers" has basis in fact. Alloyed with steel to form nickel steel it is used for armor plate and other similar products.

nickel steel

a steel with 3½ percent of nickel and 0.32 to 0.40 percent carbon, used in the making of high power rifle barrels.

nipple

the cone-shaped part of a percussion gun which is adapted to receive a percussion cap over its centrally located hole which communicates the flame from a cap to the powder charge in the barrel.

nipple pick

a short pointed metal pick either separate or in conjunction with a nipple wrench, used to clean out clogged nipples of early percussion type firearms. Sometimes called a "frizzen pick".

nipple wrench

a wrench carried as an accessory, used to unscrew broken or corroded nipples of early percussion type firearms and for screwing on replacements.

niter

a common name, just as is saltpeter and nitrate of potash, for potassium nitrate.

niter bluing process

a method of imparting a blue color to iron or steel by immersing a few seconds in molten potassium nitrate (also called nitrate of potash, niter or saltpeter) maintained in an iron pot at about 600 degrees F. Lower heats give lighter shades, higher temperatures darker colors.

nitric acid

whose chemical symbol is HNO_3 is a colorless solution, used in gunsmithing for etching steel gun parts.

nitro

sometimes used as part of the identification of a cartridge to indicate its propellent as distinguished from black powder.

nitrocellulose

the composition resulting from the treatment of cotton or other form of cellulose with a mixture of nitric and sulfuric acids. It is the base for all modern smokeless powder. Guncotton is a nitrocellulose having a very high nitrogen content.

nitrocellulose powder

high powered smokeless propellent powder. Pyro powder is a type of nitrocellulose powder.

nitrocotton

See "guncotton"

nitrogen filled

refers to rifle scopes that are filled with nitrogen gas during the final stages of manufacture in order to prevent fogging when exposed to temperature changes in the field.

nitroglycerin, nitroglycerine

a highly heavy, thick, syrupy liquid made by treating glycerin with a mixture of nitric and sulphric acids. It is very sensitive to shock and friction.

nitro wad

See "wad column"

Nobaloy

an alloy of from 90% to 95% copper and 10% to 5% of zinc with a small percentage of tin, so-called by its English manufacturer to distinguish it by name from Lubaloy.

Nobel, Alfred Bernhard *(1833-1896)*

a prolific Swedish inventor who produced dynamite in 1863, and later other explosives including a form of smokeless powder that was later developed into cordite. By his will he established the famous Nobel Prizes awarded for services to mankind.

no-bird

an illegal or broken target in skeet or trap shooting. The shooter is not required to shoot at such a target, however, if he does, it is ruled a legal bird and he must clearly hit one of the larger segments to avoid having it scored as a miss. When he does not shoot at such a target he may simply call for another bird.

Nock, Henry *(1741-1804)*

an English gunsmith, active 1772 to 1802, who invented an enclosed lock which substituted pins and hooks for the usual screws. His 1787 breech patent enabled use of a shorter barrel because it fired the propellent charge through the breech.

noise

the disagreeable effect of certain sounds upon the ears. The disagreeable effect varies with the hearer and is not susceptible to measure on a universally accepted standard. Intensity of noise and sound is measurable.
See "decibel"

nomenclature

the system of names or titles officially assigned to weapons and other material and equipment.

non-corroding, non-corrosive

as applied to ammunition, it is ammunition using a primer that does not deposit rust producing salts on the surface of the bore of a gun.

nonexplosive

a material or object that will not explode under any circumstances.

non-ferrous metals

metal alloys that do not contain iron. Steel is a ferrous alloy; brass is a non-ferrous metal.

nonhygroscopic powder

a smokeless powder having no tendency to absorb moisture from the air; used as a propelling charge. Termed in brief, NH powder.

Nordenfelt

one of the best known mechanically operated machine guns of Europe manufacture. Inventor of the system was Heldge Palmcrantz a Swedish Engineer, its promoter Thorsten Nordenfelt (1842-1920) a Swedish banker in London. The earliest design was made in 1872.

Norma

refers to those munitions manufactured by the firm Norma Projektilfabrik of Amotfors, Sweden. The name "Norma" is also used by their American representatives: Norma-Precision Company of South Lansing, New York.

normal charge

the regularly prescribed quantity of powder used with a gun. Under special circumstances a reduced or a supercharge may be used.

normal impact

the situation when a projectile squarely strikes a surface, that is, the line of flight of the projectile is normal (perpendicular) to the surface.

North, Simeon *(1765-1852)*

an American gunsmith and well known manufacturer of pistols and rifles for the United States Government.

North-South Skirmish Association

a national organization of those interested in paying tribute to the soldiers of both sides in the War between the States and to show use of their weapons. Headquarters at Pennsauken, New Jersey. Affiliated with the National Rifle Association of America.

nose

the point or foremost part of a projectile.

Nosler bullet

an American made partition bullet manufactured by the Nosler Partition Bullet Company of Bend, Oregon. At this writing Nosler bullets are not available in commercially loaded cartridges but are sold separately to those who are interested in handloading them.

notch sight

usually refers to a front sight of the post type having a notch in its top edge. An open rear sight having a V shaped notch in its top edge generally is not so called.

NRA

abbreviation for The National Rifle Association.

nutcracker tool

a colloquial name for Lyman Gun Sight Company's famous #310 Tong tool. This is a reloading tool consisting of two handles hinged together at one end (not unlike a nutcracker) and into which are fitted the required reloading dies. Entirely hand operated, this tool will perform all normal reloading operations except full-length sizing and powder measuring.

nylon

the generic term for a series of polyamide resins having many uses. It has been used for gun stocks and for barrels. Its use for barrels is as a sheath for a steel inner tube.

O

Oberndorf

the town in Bavaria, Southern Germany, where the brothers Peter and Wilhelm Mauser founded the Mauser Works — an arms manufacturing facility that achieved world-wide fame.

objective end

that portion of an optical instrument which houses the objective lens — the lens that picks up the light rays transmitting the image. The objective end is that portion of the instrument that is farthest from the eye when in use.

objective lens

the first, or light-gathering lens in an optical instrument.

obsolete

describes something no longer in use. As applied to firearms, generally taken to mean those guns no longer being manufactured, having been replaced by newer models.

obstruction

See "barrel obstruction"

obturate, obturation

(OBB too rate, OBB too RAY shun)
to seal off the breech end of a gun to prevent the escape of gases, usually by the expansion of the cartridge case against the wall of the breech chamber. Obturation is the name given the process by which the escape of such gases is prevented. Obturator the name given the device by which the breech end of a gun is made gas tight.

o'clock

according to the clock. In shooting, the standard clock having numbers 1 to 12 on its face is used to designate direction from the shooter or from the center of a target.

octagon barrel

a gun barrel having an eight sided exterior surface.

ocular

1. the eyepiece of an optical instrument.

2. pertaining to the eye.

Odkolek, Baron Adolph von

an Austrian Army Captain who, in 1893, associated himself with the Hotchkiss gun manufacturing organization and there introduced a new application of gas power to an automatic arm, — the gas piston housed in a cylinder beneath the barrel.

"Reprinted by permission of the National Rifle Association of America."

offhand

shooting from an erect standing position with the firearm supported only by the arms and hands. While this is often called the "standing" position, "offhand" is the term that is technically proper.

offset mount

a telescope mount fastened to a rifle in such a way that the axis of the scope is offset to one side of the rifle bore rather than directly above it. While this is not the most desirable mounting arrangement, it is one of the two possible methods where top ejection guns are concerned. Shooters with eye problems are often forced to use offset mounts so that they may continue to shoot from the right or left shoulder while sighting with the opposite eye.

offset trigger

a trigger that is not positioned under the center line of the firearm or one that travels in an oblique rearward direction when pulled.

ogive *(O JIVE)*

1. the curved forward part of a projectile up to, and including its pointed end.

2. the radius of the curve of the nose of a bullet commonly expressed in calibers.

oil

a liquid substance that is combustible, or meltable upon warming, and soluble in ether but not in water. The term covers a large number of substances having mineral, animal or other organic origin. A thin oil is desirable for firearms generally. Rapid fire guns such as machine guns require heavier oils because of the high heat developed in continuous firing.

oil dent

a defect in a cartridge case consisting of a smooth depression caused by the use of too much oil in its manufacture, too much oil in the chamber upon firing, or too much oil in the die upon re-sizing.

oiled case pressure gage

a device used by the British for measuring the breech pressure developed by a cartridge. A special bolt or breech block is used in which a hollow copper cylinder is placed between an anvil and a piston. A cartridge case, well oiled to prevent sticking to the walls of the chamber is inserted in the chamber, its head resting against the piston. Upon firing, the case slides backward and compresses the cylinder. The amount the cylinder is shortened will, when compared to a reference table, called a tarage table, disclose the pressure in the breech that compressed it.

oil finish

a gunstock finish created by hand-rubbing with linseed or tung oil. Contrary to popular belief, a good stock finish cannot be achieved by oil alone: the stock must first be treated with a filler and a sealer. After the sealer has dried, the stock is finely sanded and finished with light applications of oil.
Modern stock finishes, such as those made with epoxy resins have proven superior to oils and are gradually replacing oil finishes.

oilstone

a whetstone treated with oil and used for polishing or sharpening steel components.

one-piece mount

See "bridge mount"

OPE

an abbreviation for open point expanding bullets, constructed with a hollow point.

open-breech action

a system wherein the breechblock is held to the rear by a compressed spring, which, when released by pressing the trigger permits the breechblock to move forward during which time a cartridge is carried into the chamber. When the breechblock closes a firing pin strikes the primer of the cartridge. The Browning automatic rifle contains such an action.
See "closed-breech action"

open match

a target competition that is open to anyone, although participation may be limited to citizens of the U.S. and members of The National Rifle Association.

open point

a bullet having a cavity in its nose to increase the expansion of the bullet when it hits. Also called "hollow point".

open sight

a sight that is not a fully encircled opening.

operating handle

the handle or grip by which a shooter may move the operating lever, to open and close the breech of a gun.

operating lever

a lever device to open and close the breech of a gun.

operating slide

the mechanism in a Browning machine gun that permits the opening of the breech for loading, unloading, clearing out stoppages, and closing the breech for firing.

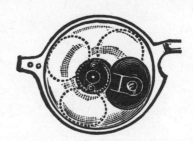

optical attachment

an eyepiece sighting disc (for a receiver sight) made to hold a prescription lens. Intended for shooters who ordinarily must wear glasses.

optical sight

a sight that employs an optical system of lenses, prisms or mirrors, to aim a gun.

optics

the science of light and vision.

ordnance *(ORD nance)*

military material of many kinds but principally combat weapons, ammunition, bombs, rockets, mines, explosives, pyrotechnics, combat vehicles, and accessories. Abbreviated as ORD.

ordnance steel

a steel containing from 0.45 to 0.55 percent of carbon, 1.00 to 1.30 percent manganese, and up to 0.05 percent of phosphorus and 0.05 percent of sulphur used until about 1941 for rifle and shotgun barrels, having been introduced at the start of the 20th century.

Oregon myrtle

wood from the myrtle tree of the Pacific Northwest which is used more and more frequently in gunstock work. Varies greatly in color (from orange to dark brown) and in grain figuration; resembles walnut in weight and working characteristics but has frustrating warping tendencies.

orifice

an aperture, opening, port or vent. The gas vent in the receiver of a rifle is an example.

origin of the trajectory

the center of the muzzle of a gun at the instant the projectile leaves it.

ornamentation
as applicable to firearms — any form of decoration such as contrasting woods, checkering, carving, engraving or inlays made from precious metals.

O/U
abbreviation for over and under, the arrangement of the barrels of a shotgun and other long guns.

outrange
the ability of one firearm to deliver a projectile at a greater distance than some other firearm.

outshoot
to shoot more accurately or more effectively than someone else or some other weapon.

outside lubricated bullet
a bullet having a diameter for the cylindrical or bearing portion just outside the mouth of the case about equal to the outside diameter of the mouth of the case. The bullet has a smaller diameter or heel at that portion lying within the mouth. Grooves or cannelures in the exposed cylindrical portion contain a film of lubricating grease or wax.
See "inside lubricated bullet"

oval-bore rifling
an oval shaped bore, the oval being twisted to give the bullet a spinning motion, made in London about 1850. This construction was developed to take the place of lands and grooves.

over
a shot that strikes or bursts over or beyond the target. One that fails to reach the target is called a "short".

over & under gun
a type of firearm having two barrels mounted one above the other.

over bore capacity
applied in describing a cartridge case that has a capacity that exceeds the amount of powder that can be most efficiently used in it.

over powder wad
See "wad column"

overshoot
to shoot over or beyond a target.

over-shot wad
See "wad column"

overtravel
the continued movement of a trigger rearward, beyond the point at which the gun is fired.

oxidation
is the slow combining of oxygen with various elements and compounds. Rust is a form of oxidation. The rust on iron is iron oxide. Rapid oxidation is called combustion. When extremely rapid and noisy it is called an explosion.

oxyacetylene welding
   (OX ee ah SET i leen)
See "welding"

P

Pacific International Trapshooting Association
an organization of those interested in trapshooting in the Western U.S., founded 1928 and having headquarters in Salem, Oregon.

Pacific maple
a species of maple tree grown in Washington, Oregon and parts of California.
The wood from this tree is dense but soft and, though occasionally used in gunstock-making, is a poor substitute for walnut.

pack
as a slang word, to carry a gun, usually a handgun.

Packard
custom made rifles designed by Ralph G. Packard in the 1930's.

pad, recoil
See "recoil pad"

Paine, Ira Anson
a famous United States pistol shot of the late 1800's, developer of the bead front sight and U-notch rear handgun sight combination formerly very popular.

Paine sight
a "bead on a post" front sight, with a half round notch rear sight designed by Ira Paine in the late 1800's.

Palmer, William R.
an American gunsmith and inventor, who in 1863 patented a bolt breech locking design that was a step toward the bolt action later to become popular.

palm-rest
an auxiliary hand grip for a rifle that may be used when target shooting from the offhand (standing) position.
A palm-rest enables a shooter to rest the elbow of his leading arm against his hip and thereby helps him to steady the rifle.

pan
the receptacle in a matchlock, wheellock or flintlock for holding the priming powder in suitable relation between the igniting means and the propellent charge.

pan cover
a plate over the pan to protect the priming powder from spilling or getting wet.

panoramic sight
a sight usually for cannon, giving the gunner a wide field of view.

paper patched bullet
a smooth lead bullet of bore diameter, tightly wrapped with strong thin paper to increase its diameter to grove diameter. The paper was folded over the bullet base. On firing the lands cut into the paper, giving the bullet a spinning motion without marring its surface. It also served as a gas seal and reduced lead fouling of the bore. The patch left the bullet at the muzzle. Black powder cartridges were sometimes loaded with these bullets which gave excellent accuracy.

149

paper shell

a term used in referring to a paper-cased shell for a shotgun.

Parabellum

translated means "for war". It was the name for a German machine gun used in World War I and II and is the name popularly applied in Europe to the official German Army sidearm, the Pistole 08, from 1908 to 1938. It is the same pistol with the toggle action that sold in the United States under the registered trademark LUGER.

paraffin test

the common name for the diphenylamine test to detect the presence of nitrates on the human hand. It consists of applying hot clean paraffin to the hand to pick up from the hand the powder residue left by the firing of a pistol or revolver. By chemical analysis the presence of nitrates will be detected. This test is not considered to be conclusive proof that a pistol or revolver has been fired since nitrates may be found on the human hand from causes other than from powder combustion deposits.

parallax

1. the apparent difference in the location of an object when viewed from two different points. In this meaning is also called azimuth difference.

2. the apparent motion of the cross wire in a telescope across the image of the object as the eye is moved from side to side across the eyepiece — a condition caused by improper focusing.

Parker

a famous American manufacturer of double barrel shotguns. Located in Meriden Connecticut until acquired by the Remington Arms Company in 1934, when all production facilities were moved to Remington's plant at Ilion, New York. The manufacture of Parker guns was discontinued in 1942.

Parkerizing

applying a grey colored rust preventative finish to the metal surfaces of a firearm by the use of an appropriate acid solution.
See "phosphatizing"

partition bullet

a comparatively modern development in bullet design intended for big game hunting.
Controlled expansion and penetration is achieved by separating the lead core of a jacketed bullet into two parts: the forward portion expands upon impact while the rearward portion remains intact.
See "H-Mantle" and "Nosler"

paster

a piece of paper stuck on a target to cover a previously made bullet hole.

patch

1. a small piece of soft cloth adapted by size to be used in cleaning the bore of a firearm by passing it from one end to the other.

2. a piece of cloth such as linen, denim, canvas or cleaning patch materials around a bullet to serve as a gas seal for older weapons and to aid it in engaging the rifling. Common to muzzle-loading firearms.

patch box

a receptacle in the stock of a muzzle loading rifle for holding bullet patches, grease and small tools.

patent

a monopoly granted by the government to an inventor which gives him the exclusive right for a fixed term of years to designate who shall be allowed to make, use or sell the embodiment of his invention. This means that even an individual who, for his own use, wishes to make a gun that includes a patented invention is legally obligated to first obtain a license (i.e. permission) to do so from the owner of the patent. The United States Patent Office, as well as the Patent Offices of foreign countries have issued many thousands of patents for inventions relative to firearms, ammunition, accessories and supplies. The first U.S. Patent was granted on July 31, 1790 to Samuel Hopkins.

patina

a dark green film on a copper, brass, and bronze surface of a firearm caused by oxidation. This kind of surface is prized in an antique firearm.

Patridge, E. E. *(PATridge)*

former president of the United States Revolver Association, developer of the flat-top blade front sight and rectangular-notch rear open sight combination introduced in 1892 and generally used for handguns having replaced the Paine sights in popular favor with pistol shooters.

Patridge sight

a thick front sight, flat on top, with a square notch rear sight designed by E. E. Patridge in the late 1800's.

patterns

1. the distribution of a series of shots fired with the same setting.

2. in the case of a shotgun, the distribution of the pellets from a single shot at a specified distance within a circle of certain diameter. For example, a pattern test of a 12 gauge gun with a full choke would be expressed as so many pellets within a 30-inch circle at 40 yards. Smaller gauges and 12 gauge guns with open chokes should be patterned at shorter ranges.

Pauly, Johannes Samuel *(1766-c1820)*

also known as Jean Samuel and Samuel John Pauly. An English gunsmith and inventor, his best known invention being a breechloader he developed in the years 1808 and 1812, that represented the first needle gun and self consuming cartridge. The cartridge was ignited by a needle that pierced a paper detonating cap affixed to the cartridge. It preceded the Dreyse needle gun by about 30 years.

pawl

a movable piece in a mechanism, usually spring controlled, adapted to fall into notches on another movable piece so that movement of such other pieces is limited to one direction only.

Peabody

rifles using the breechblock system invented by Henry O. Peabody of Boston, Massachusetts, patented 1862, were known by this name.

Peabody, Henry O.

an American inventor of a new breechlocking system that hinged the breechblock at the rear and above the axis of the barrel bore. His basic patent was granted in 1862.

Peacemaker

the six cylindered .45 Colt Single Action Army revolver first produced in 1872 and popularly known as the Peacemaker, being much in favor with peace officers of the Old West and still being manufactured.

Pedersen device

a semiautomatic mechanism that could be used with a modified U.S. Springfield M1903 rifle to enable it to fire .30 caliber pistol cartridges. Developed by J. D. Pedersen in 1917 it was produced secretly by the U.S. Army for use in World War I. Subsequently the device was held impractical and stock on hand destroyed.

Pedersen, John D. *(-1951)*

an American gunsmith and inventor who, around 1927, developed a rifle and .276 caliber cartridge for it for the U.S. Army although it was not officially adopted for use. Patented many firearms improvements. He developed the secret Pedersen device for use in World War I.

peening

the process of hammering a metal piece to indent and compress it thus expanding or stretching it. A ball peen hammer is used by gunsmiths for this operation.

peep sight

a rear sight having a small hole to look through in aiming the gun of which it is a part. Also called an "aperture sight".

pellet

a small lead shot or small bullet.

pellet lock

See "pill lock"

Pellgun

a registered trademark for air and CO_2 pellet guns.

pendulum

See "ballistic pendulum"

penetration

the distance to which a projectile will enter a designated substance.

Pennsylvania rifle

a muzzle loading rifle in both flintlock and percussion designs, also called a Kentucky rifle.

pentolite

an explosive consisting of PETN (pentaery thritoltetranitrate) and TNT (trinitrotoluene).

pepperbox

a handgun having a cluster of barrels that revolve, each containing a charge. Made in the latter half of the 18th century and discontinued in the latter half of the 19th century.

percussion

1. the act of tapping sharply.

2. in the case of a firearm the striking of the percussion cap to set off the propellent charge.

percussion cap

an early form of primer. The first were small metal caps containing the priming mixture that could be placed open end down over the nipple and in that position exploded by the blow of the hammer. A different form was the "Maynard primer".

percussion composition

an explosive chemical mixture that may be set off by the blow of a firing pin against a primer cap.

percussion hammer

See "hammer"

percussion lock

a firearm detonating system for detonating a priming powder over a touch-hole, thereby setting off the powder charge. The priming charge was used in several ways — as a powder, a pellet, paper cap, roll of caps, tape or copper cup. Its development followed that of the flintlock.

percussion long arms

many arms using the percussion system have been developed since the advent of that system which displaced the mechanical system of producing a spark. By 1842 all British Brown Bess muskets in service were converted to percussion fire. In 1845 American sportsmen put percussion long arms in general use. With the acceptance of percussion arms came improvements in rifling, breech loading, repeating features and use of revolving cylinders.

percussion pistols

adaptation of the percussion system opened the way for development of hand guns to their present state. The first regulation U.S. percussion pistol was the Model 1842 design, but the Model 1843 was the first to be put in service. Both were .54 caliber smooth bores.

percussion primer

better known as percussion cap; a cap or cylinder containing a small charge of high explosive sensitive to a blow.

percussion system

the method of igniting a propellent charge by chemical means set in motion by striking a compound capable of being detonated by a blow. A patent issued to the Reverend Alexander Forsyth in 1807 covered a lock employing this principle. Officially adopted by the British in 1836.

performance
the degree of accuracy with which a gun or ammunition delivers a projectile to a target.

perigee
the lowest point in the orbit of a body around the earth. A non-circular orbit of a satellite has both an apogee and a perigee.

petard (*pi TARD*)
an ancient term for a container of explosives used to break into a walled fortification.

Peters
an ammunition manufacturing division of Remington Arms Co., Inc., Bridgeport, Connecticut. The Peters Cartridge Company was originally founded by G. M. Peters in 1887 as a subsidiary of the King Powder Company of Kings Mills, Ohio. It was purchased by Remington Arms Company in 1934.

Petersson, Axel Jacob
a Swedish engineer who cooperated with Ole H. Krag to produce, in 1874, a rifle that was an improvement on the first of Krag's models.

petronel
the name applied to a medium caliber carbine in the 16th and 17th century.

phalanx
a unit of armed foot soldiers in a tightly grouped battle formation.

phosphatizing
a chemical process for creating a dull grey to black rust-resistant finish on steel. Widely used on military weapons prior to World War II. Also known as "Parkerizing" or "Bonderizing". Basically, this process consists of boiling steel components in a solution of phosphoric acid and water.

photomicrography
the science of taking photographs through high power microscopes. The resulting photograph is called a photomicrograph. Finds use in the science of metallurgy and in the identification of firearms.

pi
the Greek letter π used to denote the ratio of the circumference of a circle to its diameter. It has an infinite number of decimals but in ordinary usage only the first four are used, that is, it is assumed to equal 3.1416.

Picatinny Arsenal
a U. S. Army arsenal located near Dover, New Jersey, established in 1879, important as the source for every important development in artillery ammunition, bombs, explosives and pyrotechnics. Its pilot production lines have formed the models for rapid expansion of private industry in times of national emergency.

picket bullet
a bullet of conical shape having a flat nose. Also called a "sugarloaf" bullet.

picric acid
a high explosive more powerful than TNT, but since the introduction of TNT its use as a military explosive has decreased. It is used in mixtures with other nitro compounds; as a substitute for part of the mercury fulminate charge in detonators; and in converted form in the manufacture of explosive D as a booster explosive.

piece
a single firearm, such as a musket, rifle, carbine, or shotgun or an artillery weapon. The origin of this term for a firearm is unknown.

Piezo gauge (*pie EE zo*)
more correctly known as the Piezo quartz crystal gage or the electric strain gage, used to measure the pressure developed by a fired cartridge in the barrel of a gun. It makes use of the principle that when pressure is applied to a quartz crystal in a certain direction to its grain, an electromotive force is developed which is in direct proportion to the pressure.

pigeon
See "clay pigeon"

pigeon gun

a special gun developed and used in the period 1810 and 1860 for the sport of pigeon shooting. Usually a single barrel, large bore muzzle loader. The present day pigeon gun is usually an over & under or side by side shotgun of 12 gauge having 30-inch barrels bored modified and full or full and full.

pillar breech

a part of a muzzle loading system used for a time in the first half of the 19th century. It comprised a breech plug that had a pin or pillar projecting from its center into the bore. This pin was called a tige. Loading the gun consisted in placing powder around the pin, leaving it projecting above the surface of the surrounding powder to act as an anvil against which a loose fitting bullet could be rammed so it entered the grooves of the rifling.

pill lock

a percussion lock firearm employing fulminate pellets or pills, which in America gave rise to the name.

pinfire

a cartridge that appeared prior to 1850. It contained a cap containing fulminating powder against one side of the case and had a pin projecting outward from the case at the other side. When the hammer struck the pin, its inner end penetrated the cap and fired the cartridge.

pinfire ignition system

utilizes a pin that protrudes at a right angle from the cartridge case adjacent its base. The pin within the case bears upon fulminate in a percussion cap. Invented by Lefaucheux and Houllier, Frenchmen, about 1836. Pinfire revolvers were used in the Civil War.

pin, firing

See "firing pin"

pinion

a gear having a small number of teeth designed to mesh with the teeth of a larger wheel or rack.

pinning

a condition that arises in a file when cuttings removed from the work clog or jam in the teeth of the file.

pipe

in addition to other meanings also refers to the cone shaped cavity that forms in the ingot of steel as it cools from its molten state. Unless the portion of steel containing the pipe is discarded it will constitute a defect in the steel shapes fabricated from that portion of the ingot.

pistol

a handgun having a short barrel, adapted to be aimed and fired with one hand. Pistols may be single shot, repeating or self loading (semi-automatic). They do not have cylinders as do revolvers.

pistol belt

a belt made to hold a pistol or revolver holster.

pistol carbine

a pistol with a detachable shoulder stock so it can be fired from the shoulder or the hand as the shooter may elect. Used as early as the mid-19th century.

pistol grip adapter

an accessory designed to enlarge the gripping surfaces of a revolver.

pistol grip stock

See "stock, pistol grip"

pistol holster

a sheath for holding a pistol, usually worn at a belt or carried on a saddle, made of leather, webbing or some other durable material.

pitch

1. in the case of rifling it means the angle at which the spiral is cut in relation to the axis of the bore and usually stated in terms of the number of inches of bore required for one complete spiral, such as "one turn in 12 inches". Also called "twist". In the case of rifle and shotgun stocks it is the angle at which the butt plate slopes in relation to the axis of the bore. See "pitch down"

2. in the case of handgun grips the angle at which the grip slopes in relation to the axis of the bore.

pitch down

"pitch" (as described in the preceding definition for gunstocks) is the *angle* of the butt in relation to the axis of the bore. "Pitch down" is a measurement taken at the muzzle of the gun—a measurement that varies according to pitch.
"Pitch down" is measured by resting the butt of the gun on a floor so that the butt lies flat on the floor surface and the muzzle points up. The gun is then moved toward a wall surface until the topmost portion of the receiver makes contact with the wall. When this occurs it will be noted that the muzzle is still some distance from the wall — this measured distance is called "pitch down", and is used to provide the shooter or gunsmith with a simple reference that correlates the relationship of butt angle with the line of sight.

pitted

the term applied to a metal that has small indentations in its surface, caused by rust, acids or other harmful actions.

pivot

a point about which something turns.

Plains rifle

an American percussion lock, muzzle loading rifle, a development of the Kentucky rifle.

plane of fire

the vertical plane that contains the axis of the bore of a gun when it is ready to be fired.

plane of site

the plane made by two lines, one from the muzzle of the gun to the target, the other line horizontal but perpendicular to the first line at the muzzle of the gun.

plastic explosive

an explosive which, within normal ranges of temperature, is capable of being molded into desired shapes.

plastics

a term that covers many substances but commonly applies to synthetic moldable materials that fall into two general classes, — the thermosetting and the thermo-plastic. The first, when heated to curing temperature, undergoes a chemical change and usually results in a permanently hard, infusible and insoluble product. The second does not undergo a chemical change when heated and will soften on heating and solidify again when cooled below a certain temperature. Molded articles from this type can be remolded again when heated. Plastics are made in numerous compositions suited for an extensive varieties of use, including gun stocks, gun barrels, shotshell cases, grips, etc.
The first thermosetting man-made plastic was invented and patented in the U.S. in 1909 by Dr. Leo H. Baekeland an American.

plate

to overlay or coat with a thin metal layer.

plating

the process of applying a thin coat of metal to the surface of another material.

plinker

1. a firearm (rifle or handgun) that is used for shooting at random novelty targets such as tin cans, etc.

2. one who practices "plinking".

plinking

the sport of shooting novelty targets at random distance with rifle or pistol.

plug

1. an object used to stop up a hole or outlet.

2. a slang word for shooting a bullet into or at something.

3. a device that is used in scoring targets — employed when a given bullet hole is in questionable proximity to a scoring ring.

See "scoring plug"

4. a magazine plug is a metal or wooden device that is inserted behind the follower of a tubular magazine shotgun in order to reduce overall shell capacity from five to three shots in compliance with the Federal Migratory Bird Law.

plumbago

the common name for graphite.

plunger

the mechanism in a breech-loading gun that carries the firing pin into striking position.

plywood

glued together layers of wood arranged so that the grains of each layer are at right angles to the grains of the adjacent layers. Some gunstocks are made of plywood.

point

1. to aim or lay a gun on a target.

2. the tip of a projectile.

3. the name given to each of the lines found on the iron sight windage slide scales of many military rifles, including the M1903. Such are spaced to be the equivalent of 4 minutes of angle and the adjusting screw is arranged to click with each quarter point of movement. Shooters, in speaking of quarter points of windage, signify minutes of angle.

pointblank range

that range in which the curve of the trajectory is so slight that no allowance need be made in sighting for the drop of the projectile.

pointed bullet

a bullet whose shape is characterized by having a pointed nose.

pointing lead *(LEED)*

See "sustaining lead"

point of fall

point in the curved path of a falling projectile that is level with the muzzle of the gun. Also called "level point".

point of impact

point at which a projectile first strikes.

polarized light

light whose vibrations lie only in one plane.

polishing

referring to metal polishing — as in the preparation of a firearm for blueing or anodizing. A soft cloth wheel treated with a fine abrasive, such as jeweler's rouge, is used for this purpose. The gloss and lustre of the final finish is dependent almost entirely upon the degree of preliminary polishing.

Poly-Choke

the registered trademark for an adjustable choke device for single barrel shotguns manufactured by the Poly-Choke Company of Hartford, Connecticut.

Pomeroy, Seth *(1706-1777)*

an American gunsmith who became the first Brigadier General in the Continental Army.

pom-pom

a name first applied to a then newly developed Maxim 37mm machine gun that came on the scene during the Boer War (1899-1902) coined by African natives in describing what it sounded like. Now a common name applied to multi-barrelled guns, especially those used on ship-board for anti-aircraft fire or in aircraft.

Pope machine rest

useful for test firing older types of single shot rifles with heavy barrels, using cartridges of light recoil. Consists of two steel "V" blocks bolted to a heavy bench set in the ground, the rear block being adjustable in azimuth and elevation.

Pope rifling system

a useful rifling system for lead alloy bullets, characterized by having the bullet of such diameter and the lands and grooves so designed that the periphery of the bullet contacts the top of the lands and the center of the flat bottom grooves.

port

an opening to permit the inlet or outlet of air, gas, or a liquid.

position

any one of the standard postures assumed by a shooter in firing a weapon.
See "back", "prone", "sitting", "squatting", "kneeling" and "offhand" positions

positive lens

a lens that causes light rays to converge.

post reticle

a reticle that instead of having visible crosshairs is made with sight guide to resemble a front sight. Sometimes made in combination with a visible horizontal crosswire.

post sight

a front sight that projects upward, like a post, from the barrel of a gun.

potassium chlorate

also known as chlorate of potash, whose chemical symbol is $KClO_3$. A powerful oxidizing agent and a fire hazard with dry organic materials such as clothes, and with sulphur. Used in matches and pyrotechnics. An ingredient of the mixture patented in 1807 by Alexander Forsyth and called percussion powder by him. Combined with fulminate of mercury it constitutes the major ingredients of Forsyth's priming mixture.

potassium nitrate

also known as nitrate of potash, saltpeter or niter, whose chemical symbol is "KNO_3". Used in matches, pyrotechnics and explosives. The first gunpowder was made with it in a mixture with sulphur, and charcoal.

pot shot

an easy shot, as for example one at close range, or a random or haphazard shot.
See "snapshot" for distinction

pouch

1. a small bag for carrying ammunition.

2. relating to the muzzle loading era, leather pouches were used to carry bullets and patches. (Powder was carried in powder horns or flasks.)

pounds per square inch

the units used in the English system of measurement to denote the pressure exerted on a surface. In abbreviation form psi.

powder

an explosive compound or mixture used as a propelling or bursting charge. Two general types are black powder and smokeless powder. Black powder can be ignited by friction, a spark or a heavy blow while smokeless powder is insensitive to shock.

powder bag
a fabric container for holding the powder charge for separate loading artillery ammunition. The fabric is made of special silk or cotton cloth that is completely consumed by the explosion so that hot ashes do not remain in the barrel to pre-ignite the succeeding charge.

powder, black
See "black powder"

powder, blank
See "blank powder"

powder blast
usually called muzzle blast. The surge of hot air and gases that rushes from the muzzle of a gun as the projectile leaves it.

powder burn
the burn that results from being in close proximity to the muzzle of a gun upon firing; caused by contact with burning powder particles.

powder chamber
that part of the bore of a gun adapted to receive and hold the propelling charge of separate loading artillery ammunition and where it is ignited.

powder charge
the measured quantity of powder used as the propellent in a cartridge case, shotgun shell or artillery piece.

powder chest
a container for the storage or shipment of powder such as an airtight, zinc lined wooden box.

powder deterioration
various lots of smokeless powder have useful lives of different durations depending upon their manufacture and the conditions of storage until used. Smokeless powder, a chemical compound, in decomposing gives off nitrous oxide, a highly corrosive gas and very poisonous if inhaled. Decomposing smokeless powder gets progressively weaker and harder to ignite. In fixed ammunition, smokeless powder slowly loses its power but does not become dangerous.

powder, double base
See "double base powder"

powdered metal
See "sintered metals"

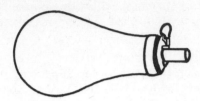

powder flask
a small, flat, narrow necked container for carrying gunpowder, usually made from non-ferrous metal or hard leather. First use believed to have been made the early part of the 15th century.

powder fouling
the solid residue remaining in the bore of a gun after it has been fired. A more serious effect when black powder was used, than with smokeless powder.

powder funnel
a funnel of such size that it may be used to conveniently fill a reconditioned cartridge case in the reloading process.

powder horn
the horn of an animal made into a container for carrying gun powder. Used first in the beginning of the 18th century.

powder keg
a small barrel for storing and transporting gun powder.

powder, Lesmok

a discontinued DuPont semi-smokeless propellent powder made from nitrated wood cellulose, saltpeter, charcoal and sulphur. At one time widely used in charging .22 caliber match ammunition. A very sensitive and difficult powder to handle, Lesmok was considered even more dangerous than black powder.

powder lot

a batch of powder made at one time by the powder plant and thus every portion of it has identical characteristics. Batches may vary from several to many thousands of pounds. In packaging, the manufacturer's lot number is generally noted on each canister or container. In this way different batches of the same powder are called to the user's attention.

powder measure

a calibrated dipper or other type of container for measuring out a charge of powder by volume rather than weight.

powder metallurgy

the art of forming articles of manufacture by subjecting powdered metal to intense heat and pressure.

powder mill

the name applied to a plant manufacturing powder or to the mechanical equipment used to shape the powder.

powder, priming

See "priming powder"

powder, propellent

See "propellent powder"

powder room

a room set apart for storage of powder, usually termed a magazine.

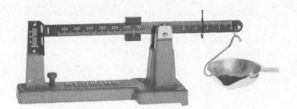

powder scale

a balance scale for weighing powder charges, usually calibrated in grains of weight and frequently equipped to permit measurements as fine as tenths-of-grains.

powder shape

for small arms, powders take several shapes. Black powder is made up of small irregular lumps better termed as granules or pellets and not grains since the latter is a unit of weight; smokeless powder is formed into small thin flakes, very small balls or small cylinders with a longitudinal hole much like spaghetti.

powder, single base

See "single base powder"

Powell

a prominent British gunmaking firm established in Birmingham, England in 1802. Famous for its fine double barrel shotguns and double barrel rifles.

power

the capacity to perform an act as in the case of the expanding gases of the ignited propellent powder which have the capacity to propel a bullet. In optics it is the degree to which the optical instrument magnifies.

practice ammunition

ammunition used for target practice. Sometimes lots of poorer grade ammunition are so designated and employed.

practice fire

target practice with live ammunition.

preliminary firing

practice firing undertaken before "record firing".

prescribed load
the combination of primer, powder and bullet recommended for a specific gun and bore size or shooting result.

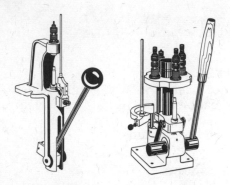

press
a tool used in the reloading of small arms ammunition.

pressure
in a gun, is the force exerted by the rapidly expanding gases of combustion of the propellent powder. Many factors in the design of a gun and a cartridge influence the pressure developed in a gun.

pressure curve
usually refers to a graphical illustration consisting of a continuous curve plotted on a time-and-energy graph to show the build up of pressure in the chamber of a gun when it is fired.

pressure equivalents
See Appendix

pressure gage
a device for measuring the pressure developed in a gun barrel by the rapidly burning propellent powder.
See "oiled case pressure gage"
    "Piezo gage"
    "radial pressure gage"

pressure lock
an improved form of matchlock, whereby the trigger releases a tumbler to revolve 90 degrees to bring the match in contact with the priming charge. Some still used in the 20th century in parts of Asia and Africa.

primer
1. the detonating mixture that ignites the propellent powder.

2. the detonating mixture together with its container or holder.

primer, Berdan
See "Berdan primer"

primer blow-back
is the term applied when a section of the primer opposite the firing pin hole is blown out by the gas pressure of the exploding propellent. May be caused by a weak main spring or a firing pin that is too light.

primer, Boxer
See "Boxer primer"

primer cup
the receptacle that holds the priming mixture and anvil. It is seated in the base of the cartridge case, or in the battery cup in the case of a shotgun shell which in turn is seated in the base of the shell.

primer leak
a defect in a cartridge which permits partial escape of hot propelling gases thru a primer, caused by faulty construction, an excessive charge, or an oversize firing pin. Black marks around the primer indicate the leakage.

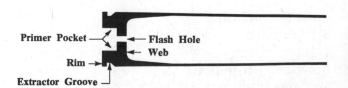

primer pocket
the receptacle in the base of a cartridge case or shell for receiving and holding the primer or primer cup.

primer seat

the chamber in the breech mechanism of a gun that uses separate loading ammunition, into which the primer is set.

primer setback

1. the term applied to a system used in a relatively small number of automatic weapons wherein the primer sets back against the bolt thus pushing a plunger mounted in the bolt face to the rear to unlock the mechanism.

2. the loosening, or partial dislodging, of the primer from the primer pocket of a cartridge case. An occurrence that points to a faulty bolt, defective cartridge, excessive powder charge, or defective chamber. Also occasionally resulting from the use of unusually high loads.

priming mixture

the tiny, highly combustible and explosive charge that is used in percussion caps and primers to ignite the main powder charge in fixed ammunition.

Primers are no doubt the most dangerous component in small arms ammunition — the hardened paste mixture is so sensitive that it is easily set off by a slight blow.

When the forerunner of the modern priming mixture was invented by the Rev. Alexander John Forsyth in 1805, the inventor chose to call it "detonating powder". Others, because of its unpredictable and often disastrous nature, simply referred to it as the "devil-mixture".

The earliest priming mixtures were comprised principally of fulminate of mercury. Later, improved mixtures added chlorate of potash and powdered glass and, when fulminate of mercury was found to have a highly corrosive effect on brass cases, a mixture of potassium chlorate and antimony sulphide was substituted.

Formulas for modern priming mixtures vary from one manufacturer to another but at least some of the following chemicals figure prominently in most of them: sulphur, lead or copper sulphocyanide, TNT, tetryl, barium peroxide, barium nitrate and lead peroxide.

priming pan

See "pan"

priming powder

gunpowder placed in the pan of a matchlock, wheellock or flintlock, used to set off the propelling charge.

priming tube

a storage tube for new primers, generally attached to the loading press, designed to facilitate the rapid feeding of single primers to the primer loading device.

prism

in optics, a transparent, light refracting body having two plane surfaces which are not parallel. Used in such devices as binoculars to change the direction of light rays so that the eyepiece lens need not be in alignment with the objective lens.

prismatic

any optical instrument, such as a binocular, camera or telescope, that makes use of a prism or prisms.

profile

the outline or contour of a firearm or portion of a firearm.

projectile

generally any object projected by an exterior force and continuing to travel by its own inertia. In the firearms usage it is any object fired from a weapon by the force of an explosive propelling charge, such as a bullet, shell, rocket or grenade. Ballistically, such an object does not become a projectile until it is in flight.

prone position
the disposition of the body of a rifleman when he shoots from the ground. The stomach is flat upon the ground, the legs spread, the insides of the feet flat on the ground, with head and shoulders raised and supported by the elbows, leaving the hands free to hold and operate the gun.

proof cartridge
a cartridge loaded to give a breech pressure about 25% greater than the pressure developed by the heaviest commercially available shell for the same caliber. The proof cartridge is used to test a new or repaired firearm for strength and safety.

proof charge
used to test the strength of a gun. It is a charge that is approximately one-fourth greater in pressure than the normal pressure intended for use in a specific gun.

proof fire
to "prove" the strength and safety of a firearm by testing with a "proof cartridge".

proof firing
the act of test firing a firearm with a "proof cartridge". Because proof firing is done with a heavily overloaded cartridge the tested firearm is never held in the hands but in a mechanical shooting device. The operator is screened by heavy protective plates.

proof house
in most foreign countries the proof testing of firearms is under strict government control; manufacturers must submit each newly made firearm to a government proof house for testing. Upon the successful completion of the test, each piece is stamped with the individual proof house mark.
In the U.S., because of traditionally high industry-wide standards, there has been no need for government regulation and each manufacturer proof tests his own wares before releasing them for sale.

proof load
See "proof cartridge"

proof mark
the distinctive stamp of acceptance pressed into the metal of a firearm by the testing government proof house (foreign) or by the manufacturer (U.S.). This mark indicates that the firearm has been successfully tested with a proof cartridge and that it may safely be used with commercially available ammunition of the appropriate caliber.

proof test

a pressure test of a gun to determine if it can withstand pressures substantially higher than those to which it will be subjected when standard ammunition is used. In the United States, manufacturers place proof marks on their guns as evidence of the proof test having been made. In many foreign countries government proof houses perform the function of testing and marking.

propellent

something capable of imparting motion to an inert body; such as the powder charge in a cartridge which, when ignited, propels the bullet. The word "propellent" may be used either as an adjective or a noun, the word "propellant" is used only as a noun.

propellent powder

the powder used in a gun to propel a projectile. Requirements for a propellent powder are that it burn quickly and at a controllable rate in a confined space. Black powder and smokeless powder meet these requirements and, by the sudden expansion of the gases they give off on burning, create the pressures needed to propel a projectile.

Prussian blue

a color pigment discovered in 1704 by a Berlin colormaker. Chemically known as ferric ferrocyanide. The dark blue powder is used on barrels being fitted to stocks to mark the uneven stock surfaces that require finishing and smoothing.

psi

abbreviation for pounds per square inch.

pull-through

a cord, cable or chain having a brush or cleaning patch holder at one end, used to clean the bore of a firearm by drawing it through the bore.

pump gun

a repeating rifle or shotgun that is operated by means of a sliding forearm. Linked to the breech block mechanism, the sliding forearm — by means of a back and forth stroke — opens and closes the breech, thereby ejecting the spent round and chambering a fresh round. The hammer is simultaneously cocked for subsequent firing. Also known as a "slide-action" or "trombone action".

pumpkin ball

a round lead ball used in shotguns for hunting deer, now almost entirely replaced by rifled slugs for that purpose.

punch

a tool used to drive a hole in a surface, or the act of doing so.

punctured primer, pierced primer

results from the hole made by the point of a firing pin and is indicative of improper correlation of firing pin and primer.

punkins, punkin shells

a local term for pumpkin balls.

punt gun

a large bore gun of approximately 4 gauge which was mounted on the front of a small boat when waterfowl hunting. Originally developed in England, punt-guns were widely used in the U. S. during the era of the market hunter. Conservation legislation and, particularly, the Federal Migratory Bird Act has now rendered them illegal.

push-button safety
a very functional and popular form of safety device that is found on many different types of firearms. A push-button safety is just what the name implies—a button-like device that is pushed to lock or unlock the firing mechanism. Usually located in the trigger guard immediately behind the trigger.

pyramid sight
a front sight that projects above the barrel of a gun and is triangular or pyramidal shape.

pyrites
sulphide of iron, a mineral that gives off sparks when it strikes iron or steel. Used in early wheellock guns and in the first of the flintlocks, being replaced by "flint" for ignition systems.

pyrites lock
a firearm type that appeared between the wheellock and snaphaunce periods. The cock terminated in a pair of jaws that held the pyrites. A sweeping motion of the pyrites against the steel of the frizzen produced the sparks that ignited the priming powder.

pyrometer
an instrument for measuring temperatures from about 300 degrees Fahrenheit upward.

pyropowder
a type of nitrocellulose powder used as a smokeless propelling charge and having a smaller nitrogen content than gun cotton. It is a single base powder.

pyrocellulose
a nitrocellulose having a lower nitration than guncotton, used in smokeless powder propellents. Also called pyrocotton.

pyrotechnic pistol
a pistol designed to fire flares or other firework signals.

pyrotechnics
1. the art and science of making fireworks.

2. fireworks or a display resembling fireworks.

Q

qualification course

practice firing for record to determine the degree of skill of a shooter as measured by his score.

qualified

a shooter who has fired for record under proper supervision and been rated according to his skill. Recognized military ratings are marksman, sharpshooter, expert.

qualify

to qualify is to undertake practice firing for record, under proper supervision and conditions, to ascertain the degree of skill of a shooter as measured by his score.

quarter point of windage

one fourth of the distance between two lines of an iron sight sliding scale found on many military rifles, including the M1903. Each quarter point represents 1 minute of angle. The adjusting screw is arranged to click with each quarter point of movement.

quenching baths

a bath of water, salt brine or one of a number of different oils alone or in various combinations used to quickly cool and thus harden heated steel. The effect of a bath upon steel depends upon its composition, temperature and volume, its heat dissipating quality largely determining what liquid is to be used for given kinds of steel.

quick draw

is the practice of reaching for and quickly producing, ready to fire, a firearm (usually a handgun) from its place of lodgement on the person. Although the sport of "quick-draw" was originally called just that, over the years the term "fast-draw" has replaced it and is now the more commonly used term.
See "fast-draw"

quick fire

very fast firing, faster than rapid fire, and used against moving or bobbing targets.

quick match

a fast-burning fuze made from a cord impregnated with black powder, used in flares.

quicksilver

the common name for the silvery metallic element mercury whose chemical symbol is Hg, which is in liquid form at atmospheric pressure and ordinary temperatures. Commonly used in thermometers and other instruments its significance to the firearms art is the fact that one of its salts, mercuric fulminate is a widely used detonator.

R

rack
See "gun rack"

radial pressure gage
a type of gage for measuring the pressure developed in a gun by the expanding gases of an exploding propellent charge. Basically it consists of a copper cylinder (for low pressures a lead cylinder) that is crushed between an anvil and a piston that is forced against the cylinder by the gas pressure. The amount of shortening of the cylinder is indicative of the pressure.
See "Piezo gage"
"pressure gage"
"oiled case pressure gage"

radiation of heat
is the emission of energy from a heated body. In firearms the heat developed in firearms is insulated from the shooter by the forearm and dissipated from the barrel.

Radom
a 9 mm, 8 shot semiautomatic pistol adopted by the Polish military in 1935.

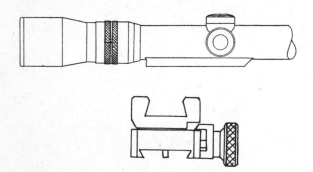

rail mount
a type of riflescope mount made with female dovetails to accommodate a railed scope. This form of telescope mounting has been practiced in Europe for quite a number of years but has never really attained acceptance in the U.S. where the traditional ring mount enjoys unimpaired popularity.

rail scope
a riflescope made with an integral rail (male dovetail). This is used in conjunction with a "rail mount" which, instead of the traditional American ring arrangement, employs a pair of female dovetail bases. Rail scopes and rail mounts are widely used in Europe but have never managed to gain acceptance in the U. S.

raise pistol
the military command to remove the pistol from its holster and hold it muzzle upward, as high as the right shoulder and about six inches in front of it.

ram
to push into position such as seating a projectile in the chamber of a gun.

rammer
as to a small arm, a ramrod hinged to the weapon so it can be used without detaching it from the gun. In a reloading tool a plunger generally mounted on a stand and used to seat a charge, as with a ramrod.

ramp
an elevated base for a front sight made with a tapered foresurface that provides a gently sloping line to the barrel. In silhouette, the combination is pleasing to the eye.

rampart gun
See "wall gun"

ramp sight

a sight that is designated for use on a ramp. Made with a narrow male dovetail so that the sight base does not protrude beyond the width of the ramp.

ramrod

a metal or wood rod used to ram the wad and bullet or shot down the barrel of a muzzle loading firearm to position them on the powder charge. Sometimes improperly used in referring to a cleaning rod.

range

1. a place where shooting is practiced.

2. the distance of travel of a projectile to a specified location expressed such as "maximum range", "effective range", "point-blank range", etc.

range deviation

the distance by which a projectile strikes beyond or falls short of the target. Also called "longitudinal deviation" or "vertical deviation".

range discipline

orderly conduct on the range in obedience to range rules and regulations.

range finder

1. an optical instrument used to determine the distance from a gun to a target. Common types are the stereoscopic range finder and the coincidence range finder.

2. a type of reticle employed in rifle scopes that enables the shooter to make range estimates.

range flag

a danger-warning flag flown on a target range to indicate that the range is in use.

range guard

a person designated to keep people away from a target range while firing is going on.

range indicator

a placard or sign displaying the distance, in yards, from the firing point to the target.

range officer

one in charge of a target range. It is the range officer's responsibility to see that the range is properly maintained and operated, and that all safety regulations are observed.

rapid fire

a rate of fire practiced in target competition in which the shooter is most severely handicapped by the time within which to complete a prescribed course of fire.

For example, in rapid fire handgun competition the shooter is usually permitted only two seconds per shot, firing a string of five shots in ten seconds.

rapid fire weapon

any gun capable of being fired rapidly.

rasp

See "barrelling rasp"

ratchet

a pivoting member adopted to engage notches in another member (such as a wheel) so as to permit motion in one direction only.

rate of fire

the number of shots per minute capable of being fired by a given weapon.

rate of twist

pertains to rifled barrels; rate of twist is the number of inches required for the rifling to make one complete revolution. This is written, for example, as "one in ten" or "1-10", meaning the rifling makes one complete revolution in ten inches.

Bullet weight and anticipated bullet speed are the governing factors in determining twist rate. Rifling that is too fast or too slow will fail to impart stable flight to the bullet and will result in loss of accuracy.

rawhide hammer
See "soft hammers"

ready position
the position in which a weapon is held just before aiming.

real image
the image formed by the convergence of light rays through an optical instrument.

reamer
a cutting tool designed for enlarging drilled holes.

rearm
1. to refuze a bomb or projectile to place it in proper condition to explode upon impact or at a predetermined time.

2. to re-equip with a weapon or weapons.

rear sight
the sight mounted nearest the breech of the gun that is used in conjunction with the front sight to enable the shooter to establish a "line of sight".

rebated rim
a type of cartridge case that has a rim diameter smaller than the diameter of the case.

rebounding lock
a type of revolver firing mechanism made with

a rebounding hammer and firing pin. Immediately after firing and upon release of trigger pressure, spring tension acts to retract the firing pin and hammer. A *non-rebounding* lock frequently permits the firing pin to stick in the primer indentation which, in turn, prevents subsequent rotation of the cylinder and results in jamming. Rebounding locks tend to eliminate jams of this kind.

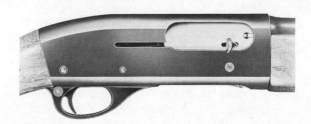

receiver
the part of a gun that takes the charge from the magazine and holds it until it is seated in the breech. Specifically the metal part of a gun that houses the breech action and firing mechanism; in revolvers and hinge frame shotguns called the "frame"; in some types of autoloading pistols the terms "frame" and "receiver" are used synonymously.

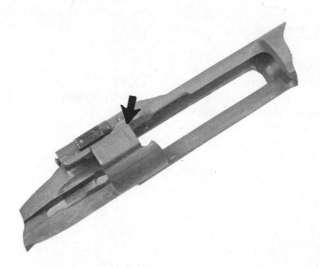

receiver bridge
the rear part of a receiver which extends partially or completely over the bolt or breech block. The solid type is typified by the Mauser bolt action rifle, the split type by the Krag-Jorgenson rifle.

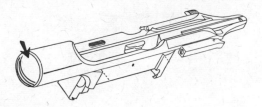

receiver ring

the cylindrical forward portion of a receiver into which the barrel is fitted. Rifles with forward locking lugs may have locking lug recesses in the receiver ring. The British term this ring a "threaded hood".

receiver sight

an adjustable, aperture-type rear sight fastened to the receiver of a firearm.

rechamber

to cut a new chamber in the barrel of a firearm by resizing its chamber; frequently employed to enlarge a weapon's case capacity without changing its bore size.

Also, in rare instances, rechambering will permit a reduction in case size when barrel wall dimensions are such that the barrel can be set back. Similarly, guns with good rifling but with eroded or faulty chambers can sometimes be corrected by the same process.

recoil

1. the rearward movement of a gun produced by its discharge. The effect upon a shooter is due largely to the weight and velocity of the bullet, the weight of the rifle and the design of the stock. The greater the weight of the bullet and the higher its velocity, the greater the effect or kick. Increase in rifle weight decreases the kick. Stocks designed to take recoil in a straight line are easier on the shooter than those with excessive cast or pitch. Gently sloped cheek pieces tend to draw away from contact with the face when recoiling.

2. the distance through which a gun recoils.

recoil calculation

is accomplished by means of a formula that relates the weight of the propelled material and its muzzle velocity to the weight of the gun. See Appendix

recoil climb

the upward swing of a firearm upon discharge due to the action of the recoil. The gun rises because the axis of the bore is above the mass-center of the gun, about which it tends to swing, as well as above the buttplate or handgun stock where recoil is resisted. The bore axis, being also above the mass-center of the shooter, causes further upward tendencies, especially when firing is done from a standing position.

recoil cylinder

a fixed cylinder containing a piston attached to the barrel of a gun filled with either air or a fluid, or both. When the gun is fired the piston is forced backward against the resistance of the air or fluid or springs, the air or fluid being permitted to pass at a predetermined rate through holes in the piston.

recoil, initial

recoil before the bullet leaves the muzzle during which a small arm moves a very small fraction of an inch.

recoilless

the term applied to certain weapons employing high velocity gas ports to counteract recoil.

recoilless rifle

a projectile firing weapon in which the rearward movement resulting from firing is essentially eliminated.

recoil lug

a projection on the bottom of the receiver of a shoulder arm that bears against a matching surface of the stock called the recoil shoulder and transmits the recoil of firing to the stock.

recoil mechanism
a mechanism designed in cannon for the purpose of absorbing the energy of recoil gradually so as to avoid violent movement of the carriage or mount. Designed in automatic, semiautomatic or selfloading weapons to perform the functions of ejecting an empty case, reloading a fresh cartridge into the chamber and restoring the weapon to a firing attitude.

recoil movement
the rearward movement of a gun which starts when it is fired and reaches a maximum when the projectile has left the muzzle a short distance.

recoil operated
in an automatic or semiautomatic firearm, the use of a barrel and breechblock locked together at the instant of firing so that, for a short distance, both are forced rearward by the expanding gases of the exploding propellent powder. Then the barrel is unlocked permitting the breechblock to continue rearward, ejecting the empty case and preparing for reloading.
The initial locking of these parts distinguishes this system from the "blowback action".

recoil plate
See "recoil shield"

recoil shield
in a revolver it is a flange on the standing breech to prevent cartridges in the chambers of the cylinder from moving backward far enough to interfere with the rotation of the cylinder.

recoil shoulder
See "recoil lug"

recoil spring
in an autoloading or automatic weapon it is the spring that is compressed by the recoiling action of the barrel and/or breechblock. When the pressure of the expanding gases has subsided, the decompressing recoil spring returns the barrel and breechblock to firing attitude. The entire sequence takes but a fraction of a second and is too fast for the eye to follow, nevertheless, in this brief period a spent casing is ejected, a fresh round chambered and, the hammer cocked for refiring.

recoil tables
tables that show recoil velocity and recoil energy for specified cartridges fired from certain guns.

record firing
firing of a weapon for the purpose of qualifying for a rating and for establishing a verified score.

record practice
practice firing for which a record is kept of the scores made, to provide a basis for marksmanship classification or qualification.

reduced charge
ammunition that has a less than normal propelling charge.

reduce jam
the act of safely removing a cartridge from a gun after it has failed to seat properly in the chamber or, of removing a fired case after it has failed to eject.

re-entry match
a target competition in which the competitor is permitted to fire more than one score for record; one or more of his best scores are then used to determine his final ranking.

reference gages

See "master gages"

reflex

response to a stimulus, such as flinching at the discharge of a gun.

refraction

the bending of a ray of light, deflecting it from a straight path. Caused by passing it obliquely from one medium to another as when passing it through an optical surface, or water, etc.

Reising

a caliber .45 submachine gun having a 20 round capacity, used by the United States in World War II, developed by Eugene Reising.

relief engraving

(more properly termed bas-relief) In gun-making it is the carving of raised figures in the surface of metal so that they appear three dimensional. Sometimes referred to as deep-relief engraving. As opposed to line engraving.

reload

1. place a fresh round or charge in a gun.

2. to assemble a new round starting with a used cartridge case, called reloading.

reloading

the hand loading of ammunition employing used cartridge cases.

reloading components

the materials required to reload used cartridge casings: i.e., primers, powders, bullets, wads, lead shot.

reloading dies

the dies or fixtures which comprise that portion of a reloading tool that actually forms and charges the casings.

reloading powders

propellent powders which are manufactured for the recharging of used casings by handloaders.

reloading press

the tool that holds the reloading dies and that provides the mechanical leverage and pressure required to shape and charge cartridge cases.

reloading tables

reloading data, compiled in chart form, which describes specific combinations of components for a given caliber or gauge. Such tables serve to guide the reloader by telling him precisely what type of powder to use, weight of powder charge in grains, and bullet style and weight. Comprehensive tables will even recommend the use of specific primers and will advise approximate muzzle velocities and chamber pressures to be expected from a given load.

When using reloading tables it is important that all recommendations be followed exactly.

reloading tools

a broad title applicable to any or all of the dies, presses and miscellaneous accessories used in reloading ammunition.

reloads
used cartridge casings that have been reloaded for re-use.

remaining velocity
the speed of a projectile at any point on its trajectory.

Remington
the trademark for firearms made by Remington Arms Co., Inc., the founder of which was Eliphalet Remington in 1816. The revolver produced in 1859 became very popular as did the single shot, black powder, rolling block military rifle which was used in the period 1870 to 1900, in various calibers, by a number of nations, including the United States.

Remington, Eliphalet *(1793-1861)*
an American firearms manufacturer whose name continues to be part of the name of a present day manufacturer. The revolver he brought out in 1859 was extremely popular because of its strong frame and simple design.

removable liner
a removable rifled cylinder, fitted in a gun tube, so designed that when worn it may be replaced.

repeater
a gun capable of being fired several times without reloading. Usually applied to rifles and carbines.

report
the sound made when a gun is discharged, caused by the sound waves created by the muzzle blast. At supersonic speeds a projectile will create a bow wave and its own sonic sharp distinctive crack that, at a distance forward of the gun, may be distinguished from the primary report.

reseat
to seat again as with replacing a bullet in a cartridge case.

residual pressure
the pressure still found in the chamber after the bullet has left the gun. It is employed in "blowback actions" to impart rearward motion to the breechblock.

resistance welding
See "welding"

resolution
the degree of image definition achieved by an optical instrument.

resolving power
the ability of an optical instrument to form separate images of closely related objects, sometimes called "definition".

rest
any support used to hold a gun steady while aiming and firing.
See "bench rest"
　　"machine rest"
　　"Mann "V" rest"
　　"Pope rest"
　　"Woodworth cradle rest"

rest, bench
See "bench rest"

rest, machine
See "machine rest"

rest, Mann "V"
See "Mann 'V' Rest"

rest, Pope
See "Pope rest"

restricted match
a match limited to specific classes of shooters.

retainer
a member for holding one or more other members of an assembly in an assigned place.

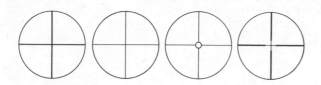

reticle, reticule
the measuring scale, aiming indicator or marks placed in the focus of an optical instrument: used in sighting telescopes, periscopes and other fire control instruments to determine the point-of-aim, size, distance, direction or position of objects sighted upon. The scale or marks are usually etched on glass and referred to as the reticle. In some rifle scopes the cross-wire reticle is made by stretching two hairs or fine wires across a ring-like disk.
"Graticule" is the British word for reticle.

retractor
better known as the slide in a semiautomatic pistol, a metal sleeve covering part or all of the barrel and the action, or merely the top of the action, usually forming the breechblock. It goes backward by recoil and is restored to its normal position by the recoil spring.

retreat gun
in the military service the firing of a gun as a signal for the lowering of the national emblem at retreat. It is fired after the sounding of the last note of the bugle call at retreat. Also called "evening gun".

return
to go back into a former position as in the case of the mechanism of an automatic or semiautomatic gun.

return pistol
a military command to restore the pistol to its holster.

reveille gun
in the military service a gun fired at the first note of reveille or at sunrise. Also called morning gun".

revolver
a repeating hand gun having a rotatable cylinder containing a series of firing chambers. The action of the trigger and firing mechanism rotates the cylinder in stages so that each chamber is sequentially aligned with the bore thereby presenting its cartridge to the action of the firing pin.

revolver action
an action that can revolve a number of cylinders on barrels to present, in succession, their contained rounds to the firing mechanism. The revolver designed by Samuel Colt in 1836 has remained a standard design in the United States.

RF
in referring to ammunition it is the abbreviation for "rimfire cartridge".

rib
a metal rail soldered to the top surface of a single barrel shotgun, or between the barrels of a side-by-side double barrel shotgun. Extending from the receiver to the muzzle, the rib is designed to facilitate aiming by providing a straight, level sighting plane. Generally found on deluxe grade shotguns — particularly target models — ribs are also occasionally used on rifles and handguns.

rib rifling
the rifling of the bore of a gun in which the lands and grooves are of equal width.

Richards, William Westley (1788-1865)

an English gunsmith who, in 1821, received a patent on a so called "detonating gun" popular in its time. It was a percussion gun that could be primed with powdered fulminate, paper caps or pellets. Westley Richards, (1814-1897) his eldest son also attained fame as a designer and manufacturer of firearms.

ricochet (RIK oh SHAY)

the skipping motion of a projectile that may result when it strikes a flat surface. Loosely used to describe a projectile that rebounds from an object. It is a phenomena of low velocity rather than of high velocity.

rifle

a shoulder arm having a long barrel whose bore has a number of shallow grooves cut into its surface longitudinally, leaving raised surfaces called lands between them. Originally some rifles had straight lands and grooves, now they follow a helical curve to impart a spinning motion to a bullet that passes through. Its long barrel distinguishes it from the carbine.

rifled slug

a conical soft lead bullet having a rifled surface and a hollow base, used in shotguns for big game hunting. (An example is the Brenneke slug). Contrary to popular belief, rifled slugs do not attain a bullet-like spin in flight but rotate slowly, making about one revolution in thirty feet. This slight rotational motion, together with the balance created by weighted nose section results in reasonable accuracy at distances up to 100 yards.

rifle grenade

a grenade or small bomb designed to be fired from a rifle by using a special device called a launcher attached to the muzzle of the gun. An early grenade launcher was made about 1760 at the Tower of London Armory to fire a spherical grenade. It was a flintlock weapon with a 14 inch long barrel, 3 inches in diameter.

rifleman

generally applied to a soldier armed with a rifle but also is applicable to a target shooter using a rifle.

rifle musket

a military muzzle loading, percussion shoulder arm having a long barrel, large caliber and other musket features but a rifled bore instead of a smooth bore.

rifle pit

a hole in the ground from which a shooter is able to fire a gun. In the Pacific theatre during World War II, rifle pits were often referred to as "spider holes".

rifle range

a range adapted for practice in rifle firing.

riflery

the sport of target shooting with a rifle.

rifle salute

as defined in the U.S. Army manual of arms is the salute in which the rifle is held at right shoulder arms or order arms position, and the left hand is carried smartly across the body to the rifle, forearm horizontal, palm down, fingers together and extended.

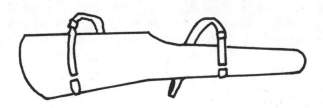

rifle scabbard

a sheath or holster for holding a rifle or carbine.

riflescope

another term for telescopic sight.
See "telescopic sight"

rifling

the helix formed in the bore of a barrel to give a spinning motion to a projectile passing through it.

Rigby

refers to John Rigby & Company of London, England, prominent manufacturer of fine quality sporting rifles and shotguns.

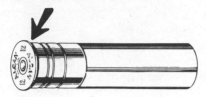

rim

that part of the base of certain cartridges that extends beyond the body of the cartridge case.

rimbase

the shoulder of a rifle stock on which the breech rests.

rimfire

a cartridge having the priming mixture lodged inside the rim of the case is termed a rim fire cartridge. The firing pin is positioned in rim fire firearms so it strikes the rim thus igniting the propellent charge in the cartridge case. Abbreviated as RF.

rimless

a cartridge whose base is the same diameter as the body of the case is so designated. All such cartridges are center-fire.

rimmed

a cartridge whose base is of greater diameter than the body of the case is so designated. The rim prevents the cartridge from entering the chamber too deeply. Such cartridges may be either center-fire or rim-fire.

ring and bead sight

the sighting system of a gun that uses a ring for the rear sight and a bead or post for the front sight.

ring bulge

a bulge in the barrel of a gun resulting from an obstruction in the bore of a gun at the time it is fired.

rings

those portions of a scope mount that are used to encircle a rifle telescope. The bottom surface of each ring is made with a locking device so that it can be securely fastened to the mount base.

ring sight

a ring through which a shooter looks to sight on a target. Generally used as a rear sight.

ring trigger

an oddity found in some old weapons having revolving cylinders in which cartridges were chambered. It was a trigger separate and apart from the firing trigger and used only to revolve the cylinder to place a new cartridge in position for firing.

ring trigger revolver

a type of revolver in the percussion period that used a ring trigger to revolve the cylinder and had a separate trigger for firing.

riot gun

any short barreled shotgun, usually one with a 20-inch cylinder bored barrel, used in guard duty or to scatter rioters.

rivet

a headed metal pin or bolt used for joining two or more pieces by passing the shank through a hole in each piece and then hammering the plain end to form an opposing head. Commonly used to fasten the metal accessories to a leather sling strap, or fittings to holsters, gun cases, etc.

rocket

a self-propelled device that derives its propelling force from gases escaping from jets or nozzles at the rear of a combustion chamber. For use in a gun.
See "Gyrojet gun"

Rock Island Arsenal

a U.S. Army manufacturing arsenal located at Rock Island, Illinois, had its origin in Civil War days in 1863. During World War II it produced small arms, field artillery, carriages and recoil mechanisms of all types. It has taken over the responsibilities for small arms formerly assigned to Springfield Arsenal.

rock maple

also known as "sugar maple" or "hard maple" this is a seldomly used gunstocker's wood that is grown widely in the Northeastern U. S. Harder than walnut and considerably more difficult to work with, rock maple is very light in color and does not easily accept staining.
Rock maple having attractive "birds-eye" figuring was widely used by American gunsmiths during the muzzle loading period.

Rockwell hardness test

a hardness test conducted with a Rockwell hardness tester which employs an initial load, then a final major load to a steel ball or a diamond sphereoconical penetrator to the surface of the metal being tested. The depth of penetration measures the relative hardness as determined by the appropriate Rockwell scale.

rod, cleaning

See "cleaning rod"

rod ejector

a rod used manually to eject a cartridge case from the chamber of a handgun.

rolled crimp

1. an all but discontinued method for closing the mouth of a shotgun shell.
In roll-crimping a cardboard wad is laid over the top of the shot column and the end of the shotshell tube is folded inwardly so that its leading edge will bear against the "over-shot wad", thereby locking it in place.

2. a crimp formed in the mouth of a cartridge case by turning the edge inward to seat in groove encircling the bullet near its base. It serves to firmly hold the bullet in place and adds to the waterproofing quality of the cartridge.

rolling block pistol

a pistol introduced in the 19th century which permitted the breech block to be pivoted backward exposing the chamber, when the hammer was at full cock. After inserting a cartridge the breech block was pivoted forward to its closed and locked position.

rolling block rifle

an early breech loading rifle mechanism credited to Joseph Rider and Leonard Geiger.
Perfected late in 1865 and manufactured by Remington Arms Co., the rolling block rifle was exceptionally strong and it attained world-wide popularity as a military weapon.
The name "rolling block" stems from the design itself: a hinged block located immediately be-

hind the breech swings back and down to facilitate loading or unloading. When closed, it effectively seals the breech for firing. A firing pin is located within the block and an exposed hammer, mounted just behind the block, provides the energy needed to propel the firing pin into the primer.

rook cartridge

a low powered cartridge developed in England for shooting pest birds and animals.

Root, Elisha King *(1808-1865)*

an American manufacturer whose inventive genius applied to machines for making firearms proved of great value to Samuel Colt with whom he worked beginning in 1849.

rosewood

a form of hardwood yielded by the rosewood tree of Brazil, Honduras and Mexico.
A very colorful wood, rosewood ranges from pale red to purple with dark brown-black streaking. It is often used in making decorative forend tips and pistol grip caps for gunstocks, but is too heavy for overall stock work. Very hard and close-grained.

Ross

a .303 caliber, 5 shot rifle formerly produced in Canada, characterized by having a straight-pull action developed in the 1890's by Sir Charles Augustus Frederick Lockhart Ross. Manufacture was discontinued in 1917.

rotary magazine

invented by Ferdinand Ritter von Mannlicher of the famous Steyr Works in Austria, this is considered the finest of all sporting rifle magazines because it perfectly aligns each cartridge with the chamber and eliminates the possibility of bullet deformation.
Rotary magazines, as used in the Mannlicher-Schoenauer rifle and Savage Model 99 rifle, are entirely contained within the receiver mechanism. They have a capacity for about five shells. A spring powered rotary follower feeds each shell for loading as the preceding shell is ejected.

rotate

to turn around or spin such as the rifling does to a projectile as it passes through the bore of a gun.
See "spin"

rotating band

a band of soft metal around a projectile near its base of slightly greater diameter than the diameter of the bore taken on the face of the lands, adapted to engage the rifling and thus cause the projectile to rotate, i.e. spin, and seal off the gases of the explosion.

rotation

the motion of turning or spinning imparted to a projectile as it passes through the rifled bore of a gun, thus imparting greater accuracy to it. Depending upon the muzzle velocity of the bullet and the twist rate of the barrel a thirty-o-six bullet may attain a speed of 213,840 revolutions per minute; a .22 long rifle bullet a speed of 50,400 revolutions per minute.

rottenstone

a friable silaceous stone used for polishing and grinding various surfaces. Finely ground rottenstone moistened with olive oil or water is used by many gunsmiths to rub on gunstocks after an oil surface has been built up, in preparation for a finishing wax.

round

all of the components required to make up the ammunition needed to fire one shot. Thus in a fixed round of ammunition the components, assembled into a single unit called a cartridge, are the bullet, propelling charge, primer and case.

round ball

a lead ball used as a single ball shotgun load.

round ball bullet

a bullet spherical in shape.

round, fixed

a completely assembled round of ammunition, all components being in a single unit that can be placed in the gun with one motion.

round nose bullet

a bullet whose shape is characterized by its round nose.

rubber

natural or synthetic, finds use in firearms products principally as the material from which recoil pads are made.

Ruger

a trademark of the firearms manufacturing firm, Sturm Ruger Company, of Southport, Connecticut.

run

the passing of a moving target once across the range.

runaway gun

an automatic or semiautomatic gun that continues to fire after the trigger is released. A defect in the mechanism causes this condition.

run-overs

a flaw common to hand checkering; it describes a condition where certain lines are seen to extend beyond the border.

rupture

a circular break in the wall of a fired cartridge case causing loss of power and difficult extraction or jamming.

Russian roulette

the extremely dangerous game of chance in which a single chamber of the cylinder of a revolver is loaded, the cylinder is spun, the revolver pointed at the head of the player and the trigger squeezed. In theory the cartridge by unbalancing the cylinder will cause the cylinder to stop with empty chambers at the top. Factors that negate this possibility are, lack of delicate balance of the cylinder and impediments in the free spinning of the cylinder such as dirt, rust, etc.

rust

the result of oxidation of the surface of a metal. In the case of iron the rust that may form is iron oxide, a chemical combination of iron and oxygen.

rusting process

a slow, tedious process for cold-blueing steel. After polishing and degreasing, an acid rusting agent is liberally applied to the metal and permitted to dry. This causes a light coating of rust which is brushed off with a soft wire wheel. The parts are then dipped in boiling water and the entire process repeated. Several applications are usually necessary over a period of three or four days before a satisfactory blue finish can be obtained.
Double barrel guns having soft soldered ribs *must* be blued by this process.

rust inhibitor

a chemical compound that will cling to the surface to be protected and shield it from rust producing conditions. Various greases are used for this purpose with firearms, particularly for periods of storage.

rust removal

from steel or iron surfaces of firearms is accomplished chemically or by the use of the finest grade of steel wool.

rust resistance in iron and steel

is continually being researched to improve that quality in iron and steel. Alloying steel with nickel or copper gives it increased resistance to corrosion. Steel with the proper chromium content is called stainless steel. Protective coatings are employed to prevent rusts, permanently, such as with copper; for limited periods by painting; and removable such as by greasing.

S

SA

abbreviation for single action.

S & W

abbreviation for Smith & Wesson and also one of its registered trademarks.

sabot *(SAB o)*

a word derived from the French, a kind of shoe. It is the name given to a separate base or cup used on certain projectiles. Formerly also so used on projectiles shot from muzzle loaders.

saddle ring

another name for a sling ring.
See "sling ring"

SAE

abbreviation for Society of Automotive Engineers.

safe working pressure

the pressure that may be safely used in a gun.

safety

a safety device on a firearm that prevents it from being fired accidentally. It may be part of the grip and automatically set, or a thumb piece may control it.
See "safety catch"
    "safety lever"
    "safety lock"
    "grip safety"
    "push button safety"

safety catch

generally refers to the accessible external piece that may be manually moved by a shooter to place a safety device in "on" or "off" position.

safety lever

a lever that sets the safety mechanism on certain types of automatic weapons.

safety limit

1. the lines that mark off the target area within which danger exists not only from direct fire but from ricocheting and rebounding projectiles and fragments.

2. the point at which maximum recommended breech pressure is met by a given powder charge.

safety lock

a device that prevents a gun from being accidentally discharged by holding the activating mechanism in fixed position.

Sako

a well known brand name for firearms made by the firm of Oy Sako Ab of Riihimaki, Finland. Particularly well known in the U.S. for their line of bolt action sporting rifles.

sal ammoniac

the common name for the chemical ammonium chloride, a soluble, white solid, used in one of the earliest known methods for browning the metal surfaces of firearms, widely practiced by early American gunsmiths.

saltpeter, saltpetre

the popular name given to potassium nitrate and to sodium nitrate.

saluting gun

a cannon used for firing salutes.

salvo

the discharge simultaneously or in regular succession of a number of small arms or of artillery pieces.

Sarasqueta

a trademark of the firearms manufacturing firm of Victor Sarasqueta, S.A., Eibar, Spain, represented in the United States by Stoeger Arms Corporation of South Hackensack, New Jersey.

Sauer

a well known German manufacturer of firearms, particularly noted for fine automatic pistols and shotguns. Until the Russians took over the occupation of East Germany, Sauer was located in Suhl. Upon fleeing to West Germany at the close of WW II, Sauer's management established a new plant in the city of Eckernforde.

Savage

a trademark of Savage Arms Company, firearms manufacturers, located in Westfield, Massachusetts.

sawed off shotgun

a shotgun whose barrel or barrels have been reduced in length thus widening the shot pattern at close ranges and making the weapon more concealable on the person. The National Firearms Act specifically includes within the scope of its application, shotguns with barrels less than 18 inches in length.

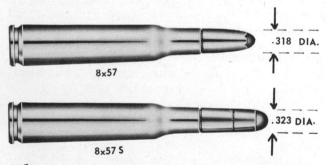

S-bore

refers to the larger of the two 8 m/m barrels used by the Germans: the original Model 88 Mauser was made with a bore measuring .318″ to .319″ in diameter. Later, upon release of the improved version Model 98 Mauser (also 8 m/m) certain changes were made in the cartridge to improve performance. The primary difference was in bullet diameter — the new 8 m/m called for a bore diameter of .323″. To prevent interchanging of the shells (both 8 m/m cartridges could be used in the 98 Mauser with the S-bore diameter of .323″, however, the .323″ cartridge *COULD NOT* safely be used in 8 m/m guns having the smaller .318″ bore) the designation "S-bore" was related to the newer cartridge and rifle combination. All 8 m/m rifles and ammunition of unknown dimensions should be examined and identified by a competent gunsmith before they are used.

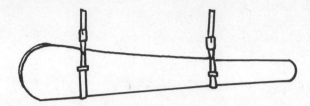

scabbard

a term for "sheath", once relating only to carrying cases for swords, knives, etc. In the field of firearms the term "scabbard" has come to mean a full length carrying case for a long gun (carbine, rifle or shotgun), frequently open-ended, used for transporting long guns by horseback or motor vehicle. Most often made of leather, a scabbard permits handy access to a weapon while simultaneously providing it with a measure of protection from weather, bumps, dirt, etc.

scatter gun

any form of shotgun, however, more appropriately used in referring to a "sawed-off" shotgun —a shotgun with a shortened barrel designed to provide the widest possible dispersion of the shot charge.

scatter shotshells

a shotgun load of shot compartmentalized in the shell so that when fired a more open pattern will be obtained. Also known as "brush", "scatter", "close-range", etc. loads.

Schmeisser

a 9 mm German machine pistol designed by Hugo S. Schmeisser, made in several models starting in 1917. Used in World War II by Japan, Germany and various European countries as a limited standard weapon.

schnabel

a German term for a particular forearm design characterized by an enlarged knob at its leading edge. Most often found on sporting rifles.

Schneider, F. E.

of Paris who was granted an English patent in 1861 for the first widely used center fire cartridge case.

Schoenauer, Otto *(SHOWN auer)*

an Austrian gunmaker and inventor, who was Director of the Austrian Arms Factory at Steyr, Austria, and in 1900 collaborated with Ferdinand Ritter Von Mannlicher to develop a spool type rotary magazine for the Mannlicher bolt action rifle. A sporting carbine followed and was called the Mannlicher-Schoenauer.

Schuetzen buttplate

a deeply curved metal buttplate with a long extension from the toe area of the stock. First used on German single shot target rifles, the Schuetzen buttplate has attained considerable popularity throughout the world. It is used when shooting from the offhand (standing) position and serves to steady the rifle.
Often referred to as a "hook" buttplate.

Schuetzen rifle

a German type of single shot target rifle designed specifically for offhand target shooting. Most commonly made for caliber 8.15 x 46 MM with a falling block action, octagonal barrel measuring approximately 28 to 30 inches, double-set target triggers, ramp front sight with fine blade, high aperture type tang sight, and a steeply dropped buttstock with hook buttplate. Weight is generally between nine and twelve pounds.

Schwartz, Berthold *(circa 1310-1384)*

a legendary German monk, erroneously credited in the past as being the inventor of gunpowder. He was concerned with the casting of cannon and in that connection experimented with gunpowder.

sclerometer

an instrument used in laboratory work for measuring the hardness of materials. Essentially it consists in scratching a line on the surface of the material tested with a diamond point, under a known pressure. The width of the line is then read and converted to an arbitrary scale of hardness.

scleroscope

an instrument for measuring the hardness of a material which basically employs a diamond tipped hammer that is dropped from a fixed height upon the surface of the metal to be tested. The higher the hammer rebounds the harder the metal. By taking readings of the height of rebound relative hardness may be ascertained.

scope

a shortened form of the word "telescope", meaning a telescopic sighting device for a firearm or, simply — "riflescope". While a telescope magnifies an image, a riflescope is made with an integral fire-direction indicator called a "reticle" which, most often, appears as crossed-hairs or crossed-wires. A riflescope is securely mounted on a firearm and adjusted so that its vertical cross-wire is aligned with the path of the fired projectile. The horizontal cross wire is then set to coincide with the projectile's point of impact at a specific distance.

scope height

refers to the distance between the axis of the bore and the axis of the scope on a given firearm. The size of a scope and mount necessitates that the axis lines of scope and bore be somewhat farther apart than would be the comparable lines if iron sights were substituted for the scope. For this reason the comb of the rifle stock is generally made higher to facilitate positioning of the shooter's eye behind the scope. Once a rifle is properly stocked for scope shooting ordinary iron sights cannot be employed — special scope height iron sights must be fitted.

scope mount

a steel or dural device used for attaching a scope to a firearm. The scope mount is generally made with a one or two-piece base plate that is fitted to the firearm with machine screws. To the base plate is then fitted a one or two piece scope-encircling ring assembly. All components must be securely locked together, looseness in any one member will preclude accuracy.

score

1. in paper target match competition a shooter's score is determined by the total value of all the required shots fired in a given match.

2. in skeet or trap competition the score is the number of clay birds broken by a competitor in a given course of fire.

3. it may mean a scratch or line in a surface such as might occur on the outside of a cartridge case.

scoring

the act of scoring targets; it is the process of determining the value of each shot and/or of tabulating total scores in accordance with the scoring procedures established for each form of target shooting.

scoring plug

a target scoring plug is designed to trace the path of a bullet through a paper target and to aid in determining the exact location and value of shots in a target. Plugs are made in various sizes to coincide with specific rifle and pistol calibers; they are shaped like bullets and are made with sharply defined collars that are matched precisely with specific bullet diameters. When a particular bullet hole is in questionable proximity to a scoring ring, the plug is placed in the bullet hole and the location of the collar examined. To aid in this examination some plugs are made with magnifying optical sleeves.

screw pitch gage

a tool designed to measure the size and pitch of screw threads.

screw thread

the projecting helical rib on a screw.

scriber

a sharply pointed tool made from hardened steel and used to scribe lines on steels or other metals.

scroll engraving

decorative patterns lightly cut into metal surfaces by means of a hand chisel and hammer.

sear

the lock or catch in a gun that holds the firing pin or hammer back until released by the trigger mechanism.

sear spring

a small spring that acts upon the sear to position it in operable relation to the trigger and hammer.

season cracking

a fine crack generally the length of the neck of a brass cartridge case appearing years after manufacture. Modern manufacture has all but eliminated this defect.

seat

1. to fit correctly in a prepared position such as placing a cartridge in the chamber of a gun.

2. in ammunition loading: to position a bullet properly in the neck of a cartridge case, or, to position a primer in the primer pocket of a cartridge case.

sectional density

is the mass of the bullet in proportion to its cross section. It is found by dividing the weight of the bullet in pounds by the square of its diameter in inches.

seize

to grasp suddenly as in the case of overheating of the parts of an automatic gun causing them to expand and become immobilized.

selective assembly

the method of assembling parts into a finished product by the trial mating of the parts to find the desired fit with a minimum of further machining or fitting. Sometimes this method is employed even with interchangeable manufacture. See "interchangeable manufacture"

selective single trigger
See "trigger, selective single"

selective trigger
See "trigger, selective single"

self loading
a firearm that has a mechanism that automatically extracts and ejects a fired case and loads another cartridge into the chamber in a firing attitude. Also called semiautomatic or auto-loading.

self lubricating
a mechanism that by its own movements introduces and spreads the required amount of lubricant over its contacting surfaces.

semiautomatic
partly self acting, thus in a gun, one that is self loading but not self firing, requiring a separate squeeze of the trigger for each shot.

semiautomatic fire
fire delivered from a self loading weapon with a separate pressure on the trigger for each shot fired.
See "automatic fire"

semifixed ammunition
ammunition in which the cartridge case is not permanently attached to the projectile.

semi-inletted stock
a gun stock that is 75 to 80% inletted and shaped.

semi-pointed
a term applied to a bullet shape that is characterized by a sharply tapered pointed nose.

semi-rimmed
a cartridge having a rim that extends slightly beyond the diameter of the case and a shallow extractor groove just forward of the rim.

separate loading ammunition
ammunition not assembled as a single unit to fire one shot. For example, in large caliber cannons, the projectile, propelling charge and primer are not assembled into a case but are loaded separately in the gun.

serial number
the number stamped on an article to identify it. By such identification the manufacturer of a gun and its user may communicate with respect to performance, parts, etc.
Federal firearms laws prohibit the distortion or obliteration of firearms serial numbers.

serpentine
1. an "S" shaped piece of iron used as a holder for the slow match of a Matchlock. It was the equivalent of the later day hammer. The jaws of its upper end held the match and its lower end served as the trigger, the piece being centrally pivoted.

2. the name applied to a type of cannon used in the 15th to 17th centuries.

serpentine powder
saltpeter, charcoal and sulphur ground dry to a flour-like composition, used as gunpowder until the middle of the 15th century when it was supplanted by corned powder. Sometimes just called "serpentine".
See "corned powder"

serve
to operate a gun or keep it in action by supplying ammunition to it. Thus the expression "to serve the piece" means to perform the function required to fire a gun or make it ready for firing.

service
the operation of a gun or supplying it with ammunition.

service ammunition
ammunition intended for military use in combat rather than for training.

service marking
symbols, numerals or letters that are placed on military items of issue to give information needed for proper handling, storage or use.

service match
a target shooting competition held in accordance with military practices or a match restricted to military competitors.

service of the piece
operation and maintenance of a gun.

service pistol
the .45 caliber model 1911 or 1911A1 automatic pistol as issued to the military. Under National Rifle Association service match rules the specifications for handguns used in these matches are strictly regulated.

service test
the test given to a military item in the field after it has passed through the engineering, experimental and development stages and before it is classed as standard.

setback
the rearward jerk, caused by inertia, of free moving parts in a projectile when it is fired. The force is used to push back a spring or plunger in a time fuze to start its operation.

set-screw
a screw positioned so it may be brought to bear on another screw in a firearm and thus prevent it from loosening. The screw that adjusts the pressure required to release a trigger is also called a set-screw.

setting
1. the adjustment of a device to predetermined position such as the scale of an aiming device of a gun.

2. cocking the trigger mechanism in a set-trigger firearm.
See "set trigger"

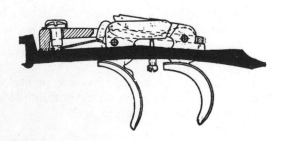

set trigger
a trigger mechanism that may be adjusted for a very light pull — may be a single set trigger or double set trigger. In either case the trigger is made with a spring powered trigger lever.
The term "set" stems from the fact that the trigger must be set (cocked) by pushing it forward. Upon setting, the single trigger is pulled in the conventional manner resulting in a weight of pull that is extremely light, and usually adjustable from a fraction of an ounce to eight ounces. The set trigger can also be used without setting but weight of pull is considerably heavier. Double set triggers are two triggers mounted one behind the other. The rear trigger is generally the setting trigger and is pulled rearward to cock the spring powered lever. Subsequent pressure on the forward trigger will then fire the gun. Some trigger manufacturers reverse this procedure by making the forward trigger the setting trigger in which case it is pushed forward instead of rearward.
Like the single set trigger, most double trigger mechanisms will permit firing by pressure on the firing trigger above (without setting) but the resultant weight of pull is, again, considerably heavier.

shaped charge
a high explosive in a projectile characterized by its hollowed out front which produces its ability to penetrate armor plate with a long thin jet of extremely hot gases of great intensity.

Sharps
famous breech loading percussion rifles and carbines using the invention of Christian Sharps, patented in 1848. Made for both military and civilian use. It embodied a sliding vertical breech block opened and closed by a lever under the gun which also served as a trigger guard.

Sharps buffalo gun
a gun of the gold rush days made in calibers of from .40 to .50.

Sharps, Christian *(1811-1874)*
an American gunsmith who, in 1848, patented his basic breech loading mechanism introducing the principle of the drop block action. Arms of his design were made by many different manufacturers but in 1863-1867 he produced the famous Sharps and Hankins carbines and rifles. When adapted to metallic cartridges they became famous as the guns of the buffalo hunters.

Sharpshooter

a marksmanship classification for skill in the use of small arms. It ranks above "Marksman" and below "Expert".

Sharps rifle

an American percussion lock breech loading weapon patented in 1848 by Christian Sharps, noted for having introduced the principle used in the "drop block" breech loading actions. First used with paper cartridges, later metallic cartridges. Both rifle and carbine used during and subsequent to Civil War. Many variations were produced. The buffalo gun of the early West was known as the Sharps buffalo gun. A carbine was also made.

Shattuck "Unique" pistol

an oddity made with four .22 caliber 1⅜ inch barrels bored in a blank that tips down to unload. Instead of a trigger a movable portion of the frame, if squeezed, will revolve the firing pin and fire each barrel in rotation. It is a true palm pistol.

Shaw, Joshua (1777-1860)

an English born American inventor who, while working in Philadelphia, Pennsylvania in 1814, became known for having developed the copper cap to hold fulminate. He may have been the first to do so.

sheaf of fire

See "cone of dispersion"

sheath trigger

an old trigger type having no trigger guard but having the trigger extending only slightly from the frame just ahead of the grip.

shell

a shotgun cartridge. In military usage it means a hollow projectile adapted to be filled with an explosive or other filler. Any empty cartridge case is sometimes loosely referred to as a "shell".

shellac

a resin, soluble in alcohol, used in the making of spirit varnishes and as an electrical insulator and in various compositions of matter as a binder. Gunsmiths do not consider it much better than varnish as a gunstock finishing agent. For a quick finish, they suggest lacquer.
A pad of lint free cloth wrapped about a tuft of alcohol soaked cotton can be dipped alternately into boiled linseed oil and shellac to achieve (through handrubbing) a glossy gunstock finish known as French polish.

shell extractor

See "extractor"

shell fire

a bombardment by artillery projectiles, especially those exploding on impact or upon the lapse of a set time.

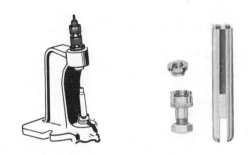

shell holder

a device designed to hold a cartridge as employed in the reloading of fired cases.

shell proof

immune to damage from shells or bombs, such as a shell proof shelter.

shell shock

a broad term covering mental and nervous disorders brought on by the cumulative emotional and psychological strain of warfare, formerly believed to have been brought about only by the exposure to exploding shells in battle.

shell wave

See "ballistic wave"

shield

See "recoil shield"

shim

a thin sheet usually of brass, steel or some other metal placed between parts to make compensating adjustments for wear, weight, or for other reasons.

shocking power

the ability to move a target or other body. Also referred to as knockdown effect.
See "knockdown effect"

shoot

to discharge a gun.

shooter

one who discharges a firearm. One who discharges a cannon is more appropriately called a gunner.

shooting box

1. a box used by shooters to carry ammunition and accessories.

2. a box shaped shooting stand — usually camouflaged and more properly known as a "blind box".

shooting eye

refers to the dominant eye, the one used by a shooter to align his sights. The dominant eye may be identified by holding a finger at arm's length and with both eyes open lining it up with a distant object. If the finger remains stationary when one eye is closed, it is the open eye that is dominant and should be used to sight a firearm.

shooting gallery

See "gallery range"

shooting glasses

protective eye glasses (not unlike sunglasses in appearance) colored to minimize glare and made from tempered, shatterproof glass.
The use of such protective glasses while shooting is strongly recommended by the firearms industry, particularly when reloaded cartridges are employed.

shooting iron

a slang expression for a firearm, usually a hand gun.

shooting lodge

a lodge used as a base of operations by sportsmen, generally during the hunting season.

shooting positions

the various positions that may be assumed by a shooter in aiming a rifle at a target.

see "fire position", "back position", "kneeling position", "offhand position" ("standing position"), "prone position" and "squatting position"

shooting stake

a rifle rest consisting of a "U" shaped fork atop a pointed stake. At a given shooting site the stake is driven into the ground and the forearm of the rifle is then placed in the fork as the marksman assumes his shooting position. Generally intended for long range shooting from a sitting or kneeling position.

shootoff

a tie-breaking system, frequently employed in skeet and trap shooting, in which the tied competitors fire at additional targets (usually 25) until one shooter emerges as the winner.

shoot out

a slang expression for a gunfight.

Shore scleroscope

a device for testing the hardness of metal. A diamond tipped hammer is allowed to drop from a known height upon the metal being tested and the extent of rebound is used to calculate the measure of hardness. The higher the rebound, the harder the metal.

short

a shot that fails to reach the target. One that goes beyond the target is an "over".

short range

1. a range of limited distance for firing.

2. ammunition having a range of relatively short distance.

short round

a defective cartridge having its bullet seated too deeply.

shot

1. the single firing of a gun.

2. spheres of lead or lead alloy used as projectiles in smooth bore weapons. Also solid balls used in cannon or cannisters.
See Appendix

shot bridging

the term applied to a condition of stoppage that sometimes occurs in the drop tube of a shotshell reloader when the shot wedges together in the tube.

shot cartridge

a metallic cartridge case loaded with small shot. A shotgun shell likewise loaded with small shot, is more properly called a "shotshell".

shot concentrators

means for concentrating a shot pattern. The most reliable means is a choke in the barrel.

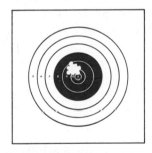

shot group

the design or pattern that is made on a target by a series of shots fired under similar conditions.

shotgun

a smoothbore shoulder arm adapted for firing of a charge containing one or more round balls or pellets. By way of illustration, the average twelve gauge shell loaded with one and one-eighth ounces of number six shot contains approximately 253 individual lead pellets.
The shotgun was designed for shooting small, winged game such as duck, pheasant, etc.

shotgun shell, shotshell

is the fixed round of ammunition designed for use in a shotgun. It consists of a paper or plastic body, a thin brass head at one end, a battery-cup primer, base wad, powder charge, over powder wad, filler wads, shot charge and folded crimp. Some modern plastic shells make use of a one piece plastic wad that replaces the cardboard and fibre wads used in the older paper shells. Rolled crimp shotshells (now obsolete) require, in addition, the use of a thin cardboard wad over the shot charge. The first shotshell was patented in 1855 by Clement Potter.

shotgun wedding, shotgun marriage

a slang expression for a union forced by a third party.

shot in the dark, a

a common expression to describe an action taken blindly and having the same chance of success as a shot fired in the dark at an unseen target.

shot locker

an old naval designation for a compartment in the hold of a vessel for storing shot and shell.

shot manufacture

lead shot reputedly was made as far back as 1420 and used as grapeshot, and by 1510 used in early hand held firearms. A British patent issued in 1758 covered a method of making lead balls by pouring and then polishing in drums. Improvements in manufacture were made in 1782. Initially shot was made by dropping molten lead, having a little arsenic added, through sieves from high towers, called shot towers, into water 100 to 200 feet below. Screening then separated the various sizes of shot made by this method. Later manufacture consisted in discharging molten lead against a rapidly rotating screen that propelled the drops into water. This dispensed with the need for shot towers. Three general types of shot have been made, soft or drop shot, chilled or hard shot, and coated or plated shot.

shot pattern
the design made on a surface by all the impacts of the shot fired from a shotgun shell, also the design made by a series of shots fired under similar conditions.

shot peen
a method used in metalworking consisting in the bombarding of a steel object with hard steel shot to improve its endurance.

shot pouch
a container of leather or other suitable material for shot, required in the days before shot shells.

shot size
See Appendix

shotting
the process of producing lead shot in a shot tower.

shot tower
a tall tower, as high as 200 feet, from which molten lead or lead alloy is dropped through sieves into a chilling liquid, such as water, to form shot.

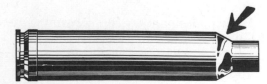

shoulder
1. the tapered portion of a cartridge case between the body of the case and the neck.

2. the process of shouldering a long gun (rifle or shotgun) prior to aiming and shooting.

shoulder arm
any small arms weapon designed to be fired while held in the hands with its butt braced against the shoulder. The rifle, carbine, shotgun, and automatic rifle are shoulder weapons.

shoulder holster
a holster for a handgun carried by a harness or shoulder strap and supported beneath the arm on the body of the wearer.

shoulder pad
a cushion of fabric, rubber or leather sewn to a shooting garment at the point where the butt of a gun is placed while firing.

shrapnel
an artillery projectile containing small lead balls that are scattered by a powder charge in the base of the shell set off by a time fuze.

shrinkage crack
in a casting arises from excessive shrinkage of the metal upon solidification.

shrinkage fit
the fitting of a cylindrical part into a hole; involves making the cylindrical part a few thousandths of an inch larger than the hole, then increasing the diameter of the hole by heating and inserting the cylindrical part. The circular part is gripped with great pressure by the contraction of the heated component upon cooling.

side arm
a weapon worn at the side or in a belt when not in use. A pistol, revolver, sword, bayonet, etc. are side arms.

side by side
a shotgun having two barrels along side of each other. Sometimes abbreviated as S/S.

BAR ACTION
SIDE LOCK

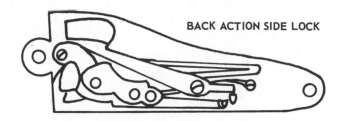

BACK ACTION SIDE LOCK

side lock

the action mechanism of a firearm assembled on two separate plates and subsequently placed into opposite sides of a gun behind the body of the breech. Common to high grade double guns. Each side lock (or plate) usually consists of a hammer, hammer spring (mainspring), sear, sear spring and intercepting safety and spring together with appropriate pins and machine screws. Firing pins and trigger mechanism are contained in the body of the breech.

Side lock action guns are more efficient than box lock types but are much more costly to produce.

Two variations of the side lock are found in common use today. The first is called a "bar action" side lock because the mainspring projects from the forward edge of the plate, necessitating the shaping of a "bar" (or arm) to cover it. The second, called a "back action" side lock, positions the mainspring behind the hammer and results in a somewhat smaller and more compact side plate. It should be noted, however, that some gunmakers will retain the profile of the bar action plate when producing a back action lock, therefore it is not always possible to determine the type of lock employed from the profile of the plate.

Box lock actions, too, are sometimes made with dummy side plates to give the appearance of a sidelock action.

See "box lock"

side plate

1. the removable plate on the side of a revolver which, when removed, gives access to the hammer and adjacent parts.

2. the plate of a side lock gun upon which is mounted the firing mechanism.

3. the dummy plates sometimes used to give a high grade box lock action the appearance of the more desirable side lock.

side split bullet

a metal cased bullet having slits in the side wall of the jacket, intended to control its expanding quality.

sight

1. to aim at a target.

2. to look through a sighting device.

3. a mechanical or optical device for aiming a gun. They may be fixed or adjustable. Mechanical sights may be classed as open or aperture; open being those sighted at or over such as post, bead, notch, etc; aperture, those sighted through such sights as peep, ring, etc. Leaf sights are those that may be folded down for protection.

sight adjustment

the adjustment of the line of sight angularly up or down to allow for range; left or right to allow for windage.

sight backlash

the play found in screw threads that may be sufficient to require that an allowance be made in setting a sight.

sight base

a mount for a gun sight.

sight blade

a thin metal post used on some firearms as a front sight.

sight bracket

a clamping device used to hold a detachable sight in position when mounted on a gun.

sight cover

a protective metal ring fastened about a sight to guard it from being moved out of adjustment by being struck or jarred, without obstructing the view of the target. Also serves to prevent light reflections off sighting surfaces. Sometimes called a sight "hood".

sight extension

any means for raising or extending a sighting device from its base. A vertical (rising) extension permits sighting at long range; a horizontal extension serves to increase the sighting radius of a firearm.

sight, front

See "front sight"

sighting bar

a wooden bar having enlarged front and rear sights at its ends with an eyepiece mounted before the sight. Used for training in small arms weapons and with movable targets. The eyepiece forces the trainee to hold his eye in proper position and because of the size of the sights, aiming errors are apparent.

sighting disk

See "aiming disk"

sighting-in

the adjustment of the sights of a gun to conform to the performance of the gun at a selected range.

i.e. aligning the sights of a firearm so that the point of impact of a fired bullet will coincide with the point of aim at a predetermined distance.

sighting shot

a trial shot fired to determine if the sights are properly adjusted.

sight inserts

See "inserts, sight"

sight, leaf

the movable hinged part of the rear sight of a gun that can be raised and set to a desired range or laid flat when not in use.

sight, line of

the line along which the sights of a gun are set and the prolongation of such line to the target.

sight radius

the distance between the front and rear sight of a gun.

sight, rear

See "rear sight"

sight, scope

an optical gun sight that employs a telescope to increase the ability of the shooter to see in proportion to its magnification.
See "scope"

signal cartridge

a cartridge loaded with pyrotechnic powders for ignition and ejection from the muzzle of a gun, usually containing vari-colored luminous balls similar to the roman candle type. Used by the military and by yachtsmen for signalling purposes.

signal pin
See "cocking indicator"

signal pistol
a pistol designed to fire pyrotechnic signals such as flares. Also called a pyrotechnic pistol.

silencer
a device for slowing down the escape of gases at the muzzle of a gun which results in the reduction of the sound of the report. It also acts as a muzzle brake and decreases the recoil of the gun. The first successful firearms silencer was developed by Hiram Percy Maxim in 1909. Production by Maxim Silencer Company discontinued in 1925 for lack of business. The National Firearms Act specifically includes silencers within the scope of its application to the making and transfer of certain firearms.

silhouette target
a practice target bearing the outline of a person, animal or object that is readily distinguishable against a light background.

silica
is amorphous silicon dioxide (SiO_2) useful as an abrasive. Finely ground into powder form and blended with varnish and drying agents to form a filling compound used in gunstock finishing.

silica gel
a colloidal form of silica, like coarse sand in appearance but having many fine pores making it a highly absorbent substance. When placed in a gun cabinet, will dry the atmosphere and prevent rusting of the metal contents. After the pores have become taxed with moisture it may be placed in an oven to be dried out and reused.

silver solder
a hard solder, usually being an alloy of silver, copper and zinc. Gunsmiths have on occasion used a silver solder of 70 per cent silver and 30 per cent copper but more often one having 49.24 per cent silver, 34.36 per cent copper and 16.4 per cent zinc.

silver soldering
the practice of joining metals (such as steel) by means of soldering with a mixture of silver and brazing alloy. Depending upon the properties of the particular silver solder used, melting points range from 900°F to 2000°F.
Makers of high quality firearms use silver solder to join the barrels of double guns and for fastening ribs to barrels.
Silver solder provides a much stronger bond than ordinary lead-tin solder, but is somewhat more difficult to work with due to its higher working temperatures and fast setting characteristics. Silver soldered components may be hot blued, soft soldered components cannot!

simulate
to pretend or feign, such as is done when practicing aiming, cocking and squeezing the trigger of an unloaded firearm.
See "dry firing"

simulated
pretended or imitated. For example, simulated ammunition may be of wood or other inert material suitable for practice purposes; simulated fire is going through the motions of firing without actually firing.

single action
in a revolver it is an action that requires the gun to be manually cocked, an operation that rotates the cylinder, places a chamber in alignment with the firing pin and holds the hammer back in readiness for a squeeze of the trigger which fires the gun. Trigger pressure will not perform such operations.

single ball load

one round lead ball used in a shotgun for large game animal shooting. The rifled slug is more accurate.
See "rifled slug"

single bore powder

made of nitrocellulose (gun cotton) dissolved in ether and alcohol then extruded, dried and formed into granules, flakes or cylinders. Also called nitrocellulose powder.

single-double triggers

an unusual and somewhat rare trigger system found in double barrel shotguns. With this mechanism the shotgun is equipped with what appears to be conventional double triggers, positioned one behind the other. However, the forward trigger is, in reality, a non-selective single trigger which will fire the right barrel with the initial trigger pull and the second (left) barrel upon a subsequent pull. (When found on over & under shotguns, the lower barrel fires first, followed by the upper barrel.) The second, or rearmost trigger fires only the left (or upper) barrel. In this manner the shooter has the advantage of a single trigger for the normal open choke, tight choke firing sequence. On those few occasions when he might need only the tighter choke he simply employs the rear trigger. Single-double triggers are generally complex, trouble-prone mechanisms.

single loader

See "single-shot weapon"

single shot

the production of a spaced shot by reason of loading by hand for each shot, or, in the case of an automatic gun by squeezing the trigger for each shot.

single shot weapon

a gun capable of receiving and firing but one hand loaded round for each shot. Also called a single loader.

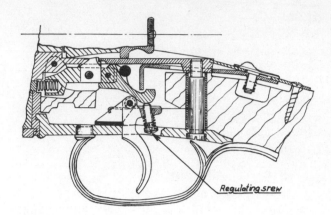

Regulating srew

single trigger

a trigger mechanism that permits both barrels of a double barrel gun to be fired by separate pulls of the same trigger: may be selective or non-selective.
A non-selective single trigger fires each of the two barrels in the same constant sequence — a sequence that cannot be reversed.
A selective single trigger permits adjustment of the trigger mechanism, by means of a selector, so that the shooter can elect which of the two barrels he prefers to fire first — the opposite barrel can then be fired upon a second pull of the trigger.

sink box

a shooting boat or moored platform once employed in waterfowl hunting. The sink box was designed to ride very low in the water so that only inches of it appeared above the water's surface. Because of the low silhouette waterfowl would come into the decoys more readily. For this reason sink boxes are now prohibited by law.

sinter

the heating and molding (usually under pressure) of a powdered material to form a solid, coherent mass. In sintering, the powdered material is never actually heated to its melting point.

sinterloy

a powdered metal that under a pressure of 50 tons per square inch is shaped and then under temperatures of 1965 to 2100 degrees F sintered to produce a dense homogeneous steel. Used in the manufacture of gun parts to avoid cutting and machining shapes from blocks of metal.

site

the location. Sometimes the angle of site is merely called "site"

See "angle of site"

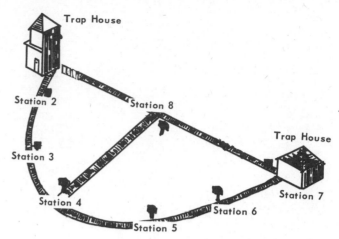

"Reprinted by permission of the National Rifle Association of America.'

sitting position

one of the standard postures used in firing a rifle. In this position the shooter sits half faced to the right, legs apart, heels well braced into the ground and body bent forward. The weight of the rifle is supported by resting the elbows inside the legs.

six gun, six shooter

a common term for revolvers arising out of the fact that most are chambered for six cartridges.

six o'clock hold

aiming a firearm by aligning the sights on the bottom edge of a bullseye rather than on its center.

sizing

as used in hand loading of cartridges it is the bringing back to proper dimension the fired case that has become enlarged as the result of its prior use. Lead bullets are also sized, after casting, to give them the desired dimensions.

sizing die

a tool used in reloading operations to restore fired cartridge casings to original dimensions.

skeet

a form of wing shooting sport in which inanimate clay targets are thrown into the air by mechanical "traps" (throwing devices) and shot at with shotguns of 12, 20, .410 or 28 gauge.

The skeet field consists of two trap houses (one high and one low house) located 120'9" apart. A segment of a 21 yard-radius circle, the base of which comprises a straight line between the trap houses, is made up of eight shooting stations. Targets from the high house, at the left of the base line emerge at a point 10 feet above ground level and are directed to fly over the "target crossing point" which is marked by a stake 18 feet directly in front of position 8.

Targets from the low house emerge at a point 3½ feet above ground level and are also aimed to fly over the target crossing point.

A skeet squad is normally composed of five shooters and one full round consists of twenty five shots, the object being to score the greatest number of "dead" targets. The round is comprised of one single target from each trap house taken at each of the eight stations. Following the singles shooting at stations 1, 2, 6 and 7, one set of doubles (one target from each trap house fired simultaneously) must be shot. This accounts for 24 targets. The 25th is made up by repeating the first missed target from whatever station the shooter happens to occupy at the same time. In the event a shooter breaks all 24 targets he is given his choice of stations for the 25th shot.

skeet field

See "skeet"

SKEET FIELD LAYOUT
SCALE: 1"= 12-0"

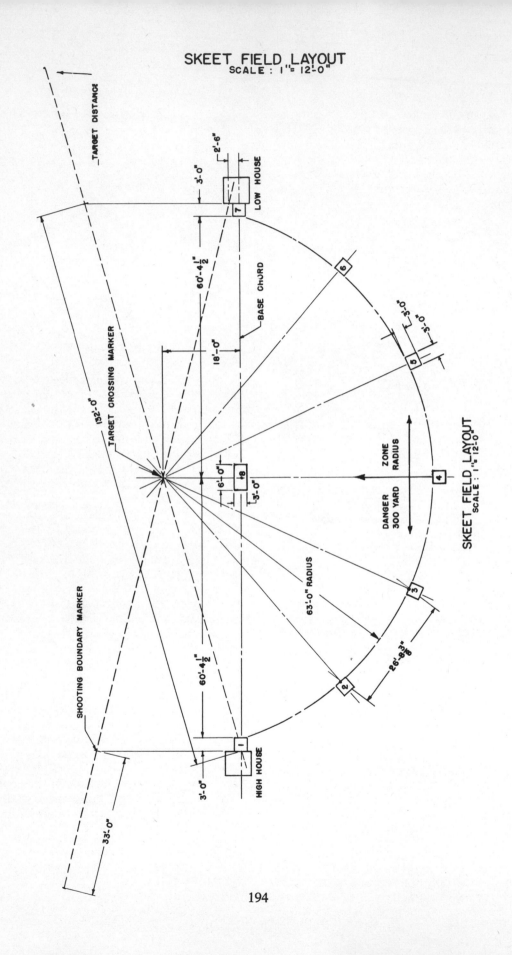

SKEET FIELD LAYOUT
SCALE: 1"= 12-0"

skeet gun

the average skeet gun is an over & under, automatic or slide action shotgun in 12, 20, .410 or 28 gauge. In the 12 or 20 gauges, the skeet gun will weigh approximately seven pounds and will be equipped with 26-inch skeet choked barrels. In .410 or 28 gauges, the skeet gun may weigh as little as six pounds and may be equipped with 28-inch barrels.

Skeet guns, in all gauges, are generally equipped with raised ventilated or solid ribs fitted with front and middle bead sights. While most skeet shooters prefer stocks made to their own specific dimensions, most factory models are made with stocks having a 14-inch length of pull, 1⅝ inch drop at comb and 2½ inch drop at heel.

Skeet guns are rarely equipped with recoil pads. Skeet Chokes: contrary to popular belief there are no prescribed dimensions for skeet chokes. The terms Skeet #1 and Skeet #2 are used by virtually all gunmakers but dimensions will vary from make to make depending upon each manufacturer's experience with pattern percentages at skeet distances.

Because the average skeet shot is made at comparatively close range, skeet chokes are designed to yield the largest possible patterns at ranges of from 15 to 20 yards. Consequently, skeet chokes are cut to dimensions somewhere between the field gun equivalents of true cylinder and improved cylinder.

Most field guns having barrels with improved cylinder chokes can be used satisfactorily on the skeet range.

skeleton buttplate

a buttplate with its center part cut away exposing the stock at its butt end.

skeleton stock

a frame, rather than a solid piece, constituting the stock of a firearm. It may be an integral or detachable piece. Designed to reduce the weight of a weapon so equipped.

skelp

strips of wrought iron, steel, etc. that are used for making tubes by bending around a cylindrical form and then welding. Damascus barrels were made with strips or strands of metal that can properly be referred to as skelp.

skirted pellet

a pellet for an air or CO_2 gun that flares outward from its waist-like constructed midsection to its base. Also called a waisted pellet.

Skoda

an automatic machine gun patented in 1888 and named after the famous Czech arms center. Adopted by Austria in 1893 as an official military arm and with modifications continued in use for many years.

slack

looseness or play in the mechanism of a gun, as for example the play in the trigger or distance that the trigger must be taken up before firing pressure is felt. Most noticeable in military weapons which are equipped with two stage triggers for safety. The first stage is simply travel (or slack)—the second stage, normal firing pressure.

slant range

the distance along a straight line from gun to target.

slave pin

a pin used as a temporary substitute for a pin that is normally used in firearms assembly. Its use is during maintenance or repair work and not when the gun is in service.

slew

swing a gun sidewise, that is, traverse a gun.

slide

1. the sliding member of the receiver of certain automatic weapons. In semiautomatic pistols, a metal sleeve embracing part or all of the barrel and/or the top of the action, forming or housing the breechblock. Driven back by recoil it is returned to firing position by spring action.

2. in slide action guns (sometimes called pump guns) the slide is that portion of the gun that is gripped by the forward hand and which is slid black and forth to clear and reload the weapon.

slide action

the mechanism of a repeating rifle or shotgun operated by the manual movement of a slide under, and parallel to the barrel. (Sometimes called pump action or trombone action).

sliding safety

a safety mechanism on a rifle or shotgun that is operated by means of a sliding, two position, safety button.

sling

a strap (usually of leather although occasionally of webbing) that is attached to a rifle or carbine to facilitate carrying. Also used to aid in steadying the gun while shooting.

To serve as a shooting aid a sling must be adjustable for length. A non-adjustable sling is more properly called a "carrying strap".

sling ring

a large metal ring free to move within an eyebolt or sling bar that is secured to the underside of a carbine and through which a sling may be passed. Such sling may be attached to a saddle or looped over the rider's shoulder to prevent the carbine from dropping out of reach.

slip shooting

a rapid fire method of firing a single action revolver which consists in holding the gun in one hand with the trigger held back, tied back or removed entirely, and with the other hand clasping the gun pressing the hammer back with the thumb permitting the thumb to slip off when the hammer has reached full cock.

slot

1. a narrow groove or opening.

2. a dovetail slot: tapered female slot, usually about ⅜th of an inch in width, cut into the barrel of a firearm to form a base for a sighting device. All such dovetails are tapered from right to left (as one aims the weapon) to remove them, sights should be driven out from left to right; new sights are installed from right to left.

slot blank

a dummy filler plate employed to fill an unused dovetail slot.

slotted tip

a slotted jag used on cleaning rods to hold a soft cloth cleaning patch.

slow fire

a rate of fire common to target shooting for which there is no pressing time restriction.

Although in present day competition, because of the number of competitors, slow fire matches are held under prescribed time limits, these limits are such that even the slowest shooter will find them easy to cope with.

For example, in slow fire handgun competition, the shooter is usually permitted one minute per shot, firing ten shots in ten minutes.

slow match

a wick soaked in a solution and dried, adapted to burn slowly when held in a C shaped piece of metal or in a Serpentine, to be available to ignite the powder at the touch hole of a matchlock musket.

slug

1. the British engineering term for a unit of mass, equal in pounds to the number of feet per second, per second of acceleration of a freely falling body at a specific point in its flight. It has the property that a force of one pound acting upon a mass of this unit produces an acceleration of one foot per second per second.

2. the term applied to a solid lead projectile used in shotgun shells for the shotgun hunting of big game.

3. as a colloquial expression: broadly used in referring to any size or type of bullet.
See "rifled slug"

slugging bore

the process of forcing a round ball of pure lead thru the bore of a rifle for the purpose of accurately determining the minimum groove diameter of the bore.

slush

an artillery term meaning to clean or oil the bore of a cannon with a compound or lubricating oil.

slush brush

an artillery item usually a cylindrical piece of wood fastened to a long rod and covered with a wool or carpet pad and used to coat the bore of a cannon with oil or a cleaning compound.

small arms

guns that can be carried and operated by one man. They include shoulder arms, sometimes called long guns, hand guns, (pistols and revolvers) and machine guns. Generally firearms with calibers up to 1 inch in diameter are so classified.

small arms ammunition

ammunition having a bullet diameter of one inch or less, used in small arms.

small bore

generally used to refer to anything in the .22 caliber rimfire family.

smallbore practice

shooting practice with .22 caliber rimfire ammunition.

small of the stock

that part of the stock of a small arms weapon usually gripped by the right hand, lying just behind the receiver and trigger assembly. In some stocks a pistol grip is shaped at this location. Specifically it is that portion of a long gun stock where the wood is at its thinnest dimension.

Smith

a carbine hinged at its breech, designed by Gilbert Smith and used during the Civil War. The rifle using the same system and also called Smith was well received in Europe.

Smith & Wesson

a trademark of the firearms manufacturing firm of Smith & Wesson Inc., of Springfield, Massachusetts.

Smith, Horace *(1808-1893)*

an American gunsmith and inventor obtaining his first patent, for a breechloading rifle, in 1851. He cooperated with Daniel Wesson in developing a metallic cartridge and is perhaps best known as the Smith of Smith and Wesson fame.

smokeless powder

it is neither smokeless nor a powder but when ignited burns with a minimum of ash and smoke and it is produced in the form of small flakes, strips, pellets, cylinders and other shapes. The single base powder is a chemical compound made from nitrated cellulose colloided with ether-alcohol. The double base powder uses both nitrocellulose and nitroglycerin as a base. Used as a propellent in firearms. It is no more dangerous to store, handle or use than celluloid and much less dangerous than gasoline. French chemists worked to obtain smokeless powder as early as 1832 but not until 1884 did French engineer Vielle produce the first successful smokeless powder.

smoothbore

a gun whose barrel is not rifled, such as those of former years called a musket, fowling piece, or blunderbuss. A shotgun is a smoothbore weapon.

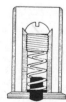

snap cap

a dummy cartridge fitted with a cushioned or spring-activated button in place of the usual primer assembly. Used to prevent damage to the firing pin tips when dry firing.

snaphaunce, snaphance

an improved muzzleloader that replaced the expensive wheel mechanism of the wheel lock. It carried a piece of pyrite or flint between jaws at the end of the spring tensioned cock. When the trigger was pulled the cock was released causing the pyrites or flint to strike a glancing blow at the steel anvil (later to be part of the frizzen of the flintlock) thus igniting the priming powder. Some authorities claim it appeared on the scene as early as 1525, others that it came into use between 1530 and 1570.

snap lock

a final form of matchlock which provided a tube as a container for a piece of tinder or short section of match thus avoiding a long piece of dangling cord whose lighted end could be seen by an enemy. Well known were the Scandinavian locks, Swedish (1547), Norwegian (1562) and Danish (1565), used from those dates on.

snapshot

a hurried or quick shot fired with little or no calculated aim — instinct shooting.
See "pot shot" for distinction

Snider

a rifle so named after Jacob Snider of New York who, in 1864, submitted what the British held to be the best method of converting its Army's muzzleloaders into breechloaders. It was the first breechloader generally issued to the British Army.

Snider, Jacob

an American whose system for converting the British muzzleloaders to breechloaders was officially adopted by the British in 1867.

sniper

military name for a concealed sharpshooter who, generally at long range and with a telescopic sight, selects as his targets, individual soldiers.

sniperscope

an electronic infrared sight scope permitting a shooter to see and aim at a target in complete darkness. Developed during World War II by the U. S. Army.

soapstone

See "talc"

Society of Automotive Engineers

abbreviated as SAE, founded 1905, annually publishes the SAE Handbook, a book of standards for various grades of materials used in the automotive industry but whose standards are frequently included in specifications for other manufacture.

sodium nitrate

also known as nitrate of soda or Chile saltpeter, whose chemical symbol is $NaCO_3$. Used as a source of nitric acid and used in fluxes and in pyrotechnics. Black powder may be made by mixing it with sulphur and charcoal.

soft hammers

hammers made of brass, babbitt metal, plastic, wood, hard rubber, copper, lead or rawhide and used to avoid marring finished surfaces or to avoid upsetting the end of a bolt, pin, or etc.

soft point, side split bullet

a lead core encased in a jacket of harder metal except at the nose where the lead is exposed. It has slits running from the open end of the jacket, part way down the side. It is used where maximum expansion on impact is sought.

soft point bullet

a lead core encased in a jacket of harder metal except at the nose where the lead is exposed. Bullets so made expand more readily and have as a result, greater stopping power.

soft shot

another name for drop shot.
See "drop shot"

solder

usually an alloy of two or more metals. Soft solder is basically lead and tin; hard solder, copper and zinc, sometimes also with silver; aluminum solder is basically tin with the addition of just zinc or zinc and aluminum. The mixes used are designed to produce a lower melting point than those of the metals to be joined, yet to have a fusing point as close as possible to that of the metals.

soldering

the practice of fusing two metallic surfaces together by means of melting a third metallic substance between them.

solid frame

in a revolver is one having no hinge in its frame. In this type the cartridges are either unloaded singly as past a loading gate or by removing the cylinder from the frame by pulling out the axis pin. In a rifle it refers to one not readily separated into its component barrel and stock portions.

solid lead bullet

a bullet made of lead alloy, the kind and amount of alloy determining the hardness of the lead. Tin and antimony are commonly used as hardening alloys.

solvent

a strong chemical solution designed to loosen or dissolve powder and lead residues in firearms. Most firearms solvents are highly errosive and should not be left in contact with metal surfaces indefinitely, but should be carefully rinsed from steel surfaces by means of a neutralizing gun oil.

sound

1. the sensation of hearing.

2. tone or noise. Sound is propagated by progressive longitudinal vibratory disturbances called sound waves. The speed of sound in air at 68° Fahrenheit is 1129 feet per second. Thus, with no wind, if the time between when an observer sees a muzzle flash and hears the report of the gun is 5 seconds the gun is over a mile away.

SP

abbreviation for soft point bullet, a bullet partially jacketed leaving some lead exposed at the nose.

spanner

a wrench or key for winding the spring on a wheel lock.

specifications

a clear and accurate technical description of the characteristics of a material, an article, or a service so that it may be faithfully reproduced.

specific gravity

is, in general terms, the ratio of the weight of any volume of a substance to the weight of an equal volume of water. Aluminum with a specific gravity of 2.7 is that many times the weight of water of equal volume. Thus, one cubic foot of aluminum weighs 2.7 x 62.5 or 168.7 pounds.

specific heat

the number of heat units required to raise the temperature of a given weight of a substance one degree. In the metric system the number of calories required to raise one gram one degree C; in the English system the number of BTU's per pound per degree F.

speed

quick motion or rate of motion (velocity).

speedlock

all firing mechanisms are called locks, however, a speedlock is a firing mechanism that is designed to transmit the trigger action to the cartridge in the shortest possible time. This is accomplished by minimizing the travel of all moving parts from the trigger, through the sear engaging surfaces, to the firing pin. True speedlocks are much desired for target shooting purposes because they help the shooter get each shot off at precisely the right moment — every split second of delay, from the time the trigger is activated, serves to handicap accuracy. Speedlock actions are most expensive to produce and, for that reason, are usually found only in high-grade target rifles.

spelter

refers to zinc, generally when in the form of ingots.

Spencer

a repeating caliber .52, 7 round carbine, the first successful repeater, made by Christian M. Spencer in 1860, put into production in 1862 and used by United States Cavalry units until about 1873. The name also was applied to rifles using Spencer's invention.

Spencer, Christopher Minor *(1833-1922)*
an American manufacturer and inventor. In 1860, he invented the first successful repeater, a 7 shot rifle with a tubular magazine in the stock. The users of the Spencer rifles and carbines during the Civil War considered them to be the finest shoulder guns then available.

spent, spent bullet
used up or without power or force, such as a bullet that has been deprived of its energy.

spin
a whirling or rotating movement such as is imparted to a projectile when it passes through the rifled bore of a gun.

spiral
another term describing the pattern of rifling lands and grooves cut into the barrel of a firearm although a spiral mathematically is a curve having a constantly increasing radius of curvature. Helical is the proper term.

spire point bullet
a term used to describe a sharply pointed bullet shape.

spitzer
a bullet having a sharp point for the purpose of giving it greater ballistic efficiency.

spline
a flat strip for insertion in a groove between parts. It also refers to the keyway for such a key.

split body
in a cartridge is a longitudinal crack in the case near the head. It is a dangerous defect since it allows gas to escape to the rear.

split neck
in a cartridge is a crack in the neck of the case, usually a season crack hastened by failure to properly anneal the neck.

spokeshave
a miniature form of drawknife used by model makers and gunstock makers for removing minute particles of wood.

spontaneous combustion
a burning that starts as the result of heat generated by chemical action without initiation from an outside source.

spool magazine
a rotary form of magazine having a spring-activated follower, believed to have been invented by Schulhof in 1885. However, the first commercially successful rotary magazine was developed by Ferdinand Ritter von Mannlicher of Austria's Steyr Works in 1887. See "rotary magazine".

sporterize
the practice of converting a military rifle into a sporting firearm. This generally involves stripping it of military accessories, cutting back or replacing the stock, replacing military sights with sporting sights, altering the bolt handle, modifying or replacing the two stage military trigger and, in some cases, cutting the barrel down to sporter length.
Most military rifles weigh nine or more pounds and it is necessary to reduce their weight to approximately seven pounds in the sporterizing process.
Sporterizing is usually limited to bolt action rifles.

Sporting Arms and Ammunition Manufacturer's Institute
a trade association comprised of the leading U.S. manufacturers of sporting firearms, ammunition and smokeless powder. Founded in 1926 and operated continuously since that date to serve the mutual interests of the industry and American sportsmen, headquartered at 420 Lexington Avenue, New York City, New York.

sporting gun
any firearm designed expressly for sporting purposes. All other weapons fall into defense, police, or military categories.

spot annealing

the softening of a small area in a hardened steel surface by spot heating, after which the work is permitted to cool slowly.

Spot annealing is often necessary where holes are to be drilled and tapped in a hardened steel receiver for the purpose of attaching a scope mount or sight.

spotter

1. a disc mounted on a long wooden pole and used by the target operator in the pit to show the shooter where his bullets are striking the target.

2. one who observes hits on target through a spotting scope from a position immediately behind the firing line.

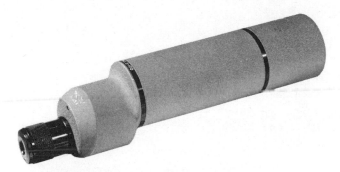

spotting scope

the term applied to a conveniently mounted telescope used to spot the hits made on a distant target. Spotting scopes are generally of about 30-power magnification.

spot welding

the welding of two parts together by having raised projections or ridges on their abutting surfaces and passing a current of electricity across them.

Springfield Armory

located in Springfield, Massachusetts was authorized by Act of Congress in April 1778 as an ammunition laboratory. In 1795 it began the manufacture of muskets. From then on it was a small arms manufacturing center for the U. S. Army. Scheduled to be phased out by April, 1968 its responsibility for research and development of rifles, pistols, machine guns, grenade launchers and weapons systems for aircraft will be taken over by Rock Island Arsenal.

Springfield rifle

United States 5-shot repeating rifle .30 caliber, model 1903. It is a breechloading, magazine fed, bolt operated weapon.

springing the rammer

a term applied to the test used in determining if a muzzleloading firearm is loaded, which consists in dropping a metal ramrod into the bore, a metallic sound denoting an unloaded condition; a dull thud, a loaded condition. Appropriate precautions are required in making this test.

spring plunger

a plunger actuated by a helical spring, but always in a fixed position until pulled back by hand or mechanical means.

springs

are resilient members used in guns to quickly restore movable parts to their normal positions or to lock parts together. For example flat springs are used to permit a gun to be cocked and fired, coiled springs to absorb recoil and restore the breechblock to normal position, a notched spring to hold a magazine within the grip of a pistol.

sprue

the hole through which molten material is poured into the gate and into the mold. Also the name given the waste piece cast in this hole.

spur hammer

a hammer having a rearward projection which may be used to cock the weapon.

spur trigger

an obsolete trigger used on old revolvers and pistols having no trigger guard, but being partly housed and protected in a spur-like projection on the bottom of the frame or receiver. The trigger extends slightly in front of this projection.

squatting position

a posture used in firing a rifle; rarely used in target competition but frequently employed in the field.

In assuming the squatting position the shooter faces half-right and, keeping his legs rather close together, squats so that his weight is evenly divided on both feet. The right upper arm is then braced against the right thigh; the left upper arm is rested against the inner flat of the left shinbone. The body weight is transferred slightly to the left foot immediately before firing.

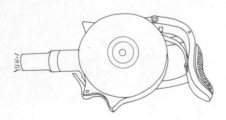

squeeze palm pistol

popular about 1880, had a circular grip and firing mechanism that would fit into the palm of the hand permitting the barrel to project outward between the fingers of the clenched hand. It was fired by squeezing the hand thus compressing the trigger against the grip portion.

squib

1. a firework characterized by a hissing noise when ignited and burning, ending in an explosion or, in some kinds, merely burning.

2. the term "squib load" refers to a cartridge or shell that does not develop normal pressures.

squirrel gun

a colloquial term for a light caliber muzzle loading weapon of the early 1800's; generally refers to weapons of .36 caliber or less.
Present day squirrel guns are usually of .22 rimfire caliber.

SS

abbreviation for single shot.

S/S

abbreviation for side by side, a shotgun having two barrels along side of each other.

ST

abbreviation for single trigger.

stabilizer

an attachment for the barrel of a small arm to minimize muzzle jump.

stacking rod

a rod projecting ahead of the upper band of certain military rifles to permit interlocking with other stacking rods to stack the arms so equipped.

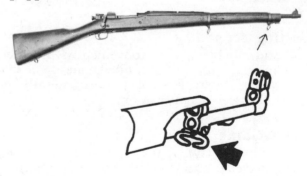

stacking swivel

the hinged hook near the muzzle end of military rifle by means of which several rifles may be fastened together to form a stack.

stage

in match competition the position, range, or timing under which a segment of the match is held.

stag grip

a pair of grips made for a pistol or revolver from genuine, or imitation, stag-horn.

stainless steel

generally a low carbon alloy steel with 9 to 20 per cent of chromium, and resistant to rust. Used for gun barrels to a limited degree. Recently adapted by the Smith & Wesson Company for their model 60 .38 caliber revolver which, it is believed, is entirely rust-proof.

stamping

basically the economical forming of a part from sheet stock by means of a press, punch and die. The product is usually referred to as a stamping. In some firearms stampings are used for floor plates, trigger guards and similar parts.
In some instances, depending upon its shape, the composition of its alloy and the uses to which it will be put, a stamping can be more desirable than a comparable machined component.

stance

the mode of standing or the standing posture of a person. In the case of a shooter a position appropriate to his weapon, target, range, rules and his own physical characteristics.

stanchion gun

a pivot gun such as a gun fixed to a boat on a pedestal mount.

stand

a vantage point selected by the hunter when game is being driven. The "stand" is a place where the hunter remains as quiet and motionless as possible in hopes of spotting a suitable target.

standard

1. an accepted or established rule or model.

2. the classification given to supplies and equipment that are accepted for general use in the United States military services.

standard muzzle velocity

the speed at which a given projectile is supposed to leave the muzzle of a gun. This depends upon the gun, the propelling charge and the size, shape and weight of the projectile. Firing tables are based on standard muzzle velocities.
See "standard trajectory"

standard nomenclature

the official name by which items of military equipment are designated so that they may be identified without confusion.

standard trajectory

the calculated path a projectile will follow through the air under given conditions of:
    gun projectile size, shape and weight
    propellent charge
    angle of fire
    weather conditions
Firing tables are based upon standard trajectories.

standing breech

that part of the frame of a gun that bears on the head of the cartridge and supports it, found in revolvers and in blow-forward and hinged frame firearms.

"Reprinted by permission of the National Rifle Association of America."

standing position

one of the standard postures in firing a rifle. The shooter stands half faced to the right, left

203

elbow well under the rifle, left hand holding rifle in front of balance point, right elbow high and cheek close to stock. Also called "offhand" position.

Star

semiautomatic pistols made in Spain for both military and civilian use and sold in the United States.

star class

a mark or symbol once used by U. S. Government arsenals to signify a high standard of excellence. In range tests Springfield rifles that grouped exceptionally well were stamped with a small star and thereafter referred to as "star" class rifles.

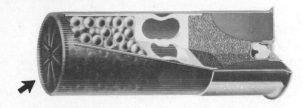

star crimp

the end closure of a paper tube shotshell in which the tube is folded into five equal segments and compressed inwardly to cover the shot column.
Modern plastic shot shells are made with six or eight segment folds treated in much the same manner as a star crimp.

star gage

an instrument that may be inserted in the bore of a gun to measure its diameter.

Starr

the name of revolvers and carbines designed by Eben T. Starr of New York who, in 1856, received a patent on his first revolver design and in 1860 a second patent.

steel

iron alloyed with carbon and certain other elements depending on intended use. Ordnance steel, for example, contained 0.45 to 0.55% of carbon, 1.00 to 1.30% manganese; max. 0.05% phosphorus; max. 0.05% sulphur. Prior to 1852 practically all small arms barrels in the United States

were made of wrought iron or soft carbon steel in view of the relatively low breech pressures then obtained with black powder. With modern pressures of 38000 psi and upward, steels of higher tensile strength are used.

steel coloring

the normal color of a steel surface may be changed by treating the surface in various ways. In gunsmithing different shades of blue, black or brown are imparted to the surface of a barrel or gun part by bluing, browning or parkerizing. See "bluing", "cold blue", "hot blue", "browning", "niter bluing process"

steel jacketed

a bullet having a soft steel jacket often flash coated or plated with gilding metal to reduce friction in the bore and prevent rusting. Not a common type in the United States.

steel surface hardening

also called case hardening, is accomplished by one of three methods depending upon the composition of the steel and the use to which it is to be put, — carburizing, cyaniding or nitriding. The first is the one most commonly employed by gunsmiths.
See "case harden"

steel wool

an abrasive made by shaving thin layers of steel from wire. The cutting characteristics vary with the size of the fiber.

stereoscopic range finder

a telescopic instrument that furnishes correct ranges when the target sighted on appears at the same distance or depth as an image or cross hair marked on its lens. Also called stereo range finder.

Stevens

a trademark applied to an assortment of firearms manufactured by the Savage Arms Corporation of Westfield, Massachusetts.

Stevens, Joshua *(1814-1907)*

an American gunsmith and inventor, who after being employed by Samuel Colt for some years began manufacture under his own name. In

1864 he founded the J. Stevens & Co., manufacturers of pistols and revolvers.

Steyr

the name of a 9 mm, 8 round semiautomatic pistol that was the official sidearm of Austria, Hungary and Romania from 1912 to 1918 and of other caliber semiautomatic pistols made for civilian use. Also site of the famous Steyr works, makers of the Mannlicher-Schoenauer rifle.

stippling

the practice of roughing a wood or metal surface with a sharply pointed instrument. The resultant random pattern provides a good gripping surface.

stirrup

as a part of some revolvers it is the latch that holds a tip up barrel in firing position. As a part of some automatic pistols it is a trigger with two rearward arms to equalize pressure on the sear when the trigger is squeezed.

stock

the rigid member of wood, plastic or other material in a rifle, carbine or shotgun to which the barrel assembly is attached and which provides a means for holding the weapon to the shoulder. In handguns the stocks form the "grip".
See "skeleton stock"

stock, ¾

a term used to describe the length of a conventional rifle stock: that is, a stock whose forend reaches to a point under the barrel about midway between the receiver and the muzzle. (Used to differentiate from full length Mannlicher style stocks.)

stock, benchrest

a true heavyweight benchrest stock is not really a gun handle but a wooden gun platform. So many different shapes and sizes are found in the benchrest field that no one stock can be made to serve as a representative specimen. Nevertheless, most are big, square-cut and bulky. Because they are not intended for carrying afield, and because their weight is designed to aid in steadying the rifle for high precision match shooting, their bulk is well suited to their function.

stock blank

a rough cut piece of gunstock wood prior to shaping.

stock, buttstock

that portion of a two piece stock that forms the butt portion, i.e. the portion which is laid in contact with the shoulder.

stock, English

a type of shotgun stock noted for its slim lines and light weight. English shotgun stocks are made with a straight grip and a small, narrow forend.

stock, free rifle

a term used to describe those target rifle stocks that are used in "open" competition. In "free" rifle competition no restrictive limits are set for stock size, weight or shape. Most free rifle stocks are made with a thumbhole, high comb, hook plate, and adjustable palm rest.

stock, full stock

a type of rifle stock that extends to the muzzle of the weapon. In sporting rifles this style is often referred to as a "Mannlicher" stock.

stock, Mannlicher

a stock design popularized by the famous Mannlicher-Schoenauer rifles of the Austrian Steyr Works. The Mannlicher stock is characterized by the extension of the wooden forend to the muzzle of the gun.

stock, modified pistol grip

a type of rifle or shotgun stock in which a small pistol grip is shaped in the form of a rounded knob.

stock, nylon

a stock for a rifle or shotgun made almost entirely of nylon.

stock, one-piece

a full length rifle or shotgun stock made from a single wood blank.

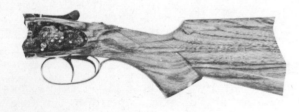

stock, pistol grip

a rifle or shotgun stock shaped with a simulated pistol grip for the trigger hand.

stock pitch

the distance between the end of the muzzle of a shoulder arm and a line perpendicular to the surface upon which the butt end of the gun rests flat, when such line just touches the receiver.

stock, semifinished

a stock maker's classification for a stock that is approximately 80% shaped and inletted.

stock, straight grip

a slim, straight line stock without pistol grip. On rifles or carbines this is often called a Western style stock. On shotguns, it is referred to as an English style stock.

stock, thumbhole

a target type stock, generally found on match rifles used in "free rifle" competition.
This stock is made with an overly large butt section and is shaped with a very full pistol grip behind which is bored a hole to accommodate the thumb of the shooter's trigger hand.
See "stock, free rifle"

stock, two piece

the wooden buttstock and forend of a firearm made as two separate pieces.

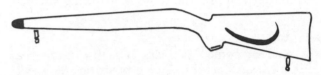

stock, Whelen

a pattern of rifle stock developed and popularized by the late Colonel Townsend Whelen. The key to the Whelen pattern is an unobstrusive cheek-piece and comb sloping gently forward and down — a feature that tends to pull the stock away from the shooter's face as the rifle recoils.

Stoeger

a trademark of Stoeger Arms Corporation of 55 Ruta Court, South Hackensack, New Jersey. Parent company of Shooter's Bible, Inc., and American representatives of such foreign firearms manufacturing firms as Franchi (Italy), Gabilondo (Spain), Sarasqueta (Spain), Steyr (Austria) and Brenneke (West Germany).

stone

a piece of cemented earthy or mineral matter certain kinds of which are important in the manufacture of firearms because of their abrasive properties. Natural stones usually employed for oilstones are the Washita and the Arkansas stones. While either oil or water may be used with those stones, another popular natural stone, the India, also called Hindustan, a coarse stone, is used only with water.

Stoner system

a U.S. military rifle, caliber 5.56 mm (.223 caliber) gas operated, air cooled, fired either automatically or semi-automatically. Magazine has 30 rounds capacity.

stop

a device that checks the movement of a part or prevents it from moving by locking it in place. The stop on a .45 caliber automatic pistol that holds the slide open after the last cartridge in the magazine has been fired, is an example.

stop watch

a time piece usually calibrated to reach to a tenth of second used in shooting events to measure the time consumed in rapid fire contests.

stoppage

the unintended stopping of fire of a gun caused by faulty action of the gun or of the ammunition.

straight *(or straight run)*

common to skeet and trap shooting: means that a shooter has broken all of the targets in a particular event.

straight-pull action

a bolt action as in the Winchester Lee and the Ross in which the bolt is moved straight back and forward instead of "up, back, forward, down" as in the turn bolt Mauser action.

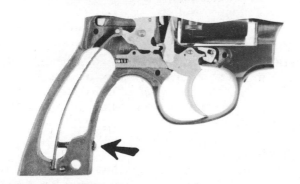

strain screw

a screw found in many revolvers, rifles and shotguns to hold and make adjustable, the tension of the mainspring.

strap

a flat, narrow band of leather, webbing or other flexible material. Also applies to any flat narrow strip of material used as a fastening.
See "sling"

stray

something that has wandered away, such as a stray bullet — beyond its intended flight path.

stress

the force exerted upon a body tending to deform it. It is generally expressed in pounds per square inch.
See "tensile strength"

striae

the markings left on the bearing surfaces of a fired bullet. They are important means for identifying the firearm from which a bullet has been fired.

striagraph

a firearms identification contour-analyzing instrument which enables an operator to obtain a photographic chart or recording of the surface contours of a bullet or gun bore.

striker

a type of firing pin, rod-like, which travels inside the breechblock and when cocked is under tension of its own spiral spring. When released by action of the trigger it projects its integral or separable pin against the primer.

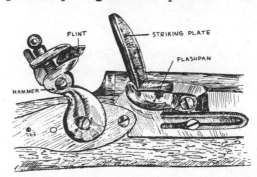

striking plate

the upright metal piece in a snaphaunce or flintlock against which a spark is produced by striking it with pyrites or flint. Properly called a "frizzen" or "batterie".

striking power

See "knockdown effect"

striking velocity

the speed of a projectile at the point of impact.

string

the number of shots fired in a given stage of match competition; usually a "string" consists of five or ten shots.

stripped action

a bare rifle or shotgun receiver lacking related parts. The comparable part in a handgun is more properly referred to as a "frame".

stripping

the disassembling of a firearm, or, when used in referring to a bullet it is the loss of some of the metal of the bullet jacket due to failure of the bullet to properly engage the rifling.

strut

the component part of the firing mechanism of a gun that puts pressure on the hammer.

stud

a projection on a gun for holding or engaging another part as for example a sight stud or a bayonet stud.

Stutzen

translated means "short rifle". It was an Austrian service rifle with a 19 inch barrel length stemming from an 1890 carbine model.

subcaliber

a caliber smaller than standard for the gun on which practice is being given. Conversion units or adapters make possible the use of cartridges smaller than those for which a gun is designed.

subcaliber equipment

items used for firing subcaliber ammunition in practice with larger guns, such as adapters, tubes, small guns, and accessories.

subcaliber firing

practice firing with subcaliber ammunition to give training in the use of guns of larger calibers.

subcaliber gun

a gun mounted on the outside and above the barrel of a cannon used in practice firing of subcaliber ammunition as part of aiming drills with the larger guns.

subcaliber range

a firing range suitable for firing of subcaliber ammunition. Such a range may be equipped with miniature landscape targets and other devices to simulate the conditions under which the regular caliber ammunition would be used.

subcaliber tube

a tube that may be fitted into the bore of a gun and which permits the use of subcaliber ammunition in practice firing.

submachine gun

a lightweight automatic or semiautomatic gun designed to be fired from the shoulder or hip. Generally air cooled and gas-operated, developed during World War II.

sugarloaf bullet

a bullet of conical shape having a flat nose. Also called a "picket" bullet.

suicide special

generally covers the multitude of cheap, poor quality pocket revolvers made in the United States during the last half of the 19th century. Apparently the term first came into use by collectors in 1948.

Sullivan Law

the New York State firearms law known for its drastic regulatory feature governing the purchase, ownership and carrying of handguns. Enacted into law in 1911.

sulphur

a chemical element whose chemical symbol is "S" and which is readily found in many areas. It was combined with charcoal and potassium nitrate (saltpeter) to make the first gunpowder. It is also used in the manufacture of sulphuric acid.

sulphur cast

a cast of sulphur made of the chamber, bullet seat and bore of a firearm to accurately ascertain the dimensions of these relatively inaccessible parts. The sulphur cast is made nonshrinking by premixing powdered lampblack and gun camphor, dissolved in alcohol, with the sulphur.

sulphuric acid

whose chemical symbol is H_2SO_4 is a colorless, oily liquid, sometimes called oil of vitriol; used in the production of explosives and the cleaning of metal surfaces.

summit of trajectory

the highest point that a projectile reaches in its flight from the gun to the target.

superelevation

the amount that the axis of the bore of a gun must be pointed above the line joining the gun and the target to allow for the curved path of the projectile in flight.

Super Speed

trade name of the Winchester Firearms Company for cartridges made by it.

Super-X

trade name of the Western Cartridge Company for cartridges made by it.

sureshot

a common expression for a proficient shooter.

surveillance

with respect to ammunition is the programmed inspection, testing and maintenance that insures its storage in usable condition.

sustaining lead *(LEED)*

tracking a moving target by keeping the sights moving at the same relative speed as the target and holding the proper lead until the gun is fired.

swab

a long handled brush used for cleaning the bore of a gun, usually of cannon size.

swage

usually applies to a number of different kinds of tools having hollow impressions in their faces for finishing round work and consisting of pairs of dies with matching tops and bottoms.

swaged choke

a choke formed during manufacture, after the finish ream of the barrel to a true cylinder, by acting on the exterior of the barrel to push material inward at the muzzle and thereafter reaming to the desired dimension.

swaging, bullet

See "bullet swaging"

sweating

1. a method of soldering two metal parts together by heating them sufficiently to melt and draw the solder, instead of using a soldering iron.

2. in the case of firearms the word applied to the condensation of moisture from the air on the metallic surfaces under certain circumstances.

swedging

better known as "swaging".

swing-out cylinder

the cylinder of a revolver that is mounted on a crane or yoke and which swings clear of the frame for loading. When latched in the frame the cylinder is rigidly held ready for firing.

swing-through leading

a method of giving lateral direction to a fired projectile by swinging the muzzle of the gun in the direction the target is moving. Its effect is relatively small, the lead being the important factor in causing a projectile to meet a moving target crossing in front of a shooter.

swivel

a link or coupling piece that permits the joined parts freedom of rotation independent of each other. For example sling swivels, a stacking swivel, or a swivel ramrod.

swivel bow

that portion of a swivel which forms the loop through which a sling or carrying strap is threaded.

swivel gun

a gun so mounted that it may be turned from side to side or up and down.

swivel hook

an English style swivel having a hooked end adapted to be readily snapped into eyes or bases protruding from the underside of a firearm, to permit quick attachment and detachment. Obsolete in the United States.

synchronism

the concurrence of events in time as typified in driven aircraft when the action of the gun had the early days of machine gun use in propeller to be synchronized with the propeller rotation so the bullets could pass between the blades of the revolving propeller.

T

tail gun

the flexibly mounted gun in the tail of an aircraft.

tail wind

a wind blowing from behind the shooter when he is facing the target.

take down

to take a gun apart, that is, to disassemble it. Also called "stripping".

talc

a mineral known as steatite or soapstone, a soft, greasy white or gray substance. It has been experimented with as a lubricant. Chemically known as hydrated magnesium silicate.

tampion, tompion

a stopper, such as a wooden plug, or a cover, especially for the muzzle of a gun to protect the bore when not in use.

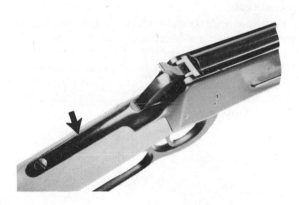

tang

a projecting prong, tongue or the like, usually forming part of one piece for joining it to another piece as for example, a trigger guard having a projection at each end for screwing it to the stock.
Most commonly used in the firearms industry to describe the top rearmost extension of a receiver at a point where it joins the stock.

tang sight

an aperture type rear sight, usually adjustable for elevation, that is anchored on the tang of a firearm.
This type of sight is used on rifles or carbines that do not lend themselves to standard side mounted receiver sights due to top ejection or mechanical complications.

tank gun

a gun mounted in a military tank.

Tannenberg gun

an ancient 13 inch bronze casting, part of a firearm, found in the ruins of Castle Tannenberg and now in a museum in Nuremberg, Germany. It is known to have predated 1399.

tap

an internal thread cutting tool having teeth to shape the thread. There are a number of classification for taps according to their use.

tapelock

an advance in the pill lock in that a strip of paper or fabric provided with percussion pellets could be fed to the firing position by the action of the lock. The percussion primer was called a tape primer.

tape primer

a row of percussion pellets enclosed between two strips of paper and in rolled up form used in a gun such as "paper caps" are used in toy guns today.

taper pin
a pin used to secure two parts together.

target
a specific point, area, object or group of objects at which fire is directed, either in practice, hunting or match competition.

target area
the area in which a target is placed and which is subject to fire.

target butt
a wall on a target range having the target pit on one side and an earthen cover on the other to protect target pit personnel. Also simply called a "butt".

target course
the path of a moving target.

target frame
a frame employed as a mounting for paper targets used in target practice.

target hammer
a wide spur hammer frequently employed on target revolvers to facilitate gripping.

target, NRA
one of a series of targets officially adopted as standard targets by the National Rifle Association.

target pit
a trench in front of a row of targets within which personnel may find security from fire and from which position they may replace or mark targets for the benefit of the shooters.

target practice
any exercise in aiming and firing at a practice target.

target range
an area set aside and equipped for shooting at targets. Also simply called "range".

target rifle
a rifle designed to be particularly adapted for target shooting.

target sled
a sled drawn by a cable and carrying a target. Used to provide a moving target in target practice.

target trigger
a trigger having a wider than normal frontal plane, designed to provide a large engaging surface for the trigger finger. When properly fitted a target trigger is adjusted to eliminate or minimize travel and to function with a crisp, light let-off.

taxidermy
the art of preparing animal skins, then stuffing and mounting them in lifelike form.

teat fire
a front loading cartridge invented in 1864 which had a rearwardly extending teat containing fulminate that was crushed by the fall of a chisel-nosed hammer.

telescope
an optical instrument that magnifies distant images in order to facilitate their viewing by the human eye. The quality of a telescope is determined by its design and construction. Four optical factors involved are illumination, definition (resolving power), size of field, and magnifying power.

telescope mount
a base or holder for a telescope, such as a bracket for securing a telescope to a gun.

telescope sight
a refracting telescope equipped with a reticle and designed to serve as an aiming device for a firearm.

temperature

the degree of heat or cold measured by a speci-fied scale and, with respect to firearms and ammunition, unless stated to the contrary, 70° Fahrenheit is the normal temperature at which velocities, pressures and trajectories are measured. Variation in the temperature of ammunition will effect pressure and velocity. A change of temperature of 10 degrees Fahrenheit could mean a change in muzzle velocity, depending on the ammunition, of 17 feet per second.

tempering

sometimes called "drawing" is the method used to reduce the brittleness in hardened steel and relieve the internal stresses caused by the sudden cooling in the quenching bath. The steel is re-heated to a specific temperature and control-cooled by means of a time-and-temperature process.

Tenite

the registered trademark for thermoplastic materials used for making wood-simulated gun stocks.

tenon

a projecting part adapted to fit into a mortise, thus forming a joint.

tensile strength

the resistance offered by a material to stress that tends to pull it apart. The stress is usually expressed in pounds per square inch. Prior to reaching the breaking point the yield point is reached, and so to properly express the breaking point it is referred to as the ultimate tensile strength. Some appropriate figures are in psi:

	Yield Point	Ultimate Tensile Strength
lead, cast	1780	
rolled	3000	
brass,		
cartridge	20,000	45,000
aluminum,		
cast	36,000	46,000
wrought		
iron	31,000	51,000
silicon steel	52,000	72,000
chrome steel	76,000	103,200
chrome moly	189,000	205,000

terminal velocity

the remaining velocity or speed of a projectile at the point in its downward path where it is level with the muzzle of the gun.
See "remaining velocity"
    "striking velocity"

testing target

a special target, used to boresight an artillery piece. It has two marks separated by the same distance that separates the axis of the bore and the axis of the sight, so that the gun barrel may be pointed at one mark and the sight brought to bear on the other.

test piece

a term used in connection with artillery usage; a gun selected to be tested for calibration by comparison with a reference piece.

test, proof

See "proof test"

tetryl *(TET rill)*

a sensitive explosive used especially in caps and bursters to detonate less sensitive explosives.

thermometer

an instrument for measuring relatively low temperatures, usually not over 200 or 300 degrees F. The scales in common use for thermometers are the Fahrenheit (F) in English speaking countries and the Centigrade (C) in continental countries and in scientific fields.

thirty-o-six

the common designation of the U. S. rifle cartridge used in both World Wars which officially is the caliber .30 M 1906. It has a rimless case about 2½" long. In figures it is abbreviated to .30-06.

thirty-thirty

the common designation for a relatively small size sporting cartridge having a rimmed base and

being about two inches long, brought out in 1895 by the Winchester Repeating Arms Company. The designation is derived from the diameter of the rifle bore and the original 30 grains weight of the powder charge. Similarity with the "thirty-o-six" lies only in their identical bullet diameter. The powder charge of the 30-06 is about 50 grains.
See "thirty-o-six"

Thompson, John Taliaferro *(1860-1940)*
a Brigadier General of the Ordnance Department, U. S. Army who designed a submachine gun that was first marketed in 1921 and which became popularly known as a tommy gun.

Thompson submachine gun
a .45 caliber, air-cooled automatic weapon that can be carried and operated by one man.

thread gage
a tool designed to measure the size and pitch of screw threads.

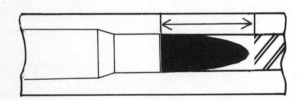

throat
the tapered portion of the bore forward of the chamber where it diminishes in cross section to meet the rifling. In a revolver it is the enlargement of the bore at the breech to facilitate the centering of the bullet in the barrel when it jumps from the cylinder into the bore. Also may be referred to as "leade".
"Jumping the throat" is an expression used to describe the initial motion of a bullet upon being fired. The throat is the area through which the bullet first moves as it starts to leave the case and before it engages the rifling.
See "leade"

thumbhole stock
a target rifle stock having a hole through it to accommodate the thumb of the firing hand to provide means for relaxing the hand and thus increasing its sensitivity to the trigger pull.
See "stock, thumbhole"

thumb piece
a latch on certain revolvers, that when pushed forward releases the cylinder.

thumb rest
a shelf or depression shaped into the gripping surface of a handgun or rifle to provide a resting platform for the shooter's trigger-hand thumb.

tige *(TEE sh)*
in an early rifle, a steel pin in the breech against which the ball was hammered by the ramrod to expand it to fit the grooves. The propellent charge was placed around the tige.

timed fire
a rate of fire practiced in target shooting which somewhat restricts the shooter in the time he is allowed to complete a prescribed course.
For example, in timed fire handgun competition the shooter is generally allowed four seconds per shot, completing a five shot string in twenty seconds.

time lag
the interval of time that elapses between the action of one part of a mechanism and the action or reaction of a connected part.

time of fall
of a bullet in air is dependent upon the force of gravity acting upon it as with any freely falling body and the resistance of the air to its passage downward through it.

time of flight
the elapsed time, in seconds, from the instant a projectile leaves the muzzle of a gun until the instant it strikes or bursts.

tin

is a soft, ductile and malleable lustrous white metal element whose chemical symbol is Sn. It has a relatively low melting point and is extensively used as an alloy with other metals and in tin plating of other metals. In the firearms art its use in bronzes, solders and babbitt metals is best known.

tinder box

once a metal container used to hold tinder, flint and steel for starting a fire.

tinder lighter

similar to the lock on a flintlock gun having instead of a barrel, a metal receptacle for holding an inflammable substance to catch the sparks. Used before the advent of friction matches.

tipping

the spiralling of a bullet in its flight through the air. Also called "air spiral" or "wabble".

tip up

a colloquial expression referring to a top-breaking revolver.

TNT

the abbreviation for the high explosives, trinitrotoluene and trinitrotoluol.

toe

the bottom part of the butt of a rifle or shotgun.

toggle joint

a joint formed by joining two members with a pin or the like to permit the members to be pivoted about it so that movement of the joint will either bring the free ends together or straighten them out. The Luger pistol is an example of use of such a joint in a firearm. See "Luger"

Tokarev

a 7.62 mm, 8 shot semiautomatic pistol, an official military weapon of Russia beginning in 1930 and used as such by various other countries allied with Russia.

tolerance

the allowable deviation from a standard dimension of a part or from the accuracy of an instrument. By keeping within prescribed tolerances the weapons and ammunition will function as intended.

toluol, toluene

toluol is the common name for the chemical toluene, a flammable liquid obtained mainly from tar oil and used in the manufacture of explosives, specifically trinitrotoluene (TNT).

tommy gun

the popular name for a submachine gun designed by Brig. Gen. John T. Thompson. It was the first American submachine gun, making its appearance in 1921. The military arm, the caliber .45 M 1928 A1 Submachine Gun has a 20 round box magazine, a 50 round drum magazine, and at one time a 100 round drum magazine. It uses a blow back system and has a cyclic rate of from 600 to 700 rounds per minute.

tompion, tampion

a stopper such as a wooden plug, or cover, especially for the muzzle of a gun to protect the bore when not in use.

top break

a form of revolver design popular during the early 1900's. Instead of the swing-out cylinder which is commonly used today, the top-break revolver was made with a hinge located in front of the cylinder where the barrel joined the frame. A spring lock was positioned at the rear of the top strap, above the firing pin port. When the lock was opened the hinge would permit the barrel to tip down at the muzzle and this would raise the cylinder, exposing the chambers for unloading or loading.

top extension
(sometimes called barrel extension) common to double barrel shotguns and some over & under guns: an extension that protrudes from the chamber area of the barrels and which fits into a corresponding recess in the face of the breech. When a cross-bolt is employed in the receiver mechanism, the sliding bolt passes through a hole cut into the barrel extension and serves to lock the barrels securely to the breech.

touchhole
the opening in early firearms that provided communication between the priming composition outside the barrel and the powder charge within the barrel which permitted the flash of the priming mixture to ignite the powder.

touch pan
the flash pan of early firearms.
See "pan"

trace
path of a tracer bullet.

tracer
1. a burning composition placed in ammunition to show the path of the projectile.

2. a type of ammunition used for observation fire, signaling and incendiary purposes.

tracer ammunition
See "tracer"

tracer bullet
a bullet containing a chemical composition that burns in flight thus making its path visible to an observer. Also called "tracer". Such bullets may also be militarily employed as incendiaries. Not recommended for use in hunting or target shooting.

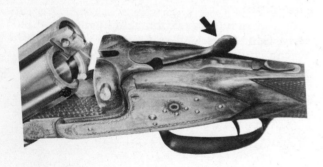

top lever
the locking lever common to break-open type guns, such as side by side or over & under double barrel shotguns.

torque
an effect noticeable in light weight rifles firing high velocity cartridges, the rifle tending to rotate in a direction opposite to the rotation of the bullet passing through the bore.

touche
a small torch, faggot or piece of wire which when lit or heated to red heat, was placed by a cannoneer to the touch hole of an early cannon to ignite the powder charge.

tracer stream
the path of a series of tracer bullets.

track
to coordinate the movement of a gun with the speed and direction of a moving target.

trade guns
a term applied to flintlocks used in trade with the natives of Africa and the Americas. Sometimes inferior in quality, sometimes specially made for the trade. They were in the hands of Indians the first half of the 17th century.

trademark

a name, letter, symbol, device, mark or combination of them used in business to distinguish the goods or services of one manufacturer or seller from the goods or services of another. Under certain conditions prescribed by law a trademark may be registered in the United States and foreign countries and be entitled to protection under the law. Frequently trademarks are incorrectly used by persons by using them to name goods without regard to the fact that many manufacturers and sellers make and sell the same goods under their respective registered trademarks. "Vaseline" for example is the registered trademark of the Chesebrough Manufacturing Company for petroleum jelly yet many erroneously refer to all petroleum jellies as "Vaseline". Another example is "Luger", the registered trademark of Stoeger Arms Corporation for firearms yet many erroneously refer to all toggle action semiautomatic pistols as "Lugers".

trade name

the name under which a person, firm or corporation does business. A trade name identifies and distinguishes a business; a trademark identifies and distinguishes a product. Manufacturers use their names as trademarks as well as trade names. In the firearms trade even though the manufacturer does not put its name to such dual use, the public frequently treats the name as though it was a trademark.

train

to bring a weapon to bear upon a target. The word also describes a line of explosive to carry fire to a charge, usually called explosive train or powder train.

trajectory *(tra JECK toe ree)*

the path of a projectile through the air. It takes the shape of a parabolic curve.

trajectory chart

a chart, consisting of numerical measurements taken from the line of sight, or patterns traced on a graph, to indicate flight characteristics of projectiles fired under prescribed conditions at various elevations. Flight characteristics vary greatly from one gun to another and are further influenced by variations in powder charge, bullet weight, etc.

trap

the name applied to mechanically or electrically operated target throwers used in skeet and trapshooting. The name appears to have originated with the box or "trap" from which live birds were released when about 1850 the sport originated in England with birds as targets.

"Trap & Field"

official magazine of the Amateur Trapshooting Association, published monthly, with editorial and business offices located at 1100 Waterway Boulevard, Indianapolis, Indiana.

trap door buttplate

a buttplate for a rifle or shotgun designed with a hinged center plate which, when opened, exposes a compartment cut inside the butt of the stock. This compartment is used for storing cleaning equipment, spare parts, or extra rounds of ammunition.

trap, electrical

an electrically operated target throwing trap as used in the sports of skeet and trap shooting.

trap field

a field upon which trapshooting competitions are held; field consists of a single trap house containing one target throwing device (trap). The trap house is positioned so that its target throwing trap is 16 yards from the nearest row of shooting stations. Shooting stations are arranged in rows of five to accommodate five competitors per round.
For handicap purposes shooters are penalized in yardage and for that reason rows of shooting stations are spaced at one yard intervals from 16 to 27 yards.

trap gun

1. a gun of the type patented in 1857 by F. Reuthe having in addition to the gun barrels a spring mechanism for discharging a spear that would supposedly hurl bait a distance away and so serve to lure animals into shooting range. The term is sometimes applied to spring guns.

2. a shotgun made for the sport of trapshooting. Trap guns are almost exclusively 12 gauge and are made with barrels measuring 30-inches or more. Barrels are usually bored with a full choke

although some shooters prefer a slightly more open boring (such as improved-modified) for 16-yard competition.

Stocks are generally made with a high comb measuring about 1⅜ inches drop at comb and 1¼ inches drop at heel. Length of pull frequently exceeds 14¼ inches. Most trap guns have high ventilated ribs equipped with front and middle bead sights.

trap gun, trip gun

a gun so equipped with a trigger actuating device such as a wire, electric eye, etc. that it will fire when a man or animal trips it.

trap, mechanical

a mechanical target throwing device that is manually operated.

trapshooter

a shooter who engages in the sport of trapshooting, i.e. shooting at flying clay targets thrown from a trap.

trapshooting

a sport originating about 1850 in England, using live birds released from a box or trap to present a flying target to the shooter. Today, in the U. S. the sport of trapshooting is regulated by the Amateur Trapshooting Association and targets are clay discs hurled into the air by a trap.

Trapshooting Association

See "Amateur Trapshooting Association"

traverse

to move a gun to the right or to the left on its mount. The amount of traverse is expressed as an angle.

trigger

that part of the lock (ignition system) pulled or squeezed by the finger to release the cock or hammer and fire the piece.

trigger creep

the slack or distance a trigger may be moved before it meets the resistance of the sear.

trigger, double pull

a firing mechanism that functions with a two stage mechanical movement distinctively felt by pulling or by squeezing the trigger and that provides an additional factor of safety.

trigger finger

any finger customarily used to squeeze the trigger of a gun, usually the forefinger of either hand.

trigger, forward set

a form of single "set" trigger; one that provides a conventional weight of pull if released in the normal manner, but which can be set for an exceptionally light pull through the forward movement of the trigger before normal rearward motion is commenced.

trigger grooves

the grooves or serrations cut into the face of a trigger to provide a non-slipping surface for the trigger finger.

trigger guard

the metal strap that partly surrounds the trigger and serves as a protecting member.

trigger happy

a colloquial expression for one, who without regard to circumstances or consequences fires a gun. It also applies to a person who acts in other matters in the same thoughtless manner.

trigger, hinged *(or folding)*

a feature sometimes found in double trigger mechanisms of better grade double barrel guns. The forward trigger is hinged to fold forward when pressure is exerted upon its rear surface. This feature serves to prevent bruising of the trigger finger under the recoil of the gun when the rear trigger is used. Especially desirable in firearms of large gauge or caliber.

trigger lock

an auxiliary locking device that anchors the trigger within the trigger guard. Frequently employed by gun owners when storing guns.

TRAP FIELD LAYOUT

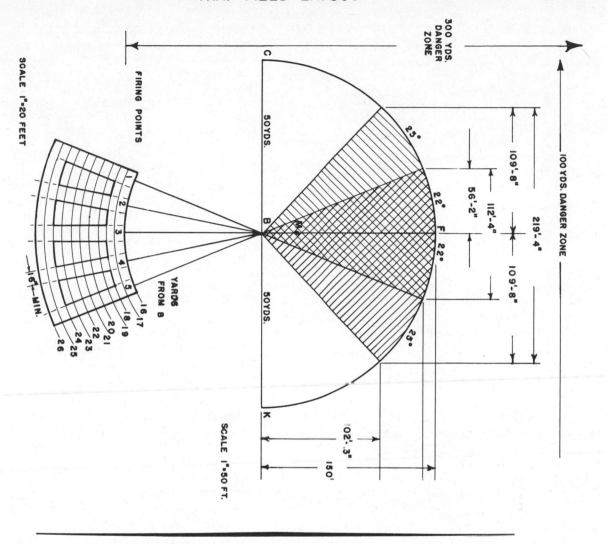

SCALE 1"=20 FEET

FIRING POINTS

YARDS FROM B

16-17
18-19
20-21
22-23
24-25
26

16" MIN.

1
2
3
4
5

300 YDS. DANGER ZONE

100 YDS. DANGER ZONE

C

50 YDS.

50 YDS.

B

F

K

25°

22°

22°

25°

109'-8"

56'-2"

112'-4"

219'-4"

109'-8"

102'-3"

150'

SCALE 1"=50 FT.

CONCRETE BLOCK TRAP HOUSE

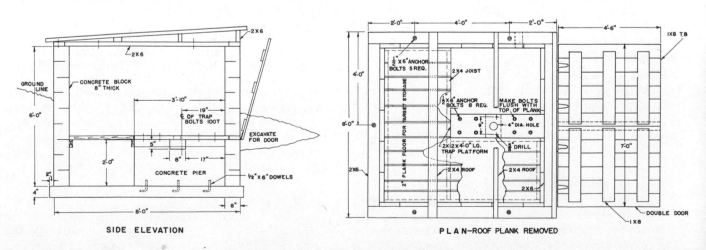

2X6

2X6

CONCRETE BLOCK 8" THICK

GROUND LINE

6'-0"

3'-10"

19"
¢ OF TRAP
BOLTS 100T

5"

8"   17"

2'-0"

CONCRETE PIER

½" X 6" DOWELS

EXCAVATE FOR DOOR

2"

4"

8'-0"

8"

SIDE ELEVATION

2'-0"   4'-0"   2'-0"

4'-6"

1X8 T.B

4'-0"

½" X 6" ANCHOR BOLTS 5 REQ.

2X4 JOIST

½" X 6" ANCHOR BOLTS 8 REQ.

MAKE BOLTS FLUSH WITH TOP OF PLANK

4" DIA. HOLE

9"

8'-0"

2" PLANK FLOOR FOR TARGET STORAGE

2X6

2X12X4'-0" LG. TRAP PLATFORM

2X4 ROOF

2X4 ROOF

2X4 ROOF

2X6

DRILL

7'-0"

DOUBLE DOOR

1X8

PLAN-ROOF PLANK REMOVED

219

triggerman

a colloquial name for a hired gunman usually a gangster who commits murder with a gun, or one of a gang of law-breakers who shoots someone in the act of committing a crime.

trigger, military

a military trigger is essentially a two stage trigger with extra long travel in both stages.
See "trigger, double pull"

trigger, non-selective single

a single trigger mechanism, such as that employed in a double barrel gun, designed to fire both barrels in unvarying sequence, i.e., the same barrel will always fire first upon the initial action of trigger and the second barrel will follow upon subsequent trigger action. The firing order cannot be reversed.
See "trigger, selective single"

trigger, offset

See "offset trigger"

trigger plate

that portion of the lock mechanism through which the trigger enters the piece.

trigger pull

the resistance offered by a trigger when pressure is put upon it. The force to overcome this is expressed in pounds. The average desirable trigger pull for rifles and shotguns lies between 3 to 6 pounds. Target guns are generally set for lighter pulls when the rules permit, and handguns, particularly when used for target shooting, are adjusted for extremely light pulling weights.

trigger, release

a most unusual and widely frowned upon trigger mechanism occasionally found in target grade shotguns. Unlike the conventional trigger which fires a gun upon being pulled rearward, the release trigger fires upon being *released*, as it starts its forward, return motion.

trigger, selective single

a single trigger mechanism found in double barrel firearms which permits the user to select the barrel he wishes to fire first. The opposite barrel will automatically follow upon a second

pull of the trigger. A selector is most often designed as part of the safety mechanism, or, at times, located near the trigger in the form of a lever.

trigger shoe

an adapter made to fit over a conventional trigger for the purpose of enlarging the trigger gripping surface. Common to target rifles and handguns.

trigger, single stage

a trigger that offers little or no perceptible movement prior to release and firing.

trigger squeeze

the proper method of firing a small arm. The whole hand is contracted to put a gradual pressure or squeeze upon the trigger.

trigger stop

an adjustable stop to arrest the travel of a trigger almost at the instant of sear release.
See "overtravel"

trigger, target

an easily adjustable single stage trigger mechanism designed to provide a pull and let-off that is light and crisp, with a minimum of travel.

trigger, two stage

See "trigger, double pull"

trinitrotoluene, trinitrotoluol

commonly known as TNT. Made by the nitration of toluene, i.e. by treating toluene with a mixture of nitric and sulphric acids. Has powerful, brisant explosive properties. Known as early as 1863, suggested as an explosive in 1890 and important militarily since 1904. The term "trinitrotoluol" is less correct chemically than "trinitrotoluene", but is also used as a name for the explosive.

trip

to release some part of a device that is being restrained. In some firearms the part of the action released by the trigger is called a trip.

tripod

a three-legged support or mount for a gun or an instrument. A bipod is a two-legged support.

trombone action

another name for slide or pump action.

troy weight

is a system of weights used for weighing gold, silver and other precious metals. One troy ounce is equal to 1.0971 avoirdupois ounces.

truncated cone bullet

a bullet whose shape is characterized by its cylindrical body and truncated cone nose portion, i.e. from its maximum diameter it slopes to a flat end.

truncated hollow point bullet

a lead core of truncated cone shaped nose portion encased in a jacket of harder metal except for its nose and base. A cavity is formed in the exposed nose of the lead core. The purpose of this construction is to give maximum expansion on impact.

trunnion

a supporting pivot for holding a gun or instrument on its mount permitting its elevation. A piece of artillery is supported by two pivots on its carriage.

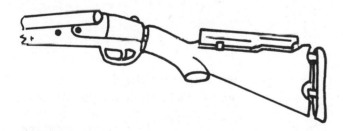

try gun

a shoulder gun used to custom fit a shooter by ascertaining the stock measurements best suited to him. It is generally adjustable for length of pull, drop at heel, comb, pitch and cast.

tube

the hollow cylinder containing the bore of a gun. "Tube" is generally a term used with artillery, while "barrel" is used with small arms.

tube lock

an ignition system employing a hollow copper tube about ⅝" long with an outside diameter of 1/16", filled with fulminate, inserted in the vent of a muzzle loader. Crushed between an anvil and the hammer it ignited the propellent charge. Patented 1818 by Joseph Manton.

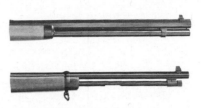

tubular magazine

a magazine common to both rifles and shotguns (usually located under the barrel though occasionally contained in the buttstock). Tubular in form and designed to store cartridges end-to-end. Common to slide action and automatic shotguns as well as lever action rifles. Also found in many varieties of .22 caliber rifles.

tumble

the term used to describe a projectile that turns end over end in flight. It is not a sought after result.

tunnel mount

a scope mount designed to permit use of iron sights through tunnelled portions of the base and/or ring assemblies.

turkey shoot

formerly a hunt for turkeys with firearms or a shoot using a live turkey as a target. Today a target shooting match with turkeys as prizes.

turnbolt action

a bolt action that requires the bolt to be turned, i.e. lifted up, to unlock its lugs from recesses in the receiver before it can be drawn back. To re-lock it the reverse motion is required.

turpentine

an oleoresin obtained from various coniferous trees, insoluable in water and having a distinctive odor and taste. Used with raw linseed oil to make a mixture found effective as an initial base coat in gunstock finishing.

turret

1. that portion of a riflescope into which is fitted the adjusting device for windage and/or elevation.

2. the rotatable cannon housing of a tank.

turret gun

1. a rifle or revolver using a cylinder resembling the turret of a battleship to hold the cartridges. The turret was mounted vertically or horizontally depending upon the particular type. Invented by John W. Cochran. Sometimes called Monitor after the Civil War vessel whose turret gave some resemblance.

2. a cannon mounted in the turret of a warship or in the turret of a military tank.

twist

in a rifled bore, the helical form of the lands and grooves between breech and muzzle. See "pitch"

twist barrel

See "Damascus barrel"

two-piece mount

a riflescope mount consisting of two separate base and ring assemblies.

type metal

lead alloys of tin and antimony used in the printing art and classified depending upon their use such as electrotype, linotype, monotype and stereotype. Also used for casting bullets.

tyro

a novice or beginner in the art of shooting, as in any endeavor.

U

ultra-violet light
an invisible "light" radiation of frequencies next higher than those of visible violet. Used in firearms identification to photograph powder combustion deposits on skin and clothing that are not otherwise detectable.

U.M.C.
initials used as the headstamp for cartridges manufactured by the Union Metallic Cartridge Company of Bridgeport, Connecticut — a firm that was founded in 1866 and which, in 1902, was merged with the Remington Arms Company.

unarmed
without weapons. Fuzes are said to be unarmed when they are neutralized by some mechanical device which keeps them from exploding.

under arms
the bearing of firearms in the hands or on the person.

underhammer firearms
firearms having the hammer beneath rather than on top of the piece. While used in Europe during the flintlock period, their greatest development occurred in the United States during the period 1835-1850.

underlugs
the locking lugs of a break-open type firearm, such as a double barrel shotgun; located on the bottom flats of the barrels, directly under the chamber area, and which lock into the forward channel of the receiver.

Union Metallic Cartridge Company
an ammunition manufacturing firm founded in Bridgeport, Connecticut in 1866 and which, in 1902, was merged with Remington Arms Company. Small arms ammunition made by this firm carried the headstamp "UMC".

United States Pigeon Shooting Association
an organization interested in pigeon shooting, having its headquarters in Fort Worth, Texas.

United States Revolver Association
a national organization of those interested in revolver and pistol shooting, founded 1900 and having headquarters in Springfield, Massachusetts.

unload
to completely remove without firing, all of the cartridges or shells from a firearm or cannon.

unserviceable
a weapon that because of its condition cannot be used for its intended purpose.

upwind
the direction from which the wind is blowing, also called windward.

usable rate of fire
the normal rate of actual fire of a gun, measured in shots per minute. The maximum rate of fire is a calculated theoretical rate and is considerably greater than the usable rate.

V

vacuum

the absence of any matter. The noise of an explosion or detonation is caused by the rush of surrounding air to fill the vacuum caused in space by the sudden removal of oxygen which unites with the chemical of the explosive or detonating mixture, resulting in shock waves in the atmosphere. The rapidity of such combustions is indicated by the rate of detonation of TNT which is from 17000 feet per second to about 25000 feet per second, depending upon its density of packing.

vanadium steel

a steel containing from 0.16 to 0.25 per cent of vanadium. It is characterized by its high tensile strength and high elastic limit.

variable scope

a riflescope that is adjustable for various powers of magnification.

varmint rifle

a rifle designed specifically for varmint hunting. Such rifles are generally made in light, high velocity calibers for precision shooting at ranges averaging 100 to 300 yards. Typical varmint rifle calibers are: .222, .223, .220, .22/250, .243 and 6MM Magnum.
Varmint rifles are generally equipped with high magnification scope sights, crisp target-type triggers and medium to heavy barrels and stocks.

varnish

a resinous solution used to provide a hard lustrous and generally transparent protective surface coating for woods. Many kinds of resins and solvents are used, but broadly, varnishes are classified according to the general character of the solvent used, or spirit varnishes or oil varnishes. The various kinds of varnishes are best sorted to specific purposes in their use. Most gunsmiths do not recommend varnish for gun stocks and especially not for walnut stocks. Lacquer, a special form of varnish is considered suitable.

velocity

speed of a projectile usually measured in feet per second (fps).

vent

a gas escape hole in modern weapons.

ventilated choke device

an adjustable choke device having a vented sleeve designed to reduce recoil.

ventilated rib

a sighting rib on top of the barrel of a shotgun, rifle, or handgun and parallel to it, provided with slots to permit the circulation of air to give a cooling effect and thus to prevent distortion of the sight picture.

ventilated sleeve

See "ventilated choke device"

verdigris *(VER di grease)*

the green or bluish deposit sometimes formed on copper, brass or bronze surfaces after lengthy exposure to the atmosphere.

verification fire

preparatory fire to test the adjustment of guns and sights.

vernier

a short graduated scale that slides along the divisions of a larger graduated scale to indicate subdivisions of the graduations of the larger scale.

vernier caliper

a caliper provided with a vernier to permit precision measurement of gun parts, cartridges, cases, bullets and firearms accessories.

vernier sight

a sight adjustable for elevation or windage by a screw having vernier calibrations marked thereon.

vertical deviation

See "range deviation"

vertical jump

the angle measuring the vertical distance the muzzle of a gun shifts between the instant of firing and the instant the projectile leaves the gun. Its horizontal equivalent is called "lateral jump".

Very pistol

a type of pistol used to fire signal flares, invented in 1877 by Lieutenant Edward W. Very of the U. S. Navy.

vibration

one of the three movements set up in a firearm upon discharge, namely recoil, jump and vibration.

Vickers hardness test

a means for determining the relative hardness of a substance by applying pressure to a square based diamond pyramid with its point resting on the surface of a material. The amount of penetration, the size of the load, and time it is applied, are the factors used to determine the Vickers hardness number.

Vickers machine gun

a modern version of the Maxim machine gun.

Vieille, Paul Marie Eugene
  (1854-1934) VYAAH yee

a French engineer who, in 1884, developed for the French Government the first successful smokeless powder for rifles. Earlier French chemists, Pelouze and Braconnet had worked on this problem as early as 1832.

vignetting *(vin YET ing)*

the effect produced by poor or faulty optical instruments in which the edges of a transmitted image tend to blur.

virtual image

an image resulting from the apparent intersection of light rays.

viscosity

the resistance offered to a flowing movement caused by a sort of internal friction in a substance. In the case of oils as temperature rises the viscosity decreases. Animal or vegetable oils maintain their viscosity better than mineral oils as temperature rises. The lower the viscosity the "lighter" the oil.

visibility

the average greatest distance toward the horizon at which prominent objects may be seen and identified by the naked eye.

Volcanic

the name given in 1855 to certain pistols and rifles whose manufacture started in 1854 and continued only to 1860. Of historical importance since it represented an intermediate stage in the development of the Jennings percussion repeating rifle into the Henry rifle which in turn became the first Winchester rifle.

volley

a burst of simultaneous fire from a number of guns. From the 14th century on, the grouping of a number of barrels together in a unitary mount, frame or carriage for simultaneous fire, has been experimented with.

Vostok TUZ-35

a Russian free pistol, .22 caliber long rifle, single shot.

W

wabble

means the same as "wobble", to rotate unevenly so that side to side movement takes place.

wad column

the plastic, or combination of cardboard and fibre devices contained in a shotgun shell which serve to contain the gases generated by the powder charge and simultaneously cushion and protect the shot charge. Also used as fillers so that various combinations of powder and shot can be made to fill the case and thus facilitate proper crimping.

Before the advent of present day one-piece plastic wads, shotshells were loaded with a heavy cardboard wad, located over the powder charge, and this was called the "nitro" or "over-powder" wad. On top of the cardboard wad there was usually placed one or more fibre or felt cushioning wads designed to raise the shot level to crimping height.

The "over-shot" wad which was common to roll crimped shotshells has been eliminated by the newer star crimp process.

wad cutter

a bullet having a square shoulder at or near the nose, so designed to produce a clean round hole in a paper target.

wadding

1. see "wad column"

2. a paper or cloth patch used by shooters of muzzleloading guns to hold the shot against the powder charge.
See "patch"

wads

See "wad column"

waisted pellet

a pellet for an air or CO_2 gun that flares outward from its waist-like constricted mid section to its base. Also called a "skirted pellet".

wall gun

a flintlock made with a leg hinged to the under side of the barrel to give it support in firing, such as behind or on top of a wall. Also called a rampart gun.

wall piece

a large sized firearm often an arquebus mounted on a swivel and placed atop the wall of a fortress, or a similar gun with a recoil plate or hook adapted to be placed against such a wall to absorb part of the recoil.

walnut *(Juglans)*

the name of the genus or family of trees whose species are found in many parts of the world. Its wood is highly prized for its gunstock qualities but the shortage of supply in the face of heavy demand has caused many other woods to be used for gunstocks.

Walther pistol

a 9 mm, 8 shot, semiautomatic pistol, an official weapon of the German Army adopted in 1938. Manufacture resumed in 1957 in Germany.

Washita oilstone

a natural stone used as for edging cutting tools. See "oilstone"

W & E

abbreviation for windage and elevation.

waste

of cotton or wool is frequently used as a bullet

stop. Especially when it is desired to recover a fired bullet without the risk of deformation that would occur if it struck a solid object.
See "identification of firearms"

water jacket

a casing for holding water, surrounding the barrel of a water cooled machine gun.

water table

the flat part of the action of a side by side double barrelled shotgun that extends forward from the bottom of the breech face substantially at right angles to it. Also called the action bar flats.

Watt, James *(1736-1819)*

the inventor of the steam engine who cooperated with Rev. Alexander John Forsyth in inventing several types of percussion locks.

wave

a series of advancing impulses set up in the air by an explosion.

wax bullet

bullets made of paraffin wax for use in primed cartridge cases without the usual powder charge. Used for short range target practice with either rifle or revolver. Cannot be used in automatic weapons.

WCF

an abbreviation for Winchester Center Fire.

weapon

any instrument capable of doing injury in combat.

weapon system

a weapon and those components required for its operation. This term is not precise unless specific parameters are established.

Weatherby

a trademark of Weatherby Inc., 2781 Firestone Boulevard, South Gate, California.

Weaverscope

the registered trademark of W. R. Weaver Company for rifle scopes.

Webley

a caliber .455, six chambered revolver adopted in 1887 as a standard by Great Britain and finally discontinued from Army use in 1947. The name also applies to other firearms made by the English firm of Webley & Scott, Ltd., successor to the businesses originally started by Philip Webley and James Webley.

weight

the weight of a firearm bears a relationship to its intended use as well as to the age and frame of the user. It is an important factor in the amount of recoil of a gun.

weld

to join two parts, usually of metal, by heating or by compression alone.
See "welding"

welding *(autogenous fusing)*

1. forge welding consists in heating two similar metals almost to the melting point and causing their abutting surfaces to fuse together under pressure. Damascus barrels were so made.

2. electric arc welding, also called resistance welding consists in passing an electric current across the juncture of two similar metals, an electro-welding rod carrying the positive charge to the grounded metal.

3. resistance forge welding combines the use of both pressure and an electric current.

4. gas welding, also known as oxyacetylene welding, accomplishes the joining of similar metals by the generation of heat with a carbine gas and oxygen fed torch.

Wesson, Daniel Baird *(1825-1906)*

an American gunsmith and manufacturer of revolvers and cartridges whose association with Horace Smith gave rise to the famous Smith and Wesson combination.

Western

a trademark of an ammunition manufacturing division of Winchester Repeating Arms Company located in East Alton, Illinois.

Westley Richards All-Range Bullet

a cylindrical lead core necked down a short distance behind its flat nose, the portion below the neck being encased in a jacket of harder metal. Designed for expansion. This bullet was originally intended for sporting use in the 7.63 mm Mauser. Introduced in England about 1900 it later was also made in Germany. This was the forerunner of the present day Westley Richards capped bullets used in large caliber hunting rifles.

Westley Richards All-Range Capped Bullet

a cylindrical lead core enclosed in a jacket of harder metal extending over the flattened nose to form a rounded protective nose cap.

Whelen, Townsend (1877-1961)

hunter, target shooter and author of a number of articles and books on those topics, served for 40 years in the United States Army reaching the rank of Colonel. In the Ordnance Department he, at one time, commanded Frankford Arsenal and later was Director of Research and Development at Springfield Armory.

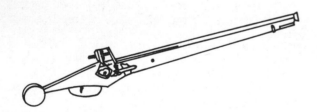

wheellock

a firearms ignition system that relied upon a revolving, spring loaded steel wheel having a roughened knurled or grooved periphery, striking a piece of pyrites or flint to cause sparks to ignite the priming powder and to flash fire down the touchhole thus setting off the powder charge. The sparking action is similar to that found in modern cigarette lighters. The wheel lock was developed about 1517 AD. It followed the matchlock and was in turn followed by the snaphaunce.

White, Rollin (1818-1892)

an American gunsmith and inventor, who, after leaving the employ of Colt's Armory, invented, and patented in 1855, the bored through revolver cylinder which permitted loading from the rear. Daniel B. Wesson in 1856 acquired exclusive rights to this patent and used it with his self primed metallic cartridges.

Whitney, Eli (1765-1825)

an American inventor; inventor of the cotton gin and manufacturer of firearms. He is best known in the firearms field for having applied the principle of interchangeable parts in the production of firearms starting in 1798. An early collaborator of Samuel Colt who participated in Colt's first Paterson (N. J.) revolver manufacturing enterprise.

wildcat cartridges

cartridges made by other than recognized commercial producers or cartridges other than standard.

wild shot

a shot completely outside the normal pattern of dispersion or one that is fired without aiming.

Wilkinson, John (1728-1808)

an ironmaster and inventor who, in 1789, received a British patent for a barrel for a percussion gun having two spiral grooves adapted to accommodate a projectile having belts or wings to fit the grooves. He is also credited with building the first boring machine in 1775.

Winchester

the trademark of Winchester Repeating Arms Company and by which firearms made by it have been known since 1866. The most famous of its firearms were the lever action repeating rifles.

Winchester, Oliver F. (1810-1880)

an American manufacturer of firearms, both rifles and pistols, but best known for production of the B. Tyler Henry repeating rifle, the forerunner of the Winchester lever action repeating rifle. Founder of Winchester Repeating Arms Co.

wind

air in motion. It exerts a force on every object in its path and depending upon the dimensions of a projectile and its time of flight, the direction and strength of the wind can materially effect the accuracy of fire.

windage

1. the influence of the wind in deflecting a projectile from its course in flight.

2. the amount of sight adjustment in azimuth to compensate or allow for the action of the wind on the projectile in flight.

3. the obsolete meaning was the space in a smoothbore firearm between the bore and its projectile which was provided by way of a tolerance to facilitate loading. In a U. S. cannon it was usually about 1/40 of the diameter and caused a loss of velocity nearly proportional to the windage.

windage knob

the rotatable knob built into the adjusting mechanism of an iron sight or telescopic sight and which is used to make horizontal adjustments in the sight setting.

windage micrometer

an instrument connected with the rear sight of a firearm to permit minute adjustments of the sight, in azimuth, for windage allowance.

windage scale

a table or scale for adjusting a sight to allow for the effect of the wind on a projectile in flight. Also called wind gage.

wind and drift chart

a chart showing the degree of sight adjustment required to allow for the effect of wind and drift of a projectile in flight, for various ranges and wind velocities.

wind component indicator

a device that mechanically determines the range and deflection components of the computed wind that is equivalent to all true winds encountered by a projectile in flight.

wind cone

a hollow truncated cone pivoted on a mount to show the direction of the wind. It performs the same function as a wind sock.

wind correction

an adjustment required in sighting to allow for the effect of wind velocity on a projectile in flight.

wind deflection

the deflection or change in course of a projectile in flight caused by wind velocity.

wind direction

is expressed in a number of terms. The system employed by shooters is known as the "horizontal clock system".

　　　　See "cross wind"
　　　　　　"fishtail wind"
　　　　　　"leeward"
　　　　　　"tailwind"
　　　　　　"upwind"
　　　　　　"wind"
　　　　　　"windward"

wind doping

the process by which each rifleman attempts to gage the effect of wind on his shooting. Mechanical wind estimating devices are usually barred from match competition. As a result, each competitor develops his own peculiar method for estimating wind: some study the effect of the wind on range flags, others study the wind's effect on grass, trees, etc.

wind gage

See "windage scale"

wind rule

the term applied to a formula that may be used to roughly determine the allowance to be made in aiming a gun when the wind is blowing at a known velocity and direction, namely, the minutes of angle to allow for a right angle cross wind equals the range in hundred of yards times the velocity of the wind in miles per hour divided by a number which is a constant for the gun being used. The constant for the M1 and M1903 rifle is 10; for the U.S. carbine caliber .30 M1 it is 5. Thus, using the formula for the M1 rifle at 300 yards, with a cross wind of 10 mph, the minutes of angle equals 3 which at 300 yards equal 9 inches. Using it with the M1 carbine under the same conditions, the minutes of angle equals 6, which at 300 yards is 18 inches.

windshield

a cap of relatively light material fixed over the head of a projectile to streamline it and thus increase its efficiency in flight.

wind sock

a cone shaped fabric sleeve which bellies out and pivots to show the direction of the wind. It performs the same function as a wind cone.

wind vane

any pivoted device capable of showing which direction the wind is blowing.

windward

the direction from which the wind blows, the side that is exposed to oncoming wind.

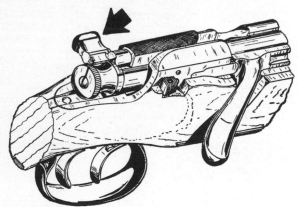

wing safety

a type of safety device frequently found on bolt action rifles. Most common to the Mannlicher, Mauser and Springfield systems.
The wing safety is located at the rear of the bolt body and is anchored at one end by a pin whose axis parallels that of the bore. The safety pivots on this pin, describing an arc of approximately 180 degrees and positively locks both the firing pin and the bolt.

wing shooting

the practice of shooting flying targets with a shotgun.

wiper

a pair of twisted pointed rods secured to the end of a ramrod or cleaning rod to hold cleaning patches when swabbing the bore of a gun.

wobble

to rotate unevenly so that side to side movement takes place. Sometimes also spelled wabble.

wood

has been used since early days for firearms stocks and grips principally to take advantage of its lightness, workability and heat insulating qualities.
See Appendix

wood filler

may be in paste or liquid form and usually contain silica or barytes, boiled oil and japan drier and sometimes a stain. Used to fill and seal the pores in gunstock woods, usually before the first finishing coat is applied.

Wood's metal

an alloy of low melting point containing bismuth, lead, tin and cadmium, melting at about 149°F.
See Appendix

Woodworth cradle rest

a cradle designed by A. Woodworth, a Springfield Armory Ordnance Engineer, whereby a conventional rifle in its stock can be held and fired in the Mann V Block.

worm

a screw secured at the end of a ramrod to permit an unfired projectile, powder and patch to be withdrawn from a muzzleloading gun.
See "ball screw"

WRF

an abbreviation for Winchester Rim Fire.

wriggle engraving

a term applied to a form of metal decoration consisting of fine parallel grooves each formed by a series of closely spaced short zig-zag lines.

wrought iron

iron containing comparatively little carbon but containing slag — the best wrought iron contains about 3% by weight of slag. It can be readily welded and it can be forged more easily than steel. While it cannot be hardened or heat treated like steel it can be case hardened by use of cyanide of potassium. It is generally unsatisfactory for bearing surfaces.

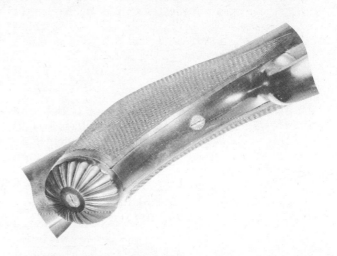

Wundhammer bulge or swell

the creation of Louis Wundhammer, an American gunsmith, the Wundhammer bulge consists of a raised area in the pistol grip of a stock that is designed to fit snugly into the palm of the shooter's trigger hand. It serves to position the hand in consistently the same attitude and adds to comfort.

X Y Z

x-ring

a small area circled in the center of a bulls-eye used to illustrate near-perfect hits. Shots within the x-ring are counted to break ties when identical scores are attained by one or more competitors. When the x-ring is employed scores are recorded in this manner: "200-15X's", "200-14X's", "200-13X's", etc. (the marksman having 15X's would be declared the winner).

yards error

the distance in yards from the point of impact to the target. A term commonly used in artillery fire. A companion term is "mils error" which measures the error by the angular unit of "mil". See "mil"

yaw

to edge sidewise from the direction of travel. Specifically the angle between the longitudinal axis of the projectile and the line drawn tangent to its trajectory at the center of gravity of the projectile.

Yerger

a corruption of the German Jaeger, also known as the Harper's Ferry Rifle.

yield point

the point at which a bar of ductile metal, when stretched under load, will further extend without an increase in the loading. It is not the same as the "elastic limit" but occurs beyond it. For example in structural steel it occurs from 3,000 to 6,000 pounds per square inch beyond the elastic limit of the steel.

yoke

See "crane"

zero

See "zero sight adjustment"

zero deflection

the adjustment of a sight exactly parallel to the axis of the gun upon which it is mounted.

zero-in

to adjust the sight settings of a rifle by calibrated firing on a standard range with no wind blowing.

zero shot

shot fired to test the alignment of sights.

zero sight adjustment

the adjustment of the rear sight in elevation and/or azimuth to place a properly aimed shot at the desired point of impact at a given range with a given load, in the absence of wind. It is the basis from which subsequent sight adjustments may be made to allow for different loads, different ranges, and/or different weather conditions.

zig-zag revolver

a Derringer in which the barrels are revolved by means of a stud engaging the angular grooves in the barrel. Among gun collectors the term "zig-zag" is generally connected with the rare Remington Ziz-Zag Derringer.

zinc

is a bluish-white crystalline metal element whose chemical symbol is Zn. It is polymorphous, its physical properties varying according to its form as well as to the heat treatment accorded it. Alloyed with copper it produces brass which finds use in the manufacture of cartridge cases and primers.

zip gun

a term commonly applied to a crude, homemade firearm whose firing pin is powered by a rubber band.

Zulu

the name under which converted French, Belgium and British military percussion muskets were sold as single barrel breech loading shotguns from 1870 on.

Appendix

TABLE I
Important Chemical Elements

Element	Symbol	Chemical Nature	First Isolated By	Time	Melting Point C	F
aluminum	Al	metal	Woehler	1827	660.2	1220
antimony	Sb	metal	Valentine	15th century	630.5	1167
arsenic	As	metalloid	Magnus	1250	817.	1503
bismuth	Bi	metal	Geoffroy	1753	271.3	520
cadmium	Cd	metal	Stromeyer	1817	320.9	610
carbon	C	metalloid	—	Prehistoric	3550	6422
chromium	Cr	metal	Varquelin	1797	1890	3434
cobalt	Co	metal	Brandt	1735	1495	2723
copper	Cu	metal	—	Prehistoric	1083	1981
gold	Au	metal	—	Prehistoric	1063	1945
iron	Fe	metal	—	Prehistoric	1535	2795
lead	Pb	metal	—	Prehistoric	327.4	621.3
magnesium	Mg	metal	Davy	1808	651	1204
manganese	Mn	metal	Gahn	1774	1244	2271
mercury	Hg	metal	—	300 B.C.	-38.87	-38
molybdenum	Mo	metal	Hjelm	1782	2610	4730
nickel	Ni	metal	Cronstedt	1751	1453	2647
palladium	Pd	metal	Wollaston	1803	1552	2826
platinum	Pt	metal	Watson	1748	1769	3216
samarian	Sa	metal	deBoisbaudran	1879	1072	1962
silicon	Si	metalloid	Berzelius	1823	1410	2570
silver	Ag	metal	—	Prehistoric	960.8	1761
sodium	Na	metal	Davy	1807	97.8	208.1
sulphur	S	metalloid	—	Prehistoric	116	241
tantalum	Ta	metal	Ekeberg	1802	2996	5425
tin	Sn	metal	—	Prehistoric	232	450
tungsten	W	metal	d'Elhujar	1783	3410	6170
vanadium	V	metal	Roscoe	1869	1890	3434
zinc	Zn	metal	Marygraf	1746	419	788
zirconium	Zr	metal	Berzelius	1824	1852	3365

TABLE II
Metals Common to Firearms

Metal	% Composition	Melting Point C	F
aluminum	100 Al	6602	1220
babbitt metal	89 Sn, 7.5 Sb, 3.5 Cu	241	466
brass, ordinary yellow	67 Cu, 33 Zn	940	1724
brass, cartridge	70 Cu, 30 Zn, Pb, Fe	916	1680
bronze, commercial	90 Cu, 10 Zn	1050	1922
bronze, gun metal	90 Cu, 10 Sn	1000	1832
cast iron, gray	94 Fe, 3.5C, 2.5 Si	1230	2246
cast iron, white	97 Fe, 3C	1150	2102
chromium	100 Cr	1890	3434
copper	100 Cu	1083	1981
iron	100 Fe	1535	2795
lead	100 Pb	327.4	621.3
lead shot	99.8 Pb, 0.2 As	327.4	621.3
manganese	100 Mg	1244	2271
manganese steel	86 Fe, 13 Mn, 1C	1510	2750
nickel	100 Ni	1453	2647
nickel steel	96.5 Fe, 3.5 Ni	1530	2786
nickel chrome steel	95.1 Fe, 3 Ni, 1.5 Cr, 0.4 C	—	—
silver solder *Grade 6	65 Ag, 20 Cu, 15 Zn	693	1280
*Grade 8	80 Ag, 16 Cu, 4 Zn	738	1360
solder, half and half **Grade 1A	50 Pb, 50 Sn, .12 Sb	181	357.8
soft **Grade 3A	60 Pb, 40 Sn, .12 Sb	181	357.8
soft **Grade 5B	67 Pb, 31 Sn, 2 Sb	188	370.4
stainless steel	90 Fe, 8 Cr, .4 Mn >.12 C	1450	2642
steel	99 Fe, 1 C	1430	2606
tin	100 Sn	232	450
type metal			
electrotype	94 Pb, 3 Sn, 3 Sb	299	570
linotype	84 Pb, 4 Sn, 12 Sb	246	475
monotype	76 Pb, 8 Sn, 16 Sb	213	515
stereotype	80 Pb, 6 Sn, 14 Sb	260	500
wood's metal	50 Bi, 25 Pb, 12.5 Sn, 12.5 Cd	65	149
wrought iron	98.5 Fe, slag	1510	2750
zinc	100 zn	419	788

*ASTM Spec. B73-29
**ASTM Spec. B32-21

TABLE III

Woods For Gunstocks

Below is a list of the most frequently used gun-stock woods together with an appraisal of their characteristics. Since woods of the same species may vary greatly in their physical properties, due to the many factors that influence the growth of the trees, the ratings given here are based on generally accepted values, and, in those cases where experts differ the majority opinion has been indicated.

	KEY		
H-heavy	P-poor		E-excellent
M-medium	F-fair		
L-light	G-good		

	Weight	Checkering	Strength	Hardness
acacia	M	G	E	E
apple	M	G	G	E
ash	H	F	E	E
balsimo	M	E	G	G
beech	M	F	G	G
birch	L	P	G	G
*blackwood (Australian)	M	G	E	E
butternut (white walnut)	M	E	E	E
cherry	M	G	E	E
cocobolo (See note)	H	P	G	G
desert ironwood	H	P	E	E
*ebony	H	E	E	E
*gumwood	H	P	E	E
*jarrah	H	P	E	E
maple (sugar, rock, black, etc.)	H	G	E	E
red, silver	M	P	P	F
Pacific	M	F	P	F
queensland	L	P	G	G
*mahogany, African	H	P	G	G
mesquite	H	E	E	E
myrtle, Oregon	M	F	P	F
*rosewood	H	G	G	G
pine	L	P	P	P
spruce	L	P	P	P
teak	H	P	G	E
redwood burl	L	P	G	F
walnut, American black	M	E	E	E
Argentine	L	G	G	G
New Zealand	H	G	G	G
circassian	M	E	E	E
California claro	M	F	G	G
*zebrawood (zingana)	H	P	F	F

NOTE: Care should be exercised when working with Cocobolo wood to avoid contact with its fine sawdust. This wood has a tendency to produce a skin poisoning much like ivy poisoning. Though not everyone reacts to this poisoning, the consequences can be painful to those who do.

*these woods are generally used only for fancy stock attachments, such as forend tips and grip caps. Rarely, if ever, are they used for complete stocks, however, most can be used for making handgun grips.

TABLE IV

English-Metric Length Conversions

Millimeters to Decimals of an Inch		Decimals of an Inch to Millimeters		Fractions of an Inch to Decimals and Millimeters		
mm	Decimals	Decimals	mm	Fraction	Decimal	mm
1.	.0394	.1	2.540	1/64	.0156	0.397
2.	.0787	.2	5.080	1/32	.0313	0.794
3.	.1181	.3	7.620	3/64	.0469	1.191
4.	.1575	.4	10.160	1/16	.0625	1.588
5.	.1968	.5	12.700	5/64	.0781	1.984
6.	.2362	.6	15.240	3/32	.0937	2.381
7.	.2756	.7	17.780	7/64	.1093	2.778
8.	.3150	.8	20.320	1/8	.1250	3.175
9.	.3543	.9	22.860	9/64	.1406	3.572
10.	.3937	1.0	25.400	5/32	.1562	3.969
				11/64	.1718	4.366
.1	.004	.01	.254	3/16	.1875	4.763
.2	.008	.02	.508	13/64	.2031	5.159
.3	.012	.03	.762	7/32	.2187	5.556
.4	.016	.04	1.016	15/64	.2343	5.953
.5	.020	.05	1.270	1/4	.2500	6.350
.6	.024	.06	1.524	17/64	.2656	6.747
.7	.028	.07	1.778	9/32	.2812	7.144
.8	.031	.08	2.032	19/64	.2968	7.541
.9	.035	.09	2.286	5/16	.3125	7.938
				21/64	.3281	8.334
.01	.00039	.001	.025	11/32	.3437	8.731
.02	.00079	.002	.051	23/64	.3593	9.128
.03	.00118	.003	.076	3/8	.3750	9.525
.04	.00157	.004	.102	25/64	.3906	9.922
.05	.00197	.005	.127	13/32	.4062	10.319
.06	.00236	.006	.152	27/64	.4218	10.716
.07	.00276	.007	.178	7/16	.4375	11.113
.08	.00315	.008	.203	29/64	.4531	11.509
.09	.00354	.009	.229	15/32	.4687	11.906
				31/64	.4843	12.303
				1/2	.5000	12.700

To convert inches to millimeters multiply by 25.4

To convert millimeters to inches multiply by .0394

TABLE V

English-Metric
Weight Conversions
Conversion of grams (metric) to grains (English)

Grams (g)	.00	.10	.20	.30	.40	.50	.60	.70	.80	.90
1	15.4	16.9	18.5	20.1	21.6	23.1	24.7	26.2	27.8	29.3
2	30.9	32.4	34.0	35.5	37.0	38.6	40.1	41.7	43.2	44.8
3	46.3	47.8	49.4	50.9	52.5	54.0	55.6	57.1	58.6	60.2
4	61.7	63.3	64.8	66.4	67.9	69.4	71.0	72.5	74.1	75.6
5	77.2	78.7	80.2	81.8	83.3	84.9	86.4	88.0	89.5	91.0
6	92.6	94.1	95.7	97.2	98.8	100.3	101.9	103.4	104.9	106.5
7	108.0	109.6	111.1	112.7	114.2	115.7	117.3	118.8	120.4	121.9
8	123.5	125.0	126.5	128.1	129.6	131.9	132.7	134.3	135.8	137.3
9	138.9	140.4	142.0	143.5	145.1	146.6	148.1	149.7	151.2	152.8
10	154.3	155.9	157.4	159.0	160.5	162.0	163.6	165.1	166.7	168.2
11	169.8	171.3	172.8	174.4	175.9	177.5	179.0	180.6	182.1	183.6
12	185.2	186.7	188.3	189.8	191.4	192.9	194.4	196.0	197.5	199.1
13	200.6	202.2	203.7	205.2	206.8	208.3	209.9	211.4	213.0	214.5
14	216.0	217.6	219.1	220.7	222.2	223.8	225.3	226.9	228.4	229.9
15	231.5	233.0	234.6	236.1	237.7	239.2	240.7	242.3	243.8	245.4
16	246.9	248.5	250.0	251.5	253.1	254.6	256.2	257.7	259.3	260.8
17	262.3	263.9	265.4	267.0	268.5	270.1	271.6	273.1	274.7	276.2
18	277.8	279.3	280.9	282.4	283.9	285.5	287.0	288.6	290.1	291.7
19	293.2	294.8	296.3	297.8	299.4	300.9	302.5	304.0	305.6	307.1
20	308.6	310.2	311.7	313.3	314.8	316.4	317.9	319.4	321.0	322.5
21	324.1	325.6	327.2	328.7	330.9	331.8	333.3	334.9	336.4	338.0
22	339.5	341.0	342.6	344.1	345.7	347.2	348.8	350.3	351.9	353.4
23	354.9	356.5	358.0	359.6	361.1	362.7	364.2	365.7	367.3	368.8
24	370.4	371.9	373.5	375.0	376.5	378.1	379.6	381.9	389.7	384.3
25	385.8	387.3	388.9	390.4	392.0	393.5	395.1	396.6	398.1	399.7
26	401.2	402.8	404.3	405.9	407.4	408.9	410.5	412.0	413.6	415.0
27	416.7	418.2	419.8	421.3	422.8	424.4	425.9	427.5	429.0	430.6
28	432.1	433.6	435.2	436.7	438.3	439.8	441.4	442.9	444.4	446.0
29	447.5	449.1	450.6	452.2	453.7	455.2	456.8	458.3	459.9	461.4
30	463.0	464.5	466.0	467.6	469.1	470.7	472.2	473.8	475.3	476.8

To convert grams to grains multiply by 15.432
To convert grains to grams multiply by 0.0648
To convert grains to pounds divide by 7000.

English	Metric
1 grain	= 0.0648 grams
1 ounce (avdp)	= 28.3495 grams
1 pound	= 0.4536 Kilograms
1 long ton	= 1016 Kilograms
1 short ton	= 907.18 Kilograms

Metric	English
1 gram	= 15.432 grains
1 gram	= 0.0353 ounces (avdp)
1 kilogram	= 2.2046 pounds
1000 kilograms	= 0.9842 long tons
1000 kilograms	= 1.1023 short tons

TABLE VI

Length Equivalents

Milli-meters	Centi-meters	Meters	Inches	Feet	Yards	Statute Miles
1	0.1	.001	.03937	.00328	.00109	.0000006
10	1	.01	.3937	.03281	.01094	.0000062
1000	100	1	39.37	3.2808	1.0936	.0006214
25.4	2.54	0.0254	1	0.08333	0.02778	.00001578
304.8	30.48	0.3048	12	1	0.3333	.0001894
914.4	91.44	0.9144	36	3	1	.0005682
1609300	160930	1609.3	63360	5280	1760	1

1 Mile = 1.6093 Kilometers
1 Kilometer = 0.6214 Miles

TABLE VII

Volume and Capacity Equivalents

Cubic Inches	Cubic Feet	Cubic Yards	U.S. Liquid Quarts	U.S. Liquid Gallons	Liters
1	.00057870	.00002143	.017316	.004329	.016387
1728	1	.037037	29.922	7.4805	28.317
46656	27	1	807.90	201.97	764.56
57.75	.033420	.001238	1	0.25	.94636
231	.13368	.004951	4	1	3.7854
61.023	.035315	.001308	1.0567	.26417	1

1 U.S. Liquid Quart = 2 pints = 8 gills = 32 fluid ounces = 256 fluid drams
1 Imperial Gallon = 1.201 U.S. Gallons = 0.1605 cu. ft. = 4.5460 liters
1 U.S. Gallon = 0.8327 Imperial gallons = 0.13368 cu. ft. = 3.7854 liters
1 Cubic Foot = 6.229 Imperial Gallons = 7.4805 U.S. gallons

TABLE VIII

Weight Equivalents

Kilograms	Grains	Avoir Ounces	Avoir Pounds	Short Ton 2000 lbs.	Metric Ton 1000 Kg.
1	15432	35.274	2.20461	.001102	.001
.00006480	1	.002286	.000142	—	—
.028349	437.5	1	.0625	—	—
.45359	7000.	16	1	.0005	.0004536
907.18	—	32000	2000	1	.90718
1000.	—	35274	2204.6	1.1023	1

1 avoirdupois ounce = 16 avoirdupois drams
1 dram = 27.4 grains = 1.771 grams
1 avoirdupois ounce = 0.91146 troy and apothecaries ounces
1 troy and apoth. ounce = 1.0971 avoirdupois ounces

TABLE IX

Pressure Equivalents
at 62° F

Lbs. Per sq. in.	Lbs. per sq. ft.	Atmosphere	Feet of Water	Inches of Water	Inches of mercury
1	144	.06804	2.31	27.72	2.036
.007	1	.00047	.016	.193	.014
14.696	2116.2	1	33.95	407.37	29.921
.433	62.355	.0295	1	12.0	.871
.036	5.196	.0025	.0833	1	.072
.491	70.704	.0327	1.134	13.61	1

1 U.S. gallon of water weighs 8.336 pounds at 62° F
1 cu. ft. of water weighs 62.355 pounds at 62° F
1 cu. ft. of water weighs 62.316 pounds at 68° F

TABLE X

Velocity Equivalents

Miles per hr.	Feet per sec.	Miles per hr.	Feet per sec.	Miles per hr.	Feet per sec.	Miles per hr.	Feet per sec.	Miles per hr.	Feet per sec.
1	1.47	21	30.80	41	60.13	61	89.47	81	118.80
2	2.93	22	32.27	42	61.60	62	90.93	82	120.27
3	4.40	23	33.73	43	63.07	63	92.40	83	121.73
4	5.87	24	35.20	44	64.53	64	93.87	84	123.20
5	7.33	25	36.67	45	66.00	65	95.33	85	124.67
6	8.80	26	38.13	46	67.47	66	96.80	86	126.13
7	10.27	27	39.60	47	68.93	67	98.27	87	127.60
8	11.73	28	41.07	48	70.40	68	99.73	88	129.07
9	13.20	29	42.53	49	71.87	69	101.20	89	130.53
10	14.67	30	44.00	50	73.33	70	102.67	90	132.00
11	16.13	31	45.47	51	74.80	71	104.13	91	133.47
12	17.60	32	46.93	52	76.27	72	105.60	92	134.93
13	19.07	33	48.40	53	77.73	73	107.07	93	136.40
14	20.53	34	49.87	54	79.20	74	108.53	94	137.87
15	22.00	35	51.33	55	80.67	75	110.00	95	139.33
16	23.47	36	52.80	56	82.13	76	111.47	96	140.80
17	24.93	37	54.27	57	83.60	77	112.93	97	142.27
18	26.40	38	55.73	58	85.07	78	114.40	98	143.73
19	27.87	39	57.20	59	86.53	79	115.87	99	145.20
20	29.33	40	58.67	60	88.00	80	117.33	100	146.67

1 mile = 5280 feet

To convert miles per hour to feet per second multiply by 1.4666

To convert feet per second to miles per hour multiply by .6818

TABLE XI

U.S. — Foreign Cartridge Equivalents

Comparative Auto Pistol Cartridges

.25 A.C.P. . . . . 6.35 mm. Browning
.32 A.C.P. . . . . 7.65 mm. Browning
No U.S. . . . . 7.65 mm. Long (French)
(.30) 7.65 Luger . . 7.65 mm. Parabellum
(.30) 7.63 Mauser . 7.63 Mauser
No U.S. . . . . 8 mm. Nambu
No U.S. . . . . 8 mm. Roth Steyr
.380 A.C.P. . . . . { 9 mm. Browning (short)
. . . . { 9 mm. Corto (Italian)
No U.S. . . . . 9 mm. Browning Long
9 mm. Luger . . . . . { 9 mm. Parabellum
. . . . { 9 mm. Glisenti
No U.S. . . . . 9 mm. Mauser
.38 A.C.P. . . . . .38 Auto (Webley & Scott)

.38 Super A.C.P. . . No European
No U.S. . . . . 9 mm. Steyr M-1911
No U.S. . . . . 9 mm. Bergmann Baynard
.45 A.C.P. . . . . No European
No U.S. . . . . 455 W & S

Comparative Revolver Cartridges

No U.S. . . . . 7.5 Nagant (Russian)
No U.S. . . . . 8 mm. French
.38 S & W . . . . { .380 MKI British
. . . . { .38-200
No U.S. . . . . 9 mm. Jap
.38 Special . . . . No European
.45 . . . . No European
.455 Webley . . . . . . .455 Webley

TABLE XII

Visual Identification of Certain Types of U.S. Military Cartridges and Shot Shells

armor piercing
bullet is black tipped

ball
conventional brass case and fully jacketed bullet

blank, rifle cartridge
no bullet in case, cannelure in neck of case

blank, revolver cartridge
.45 caliber, no bullet in case

carbine
characteristic shape and length of about 1.7 in.

dummy, rifle
tinned six fluted case, no primers, or inert primer and holes drilled in fluted case, or merely a tinned case without a primer
Revolver — tinned case with either no primer or holes in case

guard
short, round nose, lead bullet or six short corrugations, just behind neck of case

high pressure test
tinned case

incendiary
bullet is tipped with light blue color

rifle grenade
cal. 30, five petal rose crimp in mouth of case

shot shell
guard use. Brass head extends at least one inch along case

subcalibre
cal. 30 field artillery training ammunition has extracting rim on base of case

tracer
bullet is tipped with red color

243

TABLE XIII
Shotgun Bore and Chamber Sizes

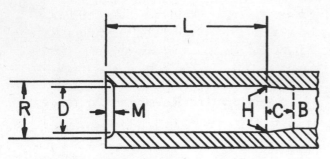

Cross Section of Shotgun Chamber

EXPLANATION OF CROSS SECTION OF SHOTGUN CHAMBER

R—Circular milling cut at the breech, which is recessed to accommodate the rim of the shell case.

M—Depth of the rim.

D—Diameter of the shell chamber when measured directly in front of the rim. The illustrations with heavy circles represent this diameter in exact true size.

L—Length of the unfired case.

H—Diameter of the head of the chamber, and because the chamber is slightly tapered, the diameter is slightly less than the diameter "D".

C—Cone of the chamber.

B—Actual beginning of the barrel proper.

CYLINDER BORES

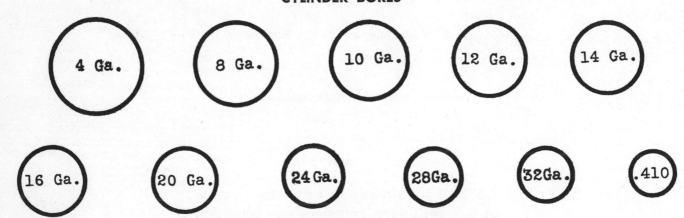

The upper two rows with light circles represent the exact natural true size of true cylinder bores of the gauges indicated. These true cylinder bore sizes represent the barrel diameter and wherever the barrel has any choke, the diameter at the muzzle will be accordingly smaller.

CHAMBER DIAMETERS

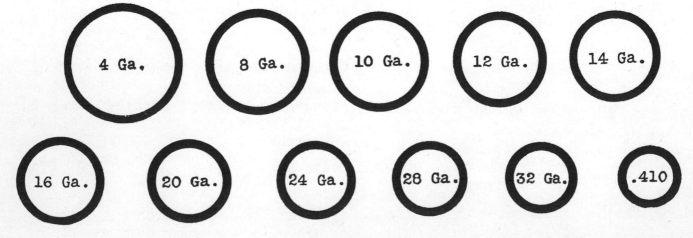

TABLE XIV

Maximum Ranges

Extreme ranges of certain small arms cartridges, determined by testing:

Bullet name	Bullet wt. (grs.)	Muzzle vel. (f.p.s.)	Ballistic co-efficient	Extreme range (yds.)
Cal. .22 long rifle	40	1145	.128	1500
Cal. .380 ACP	95	970	.08	1089
Cal. .45 ACP in pistol	234	820	.16	1640
Same in submachine gun	234	970	.16	1760
Cal. .30 Carbine M1	111	1970	.179	2200
Same, Tracer M16	107	1910	.154	1680
Cal. .30 ball, M2	152	2800	.40	3500
Cal. .30 boattail M1	172	2600	.56	5500
Same in sub-caliber gun	172	1990	.56	4300
Cal. .30-40 Krag	220	2000	.34	4050
Same in carbine	220	1920	.34	4000
Cal. .50 AP M2	718	2840	.84	7275

Calculated extreme ranges of certain small arms cartridges.

Bullet name	Bullet wt. (grs.)	Assumed M.V. (f.p.s.)	Calculated max. range (yds.)
Cal. .22 WRF	45	1450	1950
Cal. .22 WMR	40	2000	1900
Cal. .30 Mauser Pistol	86	1410	1900
Cal. .30 Luger	93	1220	1900
Cal. .32 S&W Long	98	780	1450
Cal. .38 Special	158	855	1800
Cal. .357 S&W Magnum	158	1430	2350
Cal. .38 Super Auto	130	1140	2050
9 mm. Luger	124	1140	1900
Cal. .44 Remington Magnum	240	1570	2500
Cal. .219 Zipper	56	3110	2850
Cal. .22 Hornet	45	2690	2350
Cal. .243 Winchester	100	3070	4000
Same	80	3500	3500
Cal. .250 Savage	100	2820	3500
Cal. .257 Roberts	100	2900	3850
Cal. .270 Winchester	130	3140	4000
Cal. .280 Remington	125	3140	3700
Cal. .300 H&H Magnum	180	2920	4350
Cal. .338 Winchester Magnum		2700	4660
Cal. .375 H&H Magnum	270	2740	4500
Cal. .458 Winchester F.M.J.	500	2125	4500

(Continued on following page)

Table XIV, Continued

Shot size	Diameter (ins.)	Maximum range (yds.)
Maximum ranges of shot based on journee's formula		
12-ga. round ball	.645	1420
16-ga. " "	.610	1340
20-ga. " "	.545	1200
410-ga. " "	.38	850
00 buckshot	.34	748
0 "	.32	704
1 "	.30	660
#1 shot	.16	352
#2 "	.15	330
#3 "	.14	308
#4 "	.13	286
#5 "	.12	264
#6 "	.11	242
#7½ "	.095	209
#8 "	.09	198
#9 "	.08	176
#12 " (cal. .22 shot cartridges)	.05	110

TABLE XV

Mathematical Formula

Area of a circle $= \pi r^2 = 3.1416r^2$

Circumference of a circle $= \pi d = 3.1416d$

Surface area of a sphere $= \pi d^2 = 3.1416d^2$

Volume of a sphere $= 4/3\pi r^3$ or $.5236d^3$

Surface area of a right circular cylinder $= 2\pi rh = 6.2832rh$

Volume of a right circular cylinder $= \pi r^2h = 3.1416r^2h$

In all of the foregoing $r =$ radius of the circle
$d =$ diameter of the circle
$h =$ height of cylinder

———————————————

To find the distance (D) to an object of known height (H) having the apparent height (h) of the object and a measured distance (d) from the eye of the observer

$$\frac{D}{d} = \frac{H}{h}$$

$$D = \frac{dh}{h}$$

Illustrated by the figure:

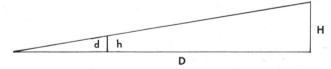

Given any three of the dimensions indicated the fourth may be found by the same formula.

TABLE XVI

Physics Formulae

Temperature reading conversions:

To convert Fahrenheit readings to degrees Centigrade:

$$°C = 5/9 \ (°F - 32)$$

To convert Centigrade readings to degrees Fahrenheit:

$$°F = 9/5 \ (°C + 32)$$

Sound and Light

Velocity of sound, still air, 68° F, at sea level = 344 meters or 1129 feet per second.

Velocity of sound, still air, 32° F, at sea level = 331.7 meters or 1088 feet per second.

For each higher degree in temperature add 1.14 feet per second to above.

For each lower degree in temperature subtract 1.14 feet per second from above.

Velocity of light in vacuum = 186,284 miles per second.

To estimate distance in feet from a gun, count the seconds that elapse between seeing the flash of gun fire and hearing the report and multiply by 1130. The velocity of light is so great it is ignored in estimating distances by the flash and sound method.

Free falling bodies, ignoring wind and air resistance

Velocity after falling two seconds = gt = 32,174t feet per second.

Distance travelled falling t seconds = $\frac{1}{2}gt^2$ = 16.087t^2 feet

Greatest height attained by a body projected with velocity of v feet per second = $\frac{v^2}{2g}$ = $\frac{v^2}{64.35}$ feet

Time to travel such height = $\frac{v}{g}$ = $\frac{v}{32.174}$

Mass and Momentum

Mass $(M) = \frac{w}{g} = \frac{w}{32.174}$

Momentum = $Mv = \frac{wv}{32.174}$ foot pounds

Energy = $\frac{1}{2} Mv^2 = \frac{1}{2} \frac{wv^2}{g} = \frac{wv^2}{64.35}$ foot pounds

In the above M = mass
w = weight in pounds
v = velocity in feet per second

TABLE XVII
Ballistics Formulae

Density of Loading

$$d = \frac{27.68w}{7000s}$$

where d = density of loading
w = weight of powder charge in grains
s = space taken up by powder charge, in cubic inches

Sectional Density

$$SD = \frac{w}{7000d^2}$$

where SD = sectional density
w = weight of bullet in grains
d = diameter of bullet in inches

Bullet Energy

$$E = \frac{1}{2} Mv^2 = \frac{1}{2} \left(\frac{w}{7000 \times 32.174} \right) v^2$$

where E = bullet energy in foot pounds
M = mass
w = weight of bullet in grains
v = velocity of bullet in feet per second

Velocity and Energy of Recoil

$$V = \frac{wv + 4700c}{7000W} \text{ feet per second}$$

$$E = \frac{W}{2g} \left(\frac{wv + 4700c}{7000W} \right)^2 \text{ foot pounds}$$

(Continued on following page)

Table XVII, Continued

where V = close approximation of velocity of recoil in feet per second

E = close approximation of energy of recoil in foot pounds

W = weight of gun in pounds

w = weight of bullet in grains

c = weight of powder charge in grains

v = muzzle velocity in feet per second

7000 converts the grains of w and c into pounds

4700 is average effective velocity of powder gases in feet per second

Range and Time of Flight in a Vacuum

Time of flight to highest point = $\dfrac{v\ \operatorname{Sin} a}{g}$ seconds

Total time to come back to original horizontal plane = $\dfrac{Z\ v\ \operatorname{Sin} a}{g}$ seconds

Maximum height reached = $\dfrac{v^2\ (\operatorname{Sin} a)^2}{2g}$ feet

Horizontal range = $\dfrac{v^2\ (\operatorname{Sin} 2a)}{g}$ feet

Maximum range (angle 45°) = $\dfrac{v^2\ (\operatorname{Sin} 90°)}{g}$ = v^2 = $\dfrac{v^2}{32.174}$ feet

Approximate maximum range = $\dfrac{v^2}{10}$ yards

In all the foregoing

v = muzzle velocity in feet per second

a = angle of elevation of gun, in degrees

g = 32.174

Trajectory

Maximum height for given range = $48t^2$ inches where t = time in flight for given range, in seconds.

Height of ordinate at a given distance from the gun = $\dfrac{d}{1000}\ (A\text{-}a)$

where d = distance at which ordinate is sought

A = angle of departure in mils, for the trajectory

a = angle of departure in mils, for a range of d length

Using what is called Sladen's formula, the height of the ordinate at desired point in the trajectory = ½ gt (T-t) feet

where T = total flight time to complete trajectory, in seconds

t = time to reach desired point in trajectory, in seconds

Wind Deflection

Deflection of bullet caused by wind = v (T-t) feet

where v = wind velocity at right angles to range, in feet per second

T = time of flight to point where deflection is sought, in seconds

t = time of flight to point where deflection is sought, in seconds if bullet travelled in a vacuum.

Note: velocity at one mile per hour equals 1.4667 feet per second

TABLE XVIII
Ballistics Tables
Remington Ballistics for Center Fire Rifle Cartridges

CARTRIDGE	BULLET Wt.-Grs.	Style	VELOCITY—Ft. Per Sec. Muzzle	100 YDS.	200 YDS.	300 YDS.	ENERGY—Foot Pounds Muzzle	100 YDS.	200 YDS.	300 YDS.	TRAJECTORY RIFLE SIGHTED IN AT 100 YDS. 50 YDS.	200 YDS.	300 YDS.	200 YDS. 100 YDS.	300 YDS.	400 YDS.
218 BEE	46	H.P.	2860	2160	1610	1200	835	475	265	145	+0.2	−6.4	−25.9			
22 HORNET	45	S.P., H.P.	2690	2030	1510	1150	720	410	230	130	−0.3	−7.8	−30.5			
220 SWIFT	48	S.P.	4110	3490	2930	2440	1800	1300	915	635	−0.2	−2.1	7.9			
222 REMINGTON.	50	H.P.P.L.	3200	2690	2230	1830	1140	800	550	370	0.0	−4.0	−15.0			
	50	Ptd.S.P., M.C.	3200	2660	2170	1750	1140	785	520	340	0.0	−4.0	−15.7			
222 REM. MAG.	55	H.P.P.L.	3300	2830	2400	2010	1330	975	700	490	0.0	−3.5	−13.1			
	55	Ptd. S.P.	3300	2800	2340	1930	1330	955	670	455	0.0	−3.6	−13.8			
22-250 REM.	55	H.P.P.L.	3810	3330	2890	2490	1770	1360	1020	760				+1.1	−5.3	−16.3
	55	Ptd. S.P.	3810	3270	2770	2320	1770	1300	935	655				−1.2	−5.8	−18.1
223 REMINGTON.	55	H.P.P.L.	3300	2830	2400	2010	1330	975	700	490	0.0	−3.5	−13.1			
(5.56 MM)	55	Ptd. S.P.	3300	2800	2340	1930	1330	955	670	455	0.0	−3.6	−13.8			
6MM REM.	80	Ptd.S.P., H.P.L.	3540	3130	2750	2400	2220	1740	1340	1018				+1.3	−6.0	−18.0
" "	100	Ptd. S.P.C.L.	3190	2920	2660	2420	2260	1890	1570	1300				+1.6	−6.5	−18.9
243 WIN.	80	Ptd. S.P.	3500	3080	2720	2410	2180	1690	1320	1030	−0.1	−2.8	−10.2			
" "	80	H.P. P.L.	3500	3110	2740	2410	2180	1720	1340	1030	−0.1	−2.7	−10.0			
" "	100	Ptd. S.P.C.I.	3070	2790	2540	2320	2090	1730	1430	1190	0.0	−3.5	−12.2			
244 REMINGTON.	90	Ptd. S.P.	3200	2850	2530	2230	2050	1630	1280	995	−0.1	−3.4	−12.3			
25-20 WIN.	86	Lead; S.P.	1460	1180	1030	940	405	265	300	170	+2.1	−23.9	−79.4			
	60	H.P.	2250	1660	1240	1030	675	365	205	140	+0.7	−11.5	−48.8			
25-35 WIN.	117	S.P.C.L.	2300	1950	1680	1460	1370	985	730	555	+0.5	−8.2	−28.6			
250 SAV.	100	Ptd. S.P.	2820	2500	2210	1940	1760	1390	1080	835	+0.1	−4.8	−16.5			
" "	100	S.P.C.L.	2820	2350	1970	1670	1760	1220	860	620	+6.1	−5.3	−19.5			
6.5MMREM.MAG.	120	Ptd. S.P.C.L.	3030	2750	2480	2230	2450	2010	1640	1330				+1.8	−7.5	−22.0
257 ROBERTS	117	S.P.C.L.	2650	2280	1950	1690	1820	1350	985	740	+0.2	−5.7	−20.6			
264 WIN. MAG.	100	Ptd. S.P.C.L.	3700	3260	2880	2550	3040	2360	1840	1440				+1.1	−5.5	−15.6
" "	140	Ptd. S.P.C.L.	3200	2940	2700	2480	3180	2690	2270	1910				+1.5	−6.1	−18.4
270 WIN.	100	Ptd. S.P.	3480	3070	2690	2340	2690	2090	1600	1215				+1.3	−6.3	−18.5
" "	150	S.P.C.L.	2800	2440	2140	1870	2610	1980	1520	1160				+2.4	−9.5	−29.6
" "	130	Ptd. S.P.C.L.	3140	2850	2580	2320	2840	2340	1920	1550				+1.6	−7.0	−20.1
" "	130	B.P.	3140	2880	2630	2400	2840	2390	1990	1660				+1.6	−6.5	−19.6
280 REMINGTON.	125	Ptd. S.P.C.L.	3190	2880	2590	2320	2820	2300	1860	1490				+1.6	−6.7	−19.8
" "	150	Ptd. S.P.C.L.	2900	2670	2450	2220	2800	2370	2000	1640				+2.0	−8.1	−23.0
" "	165	S.P.C.L.	2820	2510	2220	1970	2910	2310	1810	1420				+2.3	−9.3	−27.6
7MM REM. MAG.	150	Ptd. S.P.C.L.	3260	2970	2700	2450	3540	2940	2430	1990				+1.5	−6.3	−18.4
" "	175	Ptd. S.P.C.L.	3070	2850	2630	2430	3660	3150	2700	2290				+1.7	−6.7	−19.3
7 MM MAUSER	175	S.P.	2490	2170	1900	1680	2410	1830	1400	1100	+0.3	−6.4	−22.4			
30 CARBINE	110	S.P.	1980	1540	1230	1040	955	575	370	260	+1.0	−14.1	−51.8			
30-30 WIN.	160	M.C.	2220	1870	1600	1370	1750	1240	910	665	+0.5	−9.1	−31.7			
" "	170	HPCL., SPCL	2220	1890	1630	1410	1860	1350	1000	750	+0.7	−8.2	−29.6			
" "	150	S.P.C.L.	2410	1960	1620	1360	1930	1280	875	615	+0.4	−8.3	−29.5			
30 REMINGTON	170	S.P.C.L.	2120	1820	1560	1350	1700	1250	920	690	+0.6	−9.5	−33.8			
30-40 KRAG	180	S.P.C.L.	2470	2120	1830	1590	2440	1790	1340	1010	+0.3	−6.4	−23.4			
" "	180	Ptd. S.P.C.L.	2470	2250	2040	1850	2440	2020	1660	1370	+0.3	−6.1	−20.2			
30-06 SPRINGFIELD	220	S.P.C.L.	2410	2120	1870	1670	2830	1290	1710	1360	+0.3	−6.7	−23.6			
" "	150	Ptd. S.P.C.L.	2970	2670	2400	2130	2930	2370	1920	1510				+1.9	−7.5	−22.6
" "	150	B.P.	2970	2710	2470	2240	2930	2440	2030	1670				+1.9	−7.5	−22.6
" "	180	B.P.	2700	2480	2280	2080	2910	2460	2080	1730				+2.4	−8.5	−25.6
" "	125	Ptd. S.P.	3200	2810	2480	2200	2840	2190	1710	1340				+1.6.	−7.4	−21.4
" "	180	S.P.C.L.	2700	2330	2010	1740	2910	2170	1610	1210	+0.2	−5.6	−19.2			
" "	180	Ptd. S.P.C.L.	2700	2470	2250	2040	2910	2440	2020	1660				+2.4	−9.0	−27.1
" "	110	Ptd. S.P.	3370	2860	2400	1990	2770	2000	1410	965	−0.1	−3.4	−13.1			
" "	180	M.C.T.H.	2700	2520	2350	2190	2910	2540	2200	1900				+2.3	−8.8	−25.1
300 SAV.	180	S.P.C.L.	2370	2040	1760	1520	2240	1660	1240	920	+0.4	−7.5	−25.3			
" "	180	Ptd. S.P.C.L.	2370	2160	1960	1770	2240	1860	1530	1250	+0.4	−6.5	−22.3			
" "	150	S.P.C.L.	2670	2270	1930	1660	2370	1710	1240	915	+0.2	−5.9	−20.4			
" "	150	Ptd. S.P.C.L.	2670	2390	2130	1890	2370	1900	1510	1190	+0.2	−5.4	−17.9			
300 H&H MAG.	180	Ptd. S.P.C.L.	2920	2670	2440	2220	3400	2850	2380	1970				+1.9	−7.6	−22.5
300 WIN. MAG.	150	Ptd. S.P.C.L.	3400	3050	2730	2430	3850	3100	2480	1970				+1.5	−6.1	−18.1
" "	180	Ptd. S.P.C.L.	3070	2850	2640	2440	3770	3250	2790	2380				+1.7	−6.9	−19.4
303 SAV.	180	S.P.C.L.	2140	1810	1550	1340	1830	1310	960	715	+0.6	−10.0	−33.8			

250

Table XVIII, Continued

Remington Ballistics for Center Fire Rifle Cartridges, Continued

CARTRIDGE	BULLET WT.-GRS.	BULLET STYLE	VELOCITY—FT. PER SEC. MUZZLE	100 YDS.	200 YDS.	300 YDS.	ENERGY—FOOT POUNDS MUZZLE	100 YDS.	200 YDS.	300 YDS.	TRAJECTORY RIFLE SIGHTED IN AT 100 YDS. 50 YDS.	200 YDS.	300 YDS.	200 YDS. 100 YDS.	300 YDS.	400 YDS.
303 BRITISH	215	S.P.	2980	1900	1660	1460	2270	1720	1310	1020	+0.6	−9.1	−30.2			
" "	180	S.P.C.L.	2540	2300	2090	1900	2580	2120	1750	1440	+0.2	−5.8	−19.0			
308 WIN.	110	Ptd. S.P.	3340	2810	2340	1920	2730	1930	1340	900	+0.0	−3.7	−13.6			
" "	150	Ptd. S.P.C.L.	2860	2570	2300	2050	2730	2200	1760	1400				+2.1	−8.5	−25.6
" "	180	Ptd. S.P.C.L.	2610	2390	2170	1970	2720	2280	1870	1540	+0.3	−5.0	−17.8			
" "	180	S.P.C.L.	2610	2250	1940	1680	2720	2020	1500	1130	+0.2	−6.0	−20.8			
8MM MAUSER	170	S.P.C.L.	2570	2140	1790	1520	2490	1730	1210	870	+0.3	−6.6	−24.7			
32 REMINGTON	170	S.P.C.L.	2120	1800	1540	1340	1700	1220	895	680	+0.6	−9.5	−33.3			
32 WIN. SPCL.	170	H.P.C.L.;S.P.	2280	1920	1630	1410	1960	1390	1000	750	+0.5	−8.5	−29.8			
32-20 WIN.	100	Lead; S.P.	1290	1060	940	840	370	250	195	155	+2.8	−30.1	−97.2			
348 WIN.	200	S.P.C.L.	2530	2140	1820	1570	2840	2330	1470	1090	+0.3	−7.1	−23.7			
35 REMINGTON	150	Ptd. S.P.C.L.	2400	1960	1580	1280	1920	1280	835	545	+0.4	−8.1	−30.7			
" "	200	S.P.C.L.	2100	1710	1390	1160	1950	1300	855	605	+0.7	−109	−39.4			
350 REM. MAG.	200	Ptd. S.P.C.L.	2710	2410	2130	1870	3260	2570	2000	1550	+0.2	−5.1	−18.0			
" "	250	Ptd. S.P.C.L.	2410	2190	1980	1790	3220	2660	2180	1780	+0.4	−6.4	−21.5			
351 WIN. S.L.	180	S.P.	1850	1560	1310	1140	1370	975	685	520	+1.0	−14.5	−51.8			
375 H&H MAG.	270	S.P.	2704	2460	2210	1990	4500	3620	2920	2370				+2.4	−9.8	−27.6
" "	300	M.C.	2550	2180	1860	1590	4330	3160	2300	1680				+3.1	−12.5	−37.6
38-40 WIN.	180	S.P.	1330	1070	960	850	705	455	370	290	+2.7	−29.1	−93.7			
444 MARLIN	240	S.P.	2400	1845	1410	1125	3070	1815	1060	675	+0.6	−9.6	−36.7			
44-40 WIN.	200	S.P.	1310	1050	940	830	760	490	390	305	+2.8	−29.6	−95.2			
44 REM. MAG.	240	S.P.	1750	1360	1110	980	1630	985	655	510	+1.4	−17.5	−64.5			
45-70 GOV'T.	405	S.P.	1320	1160	1050	990	1570	1210	990	880	+2.4	−25.1	−81.2			
458 WIN. MAG.	510	S.P.	2130	1840	1600	1400	5140	3830	2900	2220	+0.6	−9.2	−32.1			
" "	500	M.C.	2130	1910	1700	1520	5040	4050	3210	2570	+0.6	−8.9	−29.4			

Ballistics figures established in test barrels in accordance with standards set by Sporting Arms and Ammunition Manufacturers' Institute .

ABBREVIATIONS: H.P. — Hollow Point S.P. — Soft Point B.P. — Bronze Point C.L. — Core-Lokt M.C. — MetalCase
H.P.C.L. — Hollow Point Core-Lokt Ptd. S.P. — Pointed Soft Point T.H. — Tapered Heel P.L. — Power Lokt
Inches above (+) or below (−) line of sight. Hold low for (+) figures, high for (−) figures.

Cartridges Interchangeable and Adapted To Same Guns

RIM FIRE
22 W.R.F.
22 Remington Special
22 Winchester M/1890

25 Stevens Short in 25
Stevens but not conversely

32 Short in 32 Long
but not conversely

CENTER FIRE
25-20 Winchester, Marlin,
Remington
25-20 Winchester and Marlin
25-20 W.C.F.
25-20 Winchester
25-20 Winchester High Velocity
25-20 Marlin

25 Colt Automatic
25 Automatic Pistol
25 (6.35 mm.) Automatic Pistol
6.35 mm. Browning Automatic

30-30 Winchester, Marlin,
Savage
30-30 Winchester
30-30 Marlin
30-30 Winchester High Velocity
30 W.C.F.

See Note A
32 Short Colt in 32 Long Colt
but not conversely

32 Colt Automatic
32 Automatic Pistol
32 (7.65 mm.) Automatic Pistol
7.65 mm. Automatic Pistol

32 Smith & Wesson in
32 Smith & Wesson Long
but not conversely

32 Smith & Wesson Long
32 Colt New Police
32 Colt Police Positive

32 Winchester, Marlin,
Remington*

32 Winchester and Marlin*
32 W.C.F.*
32 Winchester*
32-20 Winchester*
32-20 WinchesterHigh Velocity*

32-20 Marlin*
32-20 Colt L.M.R.*
32-20 W.C.F.*
32-20 Winchester and Marlin*

38 Short Colt in 38 Long Colt
but not conversely. Both
can be used in 38 Special
38 Smith & Wesson
38 Colt New Police

See Note B
38 Colt Special
38 Smith & Wesson Special
38 Special Police Match
38 Smith & Wesson Special
Mid-Range
38 Special High Velocity (†)

38-44 Special (†)
38 Special
38 Special Flat Point

38 Winchester, Marlin, Remington
38 Winchester
38 Remington
38-40 Winchester
38 W.C.F.

44 Winchester, Marlin, Remington
44 Winchester
44 Remington (not Magnum)
44 W.C.F.
44-40 Winchester

44 Smith & Wesson
in 44 Remington Mag.
but not conversely

45-70 Government
45-70 Marlin
45-70-405

9 mm. Luger Automatic Pistol
9 mm. Parabellum

NOTE: *High Velocity, Hi-Speed Cartridges must not be used in Revolvers, they should be used only in rifles made especially for them. Exceptions: items marked (†) are designed especially for the 38-44 Smith & Wesson Revolver and the 38 Colt Shooting Master. Pressure of these two cartridges is safe for lighter guns, but the recoil is likely to be more unpleasant and the frame may be shaken loose in time.

NOTE A: Not for use in revolvers chambered for 32 Smith & Wesson Long, or 32 Smith & Wesson.

NOTE B: All 38 Special cartridges can be used in 357 Magnum revolvers but not conversely.

Table XVIII, Continued

Remington Ballistics for Center Fire Pistol & Revolver Cartridges

CARTRIDGE	PRIMER	BULLET WT. IN GRAINS	BULLET STYLE	VELOCITY—FEET PER SECOND MUZZLE	50 YDS.	100 YDS.	ENERGY—FOOT POUNDS MUZZLE	50 YDS.	100 YDS.	MID-RANGE TRAJECTORY 50 YDS.	100 YDS.	BARREL
22 REM. "JET" MAG.	6½	40	S.P.	2100	1790	1510	390	285	200	0.3″	1.4″	8⅜″
221 REM. "FIRE BALL"	7½	50	Ptd. S.P.	2650	2380	2130	780	630	505	0.2″	0.8″	10½″
25 (6.35 MM) AUTOMATIC PISTOL	1½	50	M.C.	810	755	700	73	63	54	1.8″	7.7″	2″
30 (7.63MM) MAUSER AUTOMATIC PISTOL	1½	85	M.C.	1410	1210	1070	375	270	215	0.6″	3.0″	5½″
30 (7.65 MM) LUGER AUTOMATIC PISTOL	1½	93	M.C.	1220	1110	1040	305	255	225	0.9″	3.5″	4½″
32 SHORT COLT	1½	80	Lead	745	665	590	100	79	62	2.2″	9.9″	4″
32 LONG COLT	1½	82	Lead	755	715	675	100	93	83	2.0″	8.7″	4″
32 COLT NEW POLICE	1½	100	Lead	680	635	595	100	88	77	2.5″	11.0″	4″
32 (7.65 MM) AUTOMATIC PISTOL	1½	71	M.C.	960	905	850	145	130	115	1.3″	5.4″	4″
32 S. & W.	5½	88	Lead	680	645	610	90	81	73	2.5″	10.5″	3″
32 S. & W.	1½	98	Lead	705	670	635	115	98	88	2.3″	10.5″	4″
32-20 WINCHESTER	6½	100	Lead	1030	970	920	271	209	188	1.2″	4.4″	6″
	6½	100	S.P.	1030	970	920	271	209	188	1.2″	4.4″	6″
357 MAGNUM HI-SPEED	5½	158	Hi-Speed S.P.	1550	1380	1230	845	665	530	0.5″	2.5″	8⅜″
"	5½	158	Hi-Speed M.P.	1410	1240	1120	695	540	440	0.6″	2.8″	8⅜″
"	5½	158	Hi-Speed Lead	1410	1240	1120	695	540	440	0.6″	2.8″	8⅜″
9 MM. LUGER AUTOMATIC PISTOL	1½	124	M.C.	1120	1030	965	345	290	255	1.0″	4.1″	4″
38 S. & W.	1½	146	Lead	685	650	620	150	135	125	2.4″	10.0″	4″
38 SPECIAL	1½	158	Lead	855	820	790	255	235	220	1.6″	6.5″	6″
"	1½	158	Lead	855	820	790	255	235	220	1.6″	6.5″	6″
"	1½	200	Lead	730	695	665	235	215	195	2.2″	9.0″	6″
"	1½	158	M.P.	855	820	790	255	235	220	1.6″	6.5″	6″
"	1½	148	Lead W.C.	770	655	560	195	140	105	2.1″	10.0″	6″
"	1½	158	Lead Hi-Speed	1090	1030	980	415	370	335	1.0″	4.2″	6″
38 COLT NEW POLICE	1½	150	Lead	680	645	615	155	140	125	2.5″	10.5″	4″
38 SHORT COLT	1½	125	Lead	730	685	645	150	130	115	2.2″	9.4″	6″
38 LONG COLT	1½	150	Lead	730	700	670	175	165	150	2.1″	8.8″	6″
38-40 WINCHESTER	2½	180	S.P.	975	920	870	380	338	302	1.5″	5.4″	5″
38 SUPER AUTOMATIC COLT PISTOL	1½	130	Hi-Speed M.C.	1280	1140	1050	475	375	320	0.8″	3.4″	5″
38 AUTOMATIC COLT PISTOL	1½	130	M.C.	1040	980	925	310	275	245	1.0″	4.7″	4½″
380 AUTOMATIC PISTOL	1½	95	M.C.	955	865	785	190	160	130	1.4″	5.9″	3¾″
41 MAGNUM	2½	210	Lead	1050	985	930	515	450	405	1.0″	4.4″	8⅜″
"	2½	210	S.P.	1500	1350	1220	1050	850	695	0.5″	2.6″	8⅜″
41 LONG COLT	1½	195	Lead	730	705	680	230	205	200	2.2″	8.8″	6″
44 S. & M. SPECIAL	2½	246	Lead	755	725	695	310	285	265	2.0″	8.3″	6½″
44 REM. MAG.	2½	240	Lead	1470	1280	1120	1120	875	670	0.6″	2.7″	6½″
"	2½	240	S.P.	1470	1300	1170	1150	900	730	0.6″	2.5″	6½″
44-40 WINCHESTER	2½	200	S.P.	975	920	865	420	076	332	0.5″	5.7″	7½″
65 COLT	2½	250	Lead	860	820	780	410	375	340	1.6″	6.6″	5½″
45 AUTOMATIC	2½	230	M.C.	850	810	775	370	335	305	1.6″	6.5″	5″
"	2½	185	M.C.	775	695	625	245	200	160	2.0″	9.0″	5″
"	2½	230	M.C.	850	810	775	370	335	305	1.6″	6.5″	5″
45 AUTOMATIC RIM	2½	230	Lead	810	770	730	335	305	270	1.8″	7.4″	5½″

*Wad Cutter Targetmaster
**Targetmaster

Ballistics figures established in test barrels in accordance with standards set by Sporting Arms and Ammunition Manufacturer's Institute.

ABBREVIATIONS: S.P. — Soft Point   ●   M.C. — Metal Case   ●   M.P. — Metal Point

Table XVIII, Continued

Remington Ballistics for .22 Rim Fire Rifle Cartridges

CARTRIDGE		BULLET WEIGHT-GRS.	STYLE	VELOCITY—FT. PER SECOND MUZZLE	100 YDS.	ENERGY—FOOT POUNDS MUZZLE	100 YDS.	MID-RANGE TRAJECTORY INS.-100 YDS.
HI-SPEED RIM FIRE CARTRIDGES:								
22 SHORT	Adapted to single shot, repeating and autoloading rifle, revolvers and pistols.	29	Lead	1125	920	81	54	4.3
		27	H.P.	1155	920	80	51	4.2
22 LONG	Adapted to single shot, repeating and autoloading rifles, revolvers and pistols.	29	Lead	1240	965	99	60	3.8
22 LONG RIFLE	Adapted to single shot, repeating and autoloading rifles, revolvers and pistols.	40	Lead	1335	1045	158	97	3.3
		36	H.P.	1365	1040	149	86	3.3
22 W.R.F. (REM. SPECIAL)	Adapted to Remington 120S, 121S, and Winchester 1890 rifles; Remington, Winchester and Stevens single shot rifles; also Colt revolvers.	45	Lead	1450	1110	210	123	2.7
STANDARD VELOCITY RIM FIRE CTGES:								
22 SHORT	Adapted to single shot, repeating and autoloading rifles, revolvers and pistols.	29	Lead	1045	810	70	—	—
22 SHORT GAL. "SPATTER-LESS"	"Spatter-Less" cartridges are especially designed for shooting gallery use. Adapted to single shot, repeating and autoloading rifles, revolvers, and pistols.	29	Lead	1045	—	70	—	—
		15	Comp.	1710	—	97	—	—
22 LONG RIFLE	Adapted to single shot, repeating and autoloading rifles, revolvers and pistols.	40	Lead	1145	975	116	84	4.0
22 WIN. AUTO.	Adapted to Winchester Model 03 automatic rifle.	45	Lead	1055	930	111	86	4.6

Ballistics figures established in test barrels in accordance with standards set by Sporting Arms and Ammunition Manufacturers' Institute.

ABBREVIATIONS: H.P. — Hollow Point   Comp. — Composition

Winchester-Western Ballistics for .22 Rim Fire Rifle Cartridges

CARTRIDGE	WT. GRS.	BULLET TYPE	VELOCITY (fps) MUZZLE	100 YDS.	ENERGY (ft. lbs.) MUZZLE	100 YDS.	MID-RANGE TRAJECTORY 100 YDS.
22 Short Super-X and Super-Speed	29	L, K¶	1125	920	81	54	4.3
22 Short H.P. Super-X and Super-Speed	27	L, K¶	1155	920	80	51	4.2
22 Long Super-X and Super-Speed	29	L, K¶	1240	965	99	60	3 8
22 Long Rifle Super-X and Super-Speed	40	L, K¶	1335	1045	158	97	3.3
22 Long Rifle H.P. Super-X and Super-Speed	37	L, K¶	1365	1040	149	86	3.3
22 Long Rifle Shot Super-X and Super-Speed	—#12 Shot—		—	—	—	—	—
22 WRF (22 Rem. Spl.) Super-X, Super-Speed (Ins. lub.)	45	L, K	1450	1110	210	123	2.7
22 Winchester Magnum Rimfire Super-X and Super-Speed	40	JHP	2000	1390	355	170	1.6
22 Winchester Magnum Rimfire Super-X and Super-Speed	40	FMC	2000	1390	355	170	1.6
22 Short Xpert and Leader	29	Lead*	1045	—	70	—	5.6
22 Long Rifle Xpert and Leader	40	Lead*	1145	975	116	84	4.0
22 Long Rifle Super-Match Mark III and Imp. L.V. EZXS	40	Lead*	1120	950	111	80	4.2
22 Short Kant-Splash and Spatterpruf (Gallery Pack)	29	Disinteg.*	1045	—	70	—	—
22 Short Super Kant-Splash, Super Spatterpruf (Gal. Pk)	15	Disinteg.*	1710	—	97	—	—
22 Winchester Automatic (inside lubricated)	45	L, K	1055	930	111	86	4.6

CARTRIDGE	WT. GRS.	BULLET TYPE	BARREL LENGTH	MUZZLE VELOCITY (fps)	MUZZLE ENERGY (ft. lbs.)
22 Short Super-X and Super-Speed	29	L, K¶	6″	1035	69
22 Short Xpert and Leader	29	Lead*	6″	865	48
22 Long Super-X and Super-Speed	29	L, K¶	6″	1095	77
22 Long Rifle Super-X and Super-Speed	40	L, K¶	6″	1125	112
22 Long Rifle Xpert and Leader	40	Lead*	6″	950	80
22 Long Rifle Super-Match Mark IV and EZXS Pistol Match	40	Lead*	6¾″	1060	100
22 Winchester Magnum Rimfire Super-X and Super-Speed	40	JHP	6½″	1550	213
22 Winchester Magnum Rimfire Super-X and Super-Speed	40	FMC	6½″	1550	213

ABBREVIATIONS: ¶ — Wa. Coated   * — Lubricated   L — Lubaloy   K — Kopperklad   JHP — Jacketed Hollow Point
FMC — Full Metal Case

253

Winchester-Western Ballistics for Center Fire Rifle Cartridges

CARTRIDGE	WT.GRS.	BULLET TYPE	VELOCITY (fps) MUZZLE	100 YDS.	200 YDS.	300 YDS.	ENERGY (ft. lbs.) MUZZLE	100 YDS.	200 YDS.	300 YDS.	MID-RANGE TRAJECTORY 100 YDS.	200 YDS.	300 YDS.
218 Bee Super-X and Super-Speed	46	OPE(HP)	2860	2160	1610	1200	835	475	265	145	0.7	3.8	11.5
22 Hornet Super-X and Super-Speed	45	SP	2690	2030	1510	1150	720	410	230	130	0.8	4.3	13.0
22 Hornet Super-X and Super-Speed	46	OPE(HP)	2690	2030	1510	1150	740	420	235	135	0.8	4.3	13.0
220 Swift Super-X and Super-Speed	48	PSP	4110	3490	2930	2440	1800	1300	915	635	0.3	1.4	3.8
222 Rem. Super-X and Super-Speed	50	PSP	3200	2660	2170	1750	1140	785	520	340	0.5	2.5	7.0
225 Win. Super-X and Super-Speed	55	PSP	3650	3140	2680	2270	1630	1200	875	630	0.4	1.8	4.8
243 Win.(6mm)Super-X and Super-Speed	80	PSP	3500	3080	2720	2410	2180	1690	1320	1030	0.4	1.8	4.7
243 Win.(6mm)Super-X and Super-Speed	100	PP(SP)	3070	2790	2540	2320	2090	1730	1430	1190	0.5	2.2	5.5
*25-20 Win. High Velocity Super-X	60	OPE	2250	1660	1240	1030	675	365	205	140	1.2	6.3	21.0
25-20 Winchester	86	L, Lead; SP	1460	1180	1030	940	405	265	200	170	2.6	12.5	32.0
25-35 Win. Super-X and Super-Speed	117	SP	2300	1910	1600	1340	1370	945	665	465	1.0	4.6	12.5
250 Savage Super-X and Super-Speed	87	PSP	3030	2660	2330	2060	1770	1370	1050	820	0.6	2.5	6.4
250 Savage Super-X and Super-Speed	100	ST(Exp)	2820	2460	2140	1870	1760	1340	1020	775	0.6	2.9	7.4
*256 Winchester Magnum Super-X	60	OPE	2800	2070	1570	1220	1040	570	330	200	0.8	4.0	12.0
257 Roberts Super-X and Super-Speed	87	PSP	3200	2840	2500	2190	1980	1560	1210	925	0.5	2.2	5.7
257 Roberts Super-X and Super-Speed	100	ST(Exp)	2900	2540	2210	1920	1870	1430	1080	820	0.6	2.7	7.0
*257 Roberts Super-X	117	PP(SP)	2650	2280	1950	1690	1820	1350	985	740	0.7	3.4	8.8
264 Win.Mag.Super-X and Super-Speed	100	PSP	3700	3260	2880	2550	3040	2360	1840	1440	0.4	1.6	4.2
264 Win.Mag.Super-X and Super-Speed	140	PP(SP)	3200	2940	2700	2480	3180	2690	2270	1910	0.5	2.0	4.9
270 Win. Super-X and Super-Speed	100	PSP	3480	3070	2690	2340	2690	2090	1600	1215	0.4	1.8	4.8
270 Win. Super-X and Super-Speed	130	PP(SP)	3140	2880	2630	2400	2850	2390	2000	1660	0.5	2.1	5.3
270 Win. Super-X and Supe -Speed	130	ST(Exp)	3140	2850	2580	2320	2850	2340	1920	1550	0.5	2.1	5.3
270 Win. Super-X and Super-Speed	150	PP(SP)	2900	2620	2380	2160	2800	2290	1890	1550	0.6	2.5	6.3
284 Win. Super-X and Super-Speed	125	PP(SP)	3200	2880	2590	2310	2840	2300	1860	1480	0.5	2.1	5.3
284 Win. Super-X and Supe -Speed	150	PP(SP)	2900	2620	2380	2160	2800	2290	1890	1550	0.6	2.5	6.3
7 mm Mauser (7x57) Su-X and Su-Speed	175	SP	2490	2170	1900	1680	2410	1830	1400	1100	0.8	3.7	9.5
*7mm Remington Magnum Super-X	150	PP(SP)	3260	2970	2700	2450	3540	2940	2430	1990	0.4	2.0	4.9
*7mm Remington Magnum Super-X	175	PP(SP)	3070	2720	2400	2120	3660	2870	2240	1750	0.5	2.4	6.1
†30 Carbine	110	HSP	1980	1540	1230	1040	955	575	370	260	1.4	7.5	21.7
30-30 Win. Super-X and Super-Speed	150	OPE; PP; ST	2410	2020	1700	1430	1930	1360	960	680	0.9	4.2	11.0
30-30 Win. Super-X and Super-Speed	170	PP ;ST; FMC	2220	1890	1630	1410	1860	1350	1000	750	1.2	4.6	12.5
30 Remington Super-X and Super-Speed	170	ST(Exp)	2120	1820	1650	1350	1700	1250	920	690	1.1	5.3	14.0
30-06 Super-X and Super-Speed	110	PSP	3370	2830	2350	1920	2770	1960	1350	900	0.5	2.2	6.0
30-06 Super-X and Super-Speed	125	PSP	3200	2810	2480	2200	2840	2190	1710	1340	0.5	2.2	5.6
30-06 Super-X and Super-Speed	150	PP(SP)	2970	2620	2300	2010	2930	2280	1760	1340	0.6	2.5	6.5
30-06 Super-X and Super-Speed	150	ST(Exp)	2970	2670	2400	2130	2930	2370	1920	1510	0.6	2.4	6.1
30-06 Super-X and Super-Speed	180	PP(SP)	2700	2430	2010	1740	2910	1270	1610	1210	0.7	3.1	8.3
30-06 Super-X and Super-Speed	180	ST(Exp)	2700	2570	2250	2040	2910	2440	2020	1660	0.7	2.9	7.0
30-06 Super-X and Super-Match and Wimbledn Cup	180	FMCBT	2700	2520	2350	2190	2910	2540	2200	1900	0.6	2.8	6.7
*30-06 Springfield Super-X	220	PP(SP)	2410	2120	1870	1670	2830	2190	1710	1360	0.8	3.9	9.8
30-06 Super-X and Super-Speed	220	ST(Exp)	2410	2180	1980	1790	2830	2320	1910	1560	0.8	3.7	9.2
*30-40 Krag Super-X	180	PP(SP)	2470	2120	1830	1590	2440	1790	1340	1010	0.8	3.8	9.9
*30-40 Krag Super-X	180	ST(Exp)	2470	2250	2040	1850	2440	2020	1660	1370	0.8	3.5	8.5
*30-40 Krag Super-X	220	ST(Exp)	2200	1990	1800	1630	2360	1930	1580	1300	1.0	4.4	11.0
300 Win.Mag. Super-X and Super-Speed	150	PP(SP)	3400	3050	2730	2430	3850	3100	2480	1970	0.4	1.9	4.8
300 Win.Mag. Super-X and Super-Speed	180	PP(SP)	3070	2850	2640	2440	3770	3250	2790	2380	0.5	2.1	5.3
300 Win.Mag. Super-X and Super-Speed	220	ST(Exp)	2720	2490	2270	2060	3620	3030	2520	2070	0.6	2.9	6.9
300 H&H Mag. Su-X and S-uSpeed	150	ST(Exp)	3190	2870	2580	2300	3390	2740	2220	1760	0.5	2.1	5.2
300 H&H Mag. Su-X and Su-Speed	180	ST(Exp)	2920	2670	2440	2220	3400	2850	2380	1970	0.6	2.4	5.8
300 H&H Mag. Su-X and Su-Speed	220	ST(Exp)	2620	2370	2150	1940	3350	2740	2260	1840	0.7	3.1	7.7
300 Savage Super-X and Super-Speed	150	PP(SP)	2670	2350	2060	1800	2370	1840	1410	1080	0.7	3.2	8.0
300 Savage Super-X and Super-Speed	150	ST(Exp)	2670	2390	2130	1890	2370	1900	1510	1190	0.7	3.0	7.6
300 Savage Super-X and Super-Speed	180	PP(SP)	2370	2040	1760	1520	2240	1660	1240	920	0.9	4.1	10.5
300 Savage Super-X and Super-Speed	180	ST(Exp)	2370	2160	1960	1770	2240	1860	1530	1250	0.9	3.7	9.2
303 Savage Super-X and Super-Speed	190	ST(Exp)	1980	1680	1440	1250	1650	1190	875	660	1.3	6.2	15.5
†303 British Super-Speed	180	PP(SP)	2540	2300	2090	1900	2580	2120	1750	1440	0.7	3.3	8.2
308 Win. Super-X and Super-Speed	110	PSP	3340	2810	2340	1920	2730	1930	1340	900	0.5	2.2	6.0
308 Win. Super-X and Super-Speed	125	PSP	3100	2740	2430	2160	2670	2080	1640	1300	0.5	2.3	5.9
308 Win. Super-X and Super-Speed	150	PP(SP)	2860	2520	2210	1930	2730	2120	1630	1240	0.6	2.7	7.0
308 Win. Super-X and Super-Speed	150	ST(Exp)	2860	2570	2300	2050	2730	2200	1760	1400	0.6	2.6	6.5
308 Win. Super-X and Super-Speed	180	PP(SP)	2610	2250	1940	1680	2720	2020	1500	1130	0.7	3.4	8.9
308 Win. Super-X and uper-Speed	180	ST(Exp)	2610	2390	2170	1970	2720	2280	1870	1540	0.8	3.1	7.4
308 Win Super-X and Super-Speed	200	ST(Exp)	2450	2210	1980	1770	2670	2170	1750	1400	0.8	3.6	9.0

Winchester-Western Ballistics for Center Fire Rifle Cartridges, Continued

CARTRIDGE	WT. GRS.	BULLET TYPE	VELOCITY (fps) MUZZLE	100 YDS.	200 YDS.	300 YDS.	ENERGY (ft. lbs.) MUZZLE	100 YDS.	200 YDS.	300 YDS.	MID-RANGE TRAJECTORY 100 YDS.	200 YDS.	300 YDS.
32 Win. Spec. Su-X and Su-Speed	170	PP(SP)	2280	1870	1560	1330	1960	1320	920	665	1.0	4.8	13.0
32 Win. Spec. Su-X and Su-Speed	170	ST(Exp)	2280	1870	1560	1330	1960	1320	920	665	1.0	4.8	13.0
32 Rem. Super-X and Super-Speed	170	ST(Exp)	2120	1760	1460	1220	1700	1170	805	560	1.1	5.3	14.5
*32-20 Win. High-Velocity Super-X	80	OPE	2100	1430	1090	950	780	365	210	160	1.5	8.5	24.5
(Not adapted to Pistols or Revolvers or Winchester M-73 Rifles)													
32-20 Winchester (Oilproof)	100	L, Lead; SP	1290	1060	940	840	370	250	195	155	3.3	15.5	38.0
32-40 Winchester	165	SP	1440	1250	1100	1010	760	570	445	375	2.4	11.0	28.0
†8 mm Mauser (8x57; 7.9) Super-Speed	170	PP(SP)	2570	2140	1790	1520	2490	1730	1210	870	0.8	3.9	10.5
338 Win.Mag. Super-X and Super-Speed	200	PP(SP)	3000	2690	2410	2170	4000	3210	2580	2090	0.5	2.4	6.0
338 Win.Mag. Super-X and Super-Speed	250	ST(Exp)	2700	2430	2180	1940	4050	3280	2640	2090	0.7	3.0	7.4
338 Win.Mag. Super-X and Super-Speed	300	PP(SP)	2450	2160	1910	1690	4000	3110	2430	1900	0.8	3.7	9.5
†348 Winchester Super-Speed	200	ST(Exp)	2530	2220	1940	1680	2840	2190	1670	1250	0.7	3.6	9.0
35 Rem. Super-X and Super-Speed	200	PP(SP)ST(Exp)	2100	1710	1390	1160	1950	1300	860	605	1.2	6.0	16.5
351 Win. Self-Loading (Oilproof)	180	SP	1850	1560	1310	1140	1370	975	685	520	1.5	7.8	21.5
†351 Win. Self-Loading (Oilproof)	180	FMC	1850	1560	1310	1140	1370	975	685	520	1.5	7.8	21.5
358 Win.(8.8mm) Su-X and Su-Speed	200	ST(Exp)	2530	2210	1910	1640	2840	2160	1610	1190	0.8	3.6	9.4
358 Win.(8.8mm) Su-X and Su-Speed	250	ST(Exp)	2250	2010	1780	1570	2810	2230	1760	1370	1.0	4.4	11.0
375 H&H Mag. Su-X and Su-Speed	270	PP(SP)	2740	2460	2210	1990	4500	3620	2920	2370	0.7	2.9	7.1
375 H&H Mag. Su-X and Su-Speed	300	ST(Exp)	2550	2280	2040	1830	4330	3460	2770	2230	0.7	3.3	8.3
†375 H&H Magnum Super-Speed	300	FMC	2550	2180	1860	1590	4330	3160	2300	1680	0.7	3.6	9.3
38-40 Winchester (Oilproof)	180	SP	1330	1070	960	850	705	455	370	290	3.2	15.0	36.5
†38-55 Winchester	255	SP	1320	1160	1050	1000	985	760	625	565	2.9	13.0	32.0
*44 Magnum Super-X	240	HSP	1750	1350	1090	950	1630	970	635	480	1.8	9.4	26.0
44-40 Winchester (Oilproof)	200	SP	1310	1050	940	830	760	490	390	305	3.3	16.0	36.5
†45-70 Government	405	SP	1320	1160	1050	990	1570	1210	990	880	2.9	13.0	32.5
†458 Winchester Magnum Super-Speed	500	FMC	2130	1910	1700	1520	5040	4050	3210	2570	1.1	4.8	12.0
†458 Winchester Magnum Super-Speed	510	SP	9130	1840	1600	1400	5140	3830	2900	2220	1.1	5.1	13.5

Winchester-Western Ballistics for Center Fire Pistol & Revolver Cartridges

CARTRIDGE	WT. GRS.	BULLET TYPE	BARREL LENGTH	MUZZLE VELOCITY (fps)	MUZZLE ENERGY (ft. lbs.)
25 Automatic (6.35 mm) (Oilproof)	50	FMC	9"	810	73
*256 Winchester Magnum Super-X	60	OPE	8½"	2350	735
*30 Mauser (7.63 mm) (Oilproof)	86	FMC	5½"	1410	375
30 Luger (7.65 mm) (Oilproof)	93	FMC	4½"	1220	305
32 Automatic (Oilproof)	71	FMC	4"	960	145
32 Smith & Wesson (Oilproof) (inside lubricated)	85	L, Lead	3"	680	90
32 Smith & Wesson Long (Oilproof) (inside lubricated)	98	L, Lead	4"	705	115
*32 Short Colt (Oilproof) Greased	80	Lubaloy	4"	745	100
*32 Long Colt (Oilproof) (inside lubricated)	82	Lubaloy	4"	755	105
†32 Colt New Police (Oilproof) (inside lubricated)	98	Lead	4"	680	100
32-20 Winchester (Oilproof) (inside lubricated)	100	L, Lead; SP	6"	1030	235
*357 Magnum Super-X (Oilproof) (inside lubricated)	158	Lubaloy;Met Pierc	8⅜"	1410	695
†9 mm Luger (Parabellum) (Oilproof)	115	FMC	4"	1140	330
38 Smith & Wesson (Oilproof) (inside lubricated)	145	L, Lead	4"	685	150
38 Special (Oilproof) (inside lubricated)	158	L, Lead; Met Pt.	6"	855	255
38 Special Super Police (Oilproof) (inside lubricated)	200	L, Lead	6"	730	235
*38 Special Super-X (Oilproof) (inside lubricated)	150	Lubaloy;MetPierc.	6"	1060	375
38 Special Super-Match and Match Mid-Range Clean Cutting (Oilproof) (inside lubricated)	148	Lead	6"	770	195
*38 Special Super-Match (Oilproof) (inside lubricated)	158	Lead	6"	855	255
*38 Short Colt (Oilproof) Greased	130	Lubaloy	6"	730	150
*38 Long Colt (Oilproof) (inside lubricated)	150	Lubaloy	6"	730	175
†38 Colt New Police (Oilproof) (inside lubricated)	150	Lead	4"	680	155
38 Automatic Super-X and Super-Speed	130	FMC	5"	1280	475
38 Automatic	130	FMC	4½"	1040	310
380 Automatic (Oilproof)	95	FMC	3¾"	955	190
38-40 Winchester (Oilproof)	180	SP	5"	975	380
*41 Long Colt (Oilproof) (inside lubricated)	200	Lubaloy	6"	730	230
†44 Smith & Wesson Special (Oilproof) (inside lubricated)	246	Lead	6½"	755	310
*44 Magnum Super-X (Gas Check)	240	Lubaloy	6½"	1470	1150
44-40 Winchester (Oilproof)	200	SP	7½"	975	420
45 Colt (Oilproof) (inside lubricated)	255	L, Lead	5½"	860	410
45 Automatic	230	FMC	5"	850	370
*45 Automatic Super-Match Clean Cutting (Oilproof)	210	Lead	5"	710	235
*45 Automatic Super-Match Clean Cutting	185	FMC	5"	775	245

* — Western Brand only   L — Lubaloy   PP(SP) — Power-Point Soft Point   SP — Soft Point   PSP — Pointed Soft Point
FMC — Full Metal Case   † — Winchester Brand only   HSP — Hollow Soft Point   ST(Exp) — Silvertip Expanding   HP — Hollow Point   OPE — Open Point Expanding   FMCBT — Full Metal Case Boat Tail   Met Pt — Metal Point   Met Pierc. — Metal Piercing

Table XVIII, Continued
Weatherby Ballistics for Center Fire Rifle Cartridges

BULLETS		VELOCITY feet per second				ENERGY foot-pounds				MID-RANGE TRAJECTORY in inches		
Weight	Type	Muzzle	100 yds.	200 yds.	300 yds.	Muzzle	100 yds.	200 yds.	300 yds.	100 yds.	200 yds.	300 yds.
.224 Weatherby Magnum:												
50	Pt-Ex	3750	3160	2625	2140	1562	1109	765	509	0.4	1.7	4.7
55	Pt-Ex	3650	3150	2685	2270	1627	1212	881	629	0.4	1.7	4.5
.257 Weatherby Magnum:												
87	Pt-Ex	3825	3290	2835	2450	2828	2087	1553	1160	0.3	1.6	4.4
100	Pt-Ex	3555	3150	2815	2500	2802	2199	1760	1388	0.4	1.7	4.4
117	Semi-Pt-Ex	3300	2900	2550	2250	2824	2184	1689	1315	0.4	2.4	6.8
.270 Weatherby Magnum:												
100	Pt-Ex	3760	3265	2825	2435	3140	2363	1772	1317	0.4	1.6	4.3
130	Pt-Ex	3375	3050	2750	2480	3283	2686	2183	1776	0.4	1.8	4.5
150	Pt-Ex	3245	2955	2675	2430	3501	2909	2385	1967	0.5	2.0	5.0
7MM Weatherby Magnum:												
139	Pt-Ex	3300	2995	2715	2465	3355	2770	2275	1877	0.4	1.9	4.9
154	Pt-Ex	3160	2885	2640	2415	3406	2847	2384	1994	0.5	2.0	5.0
.300 Weatherby Magnum:												
150	Pt-Ex	3545	3195	2890	2615	4179	3393	2783	2279	0.4	1.5	3.9
180	Pt-Ex	3245	2960	2705	2475	4201	3501	2925	2448	0.4	1.9	5.2
220	Semi-Pt-Ex	2905	2610	2385	2150	4123	3329	2757	2257	0.6	2.5	6.7
.340 Weatherby Magnum:												
200	Pt-Ex	3210	2905	2615	2345	4566	3748	3038	2442	0.5	2.1	5.3
250	Semi-Pt-Ex	2850	2580	2325	2090	4510	3695	3000	2425	0.6	2.7	6.7
.378 Weatherby Magnum:												
270	Semi-Pt-Ex	3180	2850	2600	2315	6051	4871	4053	3210	0.5	2.0	5.2
300	Semi-Pt-Ex	2925	2610	2380	2125	5700	4539	3774	3009	0.6	2.5	6.2
.460 Weatherby Magnum:												
500	R.N.	2700	2330	2005	1730	8095	6025	4465	3320	0.7	3.3	10.0

Federal Ballistics for Hi-Power Rim Fire Cartridges

Load Number	Cartridge	Bullet Type	Bullet Wt. in Grains	VELOCITY IN FT. PER SECOND		STRIKING ENERGY FT. LBS.		Mid-Range Trajectory in Inches—100 Yard Range
				Muzzle	100 yds.	Muzzle	100 yds.	
701	.22 Short	Solid	29	1125	920	81	54	4.3
703	.22 Short	Hollow Point	27	1155	920	80	51	4.2
706	.22 Long	Solid	29	1240	965	99	60	3.8
710	.22 Long Rifle	Solid	40	1335	1045	158	97	3.3
712	.22 Long Rifle	Hollow Point	36	1365	1040	149	86	3.3
716	.22 Long Rifle	No. 12 Shot	—					

Federal Ballistics for Monark Rim Fire Cartridges

Load Number	Cartridge	Bullet Type	Bullet Wt. in Grains	VELOCITY IN FT. PER SECOND		STRIKING ENERGY FT. LBS.		Mid-Range Trajectory in Inches—100 Yard Range
				Muzzle	100 yds.	Muzzle	100 yds.	
702	.22 Short	Solid	29	1045	—	70	—	
711	.22 Long Rifle	Solid	40	1145	975	116	84	4.0

Information is based on firing from a 24-inch barrel.
Mid-Range Trajectory shows the distance in inches that the projectile is above the line of sight at the midpoint of its 100 yard range.

Table XVIII, Continued
Federal Ballistics for Center Fire Rifle Cartridges

Load No.	Cartridge	Bullet Wt. in Grains	VELOCITY FEET PER SECOND				ENERGY FOOT POUNDS				BULLET DROP IN INCHES			Test Barrel Length
			Muzzle	100 Yds.	200 Yds.	300 Yds.	Muzzle	100 Yds.	200 Yds.	300 Yds.	100 Yds.	200 Yds.	300 Yds.	
222A	222 Remington	50	3200	2660	2170	1750	1140	785	520	340	2.0	8.9	23.5	26
223A	223 Remington	55	3300	2800	2340	1930	1330	955	670	455	1.8	8.1	21.0	26
243A	243 Winchester	80	3500	3080	2720	2410	2180	1690	1320	1030	1.5	6.7	16.5	26
243B		100	3070	2790	2540	2320	2090	1730	1430	1190	2.0	8.4	20.0	
270A	270 Winchester	130	3140	2880	2630	2400	2840	2390	1990	1660	1.9	8.0	19.0	24
270B		150	2800	2440	2140	1870	2610	1980	1520	1160	2.4	11.0	26.5	
7A	7 mm. Mauser	175	2490	2170	1890	1650	2410	1840	1390	1060	3.1	14.7	38.0	24
7B		139	2710	2440	2200	1980	2230	1810	1470	1190	2.1	11.7	36.5	
7RA	7 mm. Remington	150	3260	2970	2700	2450	3540	2940	2430	1990	1.7	7.4	17.9	26
7RB	Magnum	175	3070	2720	2400	2120	3660	2870	2240	1750	2.0	8.8	21.5	
303OA	30-30 Winchester	150	2410	2020	1700	1430	1930	1360	960	680	3.4	15.0	38.5	26
303OB		170	2220	1890	1630	1410	1860	1350	1000	750	4.2	17.5	44.0	
3006A	30-06 Springfield	150	2970	2670	2400	2130	2930	2370	1920	1510	2.1	9.1	22.0	24
3006B		180	2700	2430	2180	1940	2910	2360	1900	1500	2.5	11.0	27.0	
300WA	300 Winchester	150	3400	3050	2730	2430	3850	3100	2480	1970	1.6	7.0	17.0	26
300WB	Magnum	180	3070	2850	2640	2440	3770	3250	2790	2380	1.9	8.1	19.5	
300A	300 Savage	150	2670	2390	2130	1890	2370	1900	1510	1190	2.6	11.5	27.5	26
300B		180	2370	2160	1960	1770	2240	1860	1530	1250	3.3	14.0	34.0	
303A	303 British	180	2540	2300	2090	1900	2580	2120	1750	1440	2.9	12.5	29.5	26
308A	308 Winchester	150	2860	2570	2300	2050	2730	2200	1760	1400	2.3	10.0	24.0	24
308B		180	2610	2250	1940	1680	2720	2020	1500	1130	2.8	12.5	31.0	
8A	8 mm. Mauser	170	2500	2180	1900	1650	2370	1800	1360	1040	3.1	14.6	39.5	24
32A	32 Win. Special	170	2280	1920	1630	1410	1960	1390	1000	750	3.8	17.0	43.0	26
35A	35 Remington	200	2100	1710	1390	1160	1950	1300	855	605	4.6	21.0	55.0	22

Figures in this table are based on the barrel lengths shown in the last column.

Federal Ballistics for Center Fire Pistol Cartridges

Load No.	Caliber	Bullet Type	Bullet Wt. in Grains	Muzzle Velocity Ft. Per Sec.	Muzzle Energy Ft. Lbs.	Mid-Range Trajectory 50 Yds.	Barrel Length
38A	38 Special Mid-range (Match)	Lead Wadcutter	148	770	195	2.1	6"
38B	38 Special (Service)	Lead	158	855	256	1.6	6"
45A	45 Automatic (Match)	Metal Case	230	850	370	1.6	5"
45B	45 Automatic (Match)	Metal Case Wadcutter	185	775	247	2.0	5"

Table XVIII, Continued
Norma Ballistics for Center Fire Pistol & Revolver Cartridges

Index no.	Cartridge	Bullet Weight grs.	Velocity, feet per sec. V Muzzle	Energy, foot pounds E Muzzle	Barrel length
	.32 ACP				
86	Full jacket round nose	77	900	139	4.0 inches
	.30 Luger				
88	Full jacket round nose	93	1230	312	4.7 inches
	9 mm Luger				
91	Full jacket round nose	116	1165	350	4.7 inches
	.357 Magnum				
174	Soft point flat lead nose	158	1520	811	9.8 inches
	.38 SPL				
96	Lead wadcutter	148	770	195	6.0 inches
97	Lead round nose	158	870	266	6.0 inches
	.44 Magnum				
175	Soft point flat lead nose	240	1675	1496	18.5 inches

Norma Ballistics for Center Fire Rifle Cartridges

Index no.	Cartridge	Bullet Weight grs.	V Muzzle	V 100 yds.	V 200 yds.	V 300 yds.	E Muzzle	E 100 yds.	E 200 yds.	E 300 yds.	Tr. 100 yds.	Tr. 200 yds.	Tr. 300 yds.
	.220 Swift												
1	Soft point pointed	50	4111	3611	3133	2681	1877	1448	1090	799	.2	.9	3.0
2	Full jacket semi pointed	50	4111	3460	2850	2295	1877	1329	902	585	.2	.9	3.7
	.222 Rem.												
3	Soft point pointed	50	3200	2660	2170	1750	1137	786	523	340	.0	2.0	6.2
4	Full jacket semi pointed	50	3200	2610	2080	1630	1137	756	480	295	.0	2.1	7.1
	.243 Win.												
5	Hollow point	75	3500	3070	2660	2290	2041	1570	1179	873	.0	1.4	4.1
151	Soft point pointed	100	3070	2790	2540	2320	2093	1729	1433	1195	.1	1.8	5.0
148	Full jacket semi pointed	100	3070	2790	2540	2320	2093	1729	1433	1195	.1	1.8	5.0
	.244 Rem.												
7	Hollow point	75	3500	3070	2660	2290	2041	1570	1179	873	.0	1.4	4.1
8	Soft point pointed	90	3200	2850	2530	2230	2047	1624	1279	994	.1	1.6	4.9
	.250 Savage												
9	Soft point pointed	87	3032	2685	2357	2054	1776	1393	1074	815	.0	1.9	5.8
10	Soft point pointed	100	2822	2514	2223	1956	1769	1404	1098	850	.1	2.2	6.6
101	Soft point pointed	120	2645	2405	2177	1964	1865	1542	1263	1028	.2	2.5	7.0
	.257 Roberts												
11	Soft point pointed	100	2900	2588	2291	2020	1868	1488	1166	906	.1	2.1	6.2
12	Soft point pointed	120	2645	2405	2177	1964	1865	1542	1263	1028	.2	2.5	7.0
	6,5 Jap.												
13	Soft point pointed boattail	139	2428	2280	2130	1990	1820	1605	1401	1223	.3	2.8	7.7
14	Soft point round nose	156	2067	1871	1692	1529	1481	1213	992	810	.6	4.4	11.9
	6,5 x 54 MS												
15	Soft point pointed	77	3117	2731	2369	2036	1662	1274	960	710	.0	1.9	5.6
16	Soft point pointed boattail	139	2580	2420	2270	2120	2056	1808	1591	1388	.2	2.4	6.5
163	Full jacket boattail	139	2580	2420	2270	2120	2056	1808	1591	1388	.2	2.4	6.5
17	Soft point round nose	156	2461	2240	2033	1840	2098	1738	1432	1173	.3	3.0	8.2
164	Full jacket round nose	156	2461	2240	2033	1840	2098	1738	1432	1173	.3	3.0	8.2
	6,5 x 55												
105	Soft point pointed	77	3120	2730	2370	2040	1664	1275	961	712	.0	1.9	5.6
19	Full jacket pointed	93	3150	2705	2292	1920	2050	1512	1085	762	.0	1.9	6.0
20	Soft point pointed boattail	139	2789	2630	2470	2320	2402	2136	1883	1662	.1	2.0	5.6
21	Full jacket boattail	139	2789	2630	2470	2320	2402	2136	1883	1662	.1	2.0	5.6
22	Soft point round nose	155	2493	2271	2062	1867	2153	1787	1473	1208	.3	2.9	7.9
23	Full jacket round nose	156	2493	2271	2062	1867	2153	1787	1473	1208	.3	2.9	7.9
	.270 Win.												
24	Soft point pointed	110	3248	2966	2694	2435	2578	2150	1773	1448	.1	1.4	4.3
25	Soft point pointed boattail	130	3140	2884	2639	2404	2847	2401	2011	1669	.0	1.6	4.7
26	Hollow point boattail	130	3140	2860	2593	2338	2847	2362	1941	1578	.0	1.6	4.8
27	Full jacket boattail	130	3140	2944	2753	2568	2847	2502	2188	1904	.0	1.4	4.3
28	Soft point pointed boattail	150	2802	2616	2436	2262	2616	2280	1977	1705	.1	2.0	5.7
161	Full jacket pointed	150	2802	2616	2436	2262	2616	2280	1977	1705	.1	2.0	5.7
	7 x 57												
29	Soft point pointed	110	3068	2792	2528	2277	2300	1904	1561	1267	.0	1.6	5.0
30	Soft point pointed boattail	150	2756	2539	2331	2133	2530	2148	1810	1516	.1	2.2	6.2
31	Full jacket boattail	150	2756	2539	2331	2133	2530	2148	1810	1516	.1	2.2	6.2
32	Soft point round nose	175	2490	2170	1900	1680	2410	1830	1403	1097	.4	3.3	9.0

258

Norma Ballistics for Center Fire Rifle Cartridges, Continued

Index no.	Cartridge	Weight grs.	V Muzzle	V 100 yds.	V 200 yds.	V 300 yds.	E Muzzle	E 100 yds.	E 200 yds.	E 300 yds.	Tr. 100 yds.	Tr. 200 yds.	Tr. 300 yds.
	.30 US Carb.												
35	Soft point round nose	110	1970	1595	1300	1090	948	622	413	290	.8	6.4	19.0
34	Full jacket round nose	110	1970	1595	1300	1090	948	622	413	290	.8	6.4	19.0
	.30 - 30 Win.												
37	Soft point flat nose	170	2220	1890	1630	1410	1861	1349	1003	750	.7	4.1	11.9
	.308 Win.												
143	Soft point pointed boattail	130	2900	2590	2300	2030	2428	1937	1527	1190	.1	2.1	6.2
38	Soft point pointed boattail	150	2860	2570	2300	2050	2725	2200	1762	1400	.1	2.0	5.9
39	Soft point pointed boattail	180	2610	2400	2210	2020	2725	2303	1952	1631	.2	2.5	6.6
	.308 Norma Magnum												
179	Norma "Dual Core"	180	3100	2881	2668	2464	3842	3318	2846	2427	.0	1.6	4.6
	.30 - 06												
40	Soft point pointed boattail	130	3281	2951	2636	2338	3108	2514	2006	1578	.1	1.5	4.6
42	Full jacket boattail	130	3281	2951	2636	2338	3108	2514	2006	1578	.1	1.5	4.6
43	Soft point pointed boattail	150	2972	2680	2402	2141	2943	2393	1922	1527	.0	1.9	5.7
44	Full jacket boattail	150	2972	2680	2402	2141	2943	2393	1922	1527	.0	1.9	5.7
45	Soft point pointed boattail	180	2700	2494	2296	2109	2914	2487	2107	1778	.1	2.3	6.4
46	Hollow point boattail	180	2700	2494	2296	2109	2914	2487	2107	1778	.1	2.3	6.4
47	Full jacket boattail	180	2700	2530	2365	2206	2914	2559	2236	1946	.1	2.2	6.1
48	Soft point round nose	220	2411	2197	1996	1809	2840	2358	1947	1599	.3	3.1	8.5
49	Full jacket round nose	220	2411	2197	1996	1809	2840	2358	1947	1599	.3	3.1	8.5
	.300 H & H												
50	Soft point pointed boattail	180	2920	2706	2500	2297	3409	2927	2499	2109	.0	1.9	5.3
51	Hollow point boattail	180	2920	2706	2500	2297	3409	2927	2499	2109	.0	1.9	5.3
53	Soft point round nose	220	2625	2400	2170	1986	3367	2814	2301	1927	.2	2.5	7.0
54	Full jacket round boattail	220	2625	2400	2170	1986	3367	2814	2301	1927	.2	2.5	7.0
	7.65 Argentine												
187	Soft point pointed	150	2920	2630	2355	2105	2841	2304	1843	1476	.1	2.0	5.8
	.303 Brit.												
55	Soft point pointed	130	2789	2483	2195	1929	2246	1780	1391	1075	.1	2.3	6.7
147	Soft point pointed	150	2720	2440	2170	1930	2465	1983	1569	1241	.1	2.2	6.5
56	Soft point pointed boattail	180	2540	2340	2147	1965	2579	2189	1843	1544	.2	2.7	7.3
57	Soft point round nose	215	2182	1947	1733	1541	2273	1810	1434	1134	.5	4.1	11.2
	7,7 Jap.												
110	Soft point pointed	130	2950	2635	2340	2065	2513	2004	1581	1231	.1	2.0	5.9
58	Soft point pointed boattail	180	2493	2292	2101	1922	2484	2100	1765	1477	.3	2.8	7.7
59	Soft point round nose	215	2264	2023	1802	1603	2448	1954	1550	1227	.5	3.8	10.4
	8 x 57 JR												
61	Soft point round nose	196	2362	2045	1761	1513	2428	1820	1530	996	.4	3.7	10.6
	8 x 57 JRS												
62	Soft point round nose	196	2395	2074	1795	1535	2497	1873	1402	1026	.4	3.6	10.3
	8 x 57 J												
112	Soft point round nose	159	2723	2362	2030	1734	2618	1970	1455	1062	.2	2.6	7.9
113	Full jacket round nose	159	2723	2362	2030	1734	2618	1970	1455	1062	.2	2.6	7.9
60	Soft point round nose	196	2526	2195	1894	1627	2778	2097	1562	1152	.3	3.1	9.1
114	Full jacket round nose	196	2526	2195	1894	1627	2778	2097	1562	1152	.3	3.1	9.1
	8 x 57 JS												
63	Soft point pointed	123	2887	2515	2170	1857	2277	1728	1286	942	.1	2.3	6.8
64	Soft point pointed	159	2723	2362	2030	1734	2618	1970	1455	1062	.2	2.6	7.9
65	Soft point round nose	196	2526	2195	1894	1627	2778	2097	1562	1152	.3	3.1	9.1
67	Hollow point boattail	198	2625	2416	2216	2028	3031	2567	2160	1808	.2	2.5	6.9
68	Full jacket boattail	198	2625	2456	2294	2139	3031	2653	2314	2012	.2	2.4	6.5
69	Soft point round nose	227	2330	2085	1855	1650	2737	2192	1735	1373	.4	3.4	9.5
	.358 Win.												
71	Soft point semi pointed	200	2530	2210	1910	1640	2843	2170	1621	1195	.4	3.1	8.8
72	Soft point semi pointed	250	2250	2010	1780	1570	2811	2243	1759	1369	.6	3.9	10.4
	.358 NORMA MAGNUM												
152	Soft point semi pointed	250	2790	2493	2231	2001	4322	3451	2764	2223	.2	2.4	6.6
	9,3 x 57												
73	Hollow point boattail	232	2329	2032	1763	1527	2795	2127	1602	1202	.4	3.7	10.6
74	Soft point round nose	286	2067	1818	1595	1404	2714	2099	1616	1252	.6	4.8	13.2
	9,3 x 62												
75	Hollow point boattail	232	2625	2304	2009	1742	3551	2735	2080	1564	.2	2.8	8.1
76	Full jacket pointed	232	2625	2350	2092	1855	3551	2846	2255	1773	.2	2.7	7.6
77	Soft point round nose	286	2362	2088	1837	1612	3544	2769	2144	1651	.4	3.5	9.8
78	Full jacket round nose	286	2362	2088	1837	1612	3544	2769	2144	1651	.4	3.5	9.8
	.375 H & H												
84	Soft point semi pointed	270	2740	2460	2210	1990	4502	3629	2929	2375	.2	2.4	6.5
85	Soft point semi pointed	300	2550	2280	2040	1830	4333	3464	2773	2231	.3	2.8	7.6

Table XVIII, Continued
R.W.S. Ballistics for Center Fire Rifle Cartridges

Cartridge	Style	Weight (Grain)	110	220	330	Muzzle	110 yards	Muzzle	110 yards	Iron 55	Iron 110	Iron 165	Iron 220	Tel 55	Tel 110	Tel 165	Tel 220
6.5x54 M. Sch.	s.p.	159	161	344	555	2195	1910	1693	1288	+0.87	0	−3.54	−10.43	+0.28	0	−2.95	−9.25
	r.n.									+2.17	+2.40	0	−5.70	+1.38	+2.0	0	−5.31
6.5x54 M.Sch.	H-m.o.	159	149	317	506	2333	2072	1917	1519	+0.67	0	−3.15	−9.01	+0.08	0	−2.56	−7 84
	h.p.									+1.73	+2.13	0	−4.81	+0.94	+1.73	0	−4 41
6.5x57	s.p.	93	106	228	367	3320	2885	2255	1710	+0.04	0	−1.40	−4.25	−0 55	0	−0.79	−3.07
	r.n.									+0.51	+0.94	0	−2.36	−0.28	0.55	0	−1.97
6.5x68S	s.p. S.	93	90	194	313	3937	3389	3183	2360	−0.04	0	−0.83	−2.64	−0.63	0	−0.24	−1.46
										+0.24	+0.55	0	−1.53	−0.55	+0.16	0	−1.14
7x57 7x57R	H-m.	172.8	138	291	462	2526	2256	2452	1953	+0.51	0	−2.52	−7.36	−0.08	0	−1.93	−6.18
	l.p.									+1.34	+i.65	0	−4.02	+0 55	+1.26	0	−3.62
7x57 7x57R	s.p.	138.9	139	300	487	2561	2184	2025	1468	+0.55	0	−2.76	−7 87	−0.04	0	−2.17	−6.70
	r.n.									+1.54	+1.85	0	−4.33	+0.75	+1.46	0	−3.94
7x64	H-m. C.	172.8	123	255	398	2776	2567	2966	2532	+0.28	0	−1.93	−5.55	−0.32	0	−1.34	−4.37
	h.p.									+0.94	+1.26	0	−2.99	+0.16	+0.87	1	−2.60
7x64	s.p.	138.9	145	268	432	2913	2460	2618	1866	+0.35	0	−2.05	−6.18	−0.24	0	−1.46	−5.00
	h.p.									+1.06	+1.42	0	−3.39	+0.28	+1.02	0	−2.99
7x65R	s.p.	172.8	135	289	464	2616	2273	2633	1982	+0.47	0	−2.52	−7.28	−0.12	0	−1.93	−6.10
	r.n.									+1.34	+1.61	0	−3.94	+0.55	+1.22	0	−3.54
8x56 M. Sch.	s.p.	202.2	164	353	571	2164	1863	2105	1555	+0.90	0	−3.94	−11.30	+0.32	0	−3.35	−10.12
										+2.24	+2.64	0	−6.10	+1.46	+2.24	0	−5.71
8x57JR	H-m.	196	141	300	479	2483	2187	2683	2083	+0.51	0	−2.76	−7.91	−0.08	0	−2.17	−6.73
	l.p.									+1.41	+1.85	0	−4.25	+0.63	+1.46	0	−3.86
8x57JR	s.p.	196	152	329	534	2345	1997	2394	1736	+0.71	0	−3.35	−9.64	+0.12	0	−2.76	−8.46
	r.n.									+1.85	+2.32	0	−5.15	+1.06	+1.93	0	−4.77
8x57 JRS	s.p.	196	149	323	521	2397	2037	2503	1808	+0.63	0	−3.23	−9.37	+0.04	0	−2.64	−8.19
	r.n.									+1.69	+2.17	0	−5.08	+0.90	+1.77	0	−4.68
8x68S	H-m.l.p.o.	186	108	234	379	3280	2808	4463	3269	+0.08	0	−1.49	−4.56	−0.51	0	−0.91	−3.38
	h.p.									+0.59	+1.02	0	−2.56	−0.20	+0.63	0	−2.17
9.3x62	H-m. C.	257.7	127	264	412	2697	2487	4159	3537	+0.35	0	−2.05	−5.94	−0 23	0	−1.46	−4.77
	h.p.									+1.02	+1.38	0	−3.23	+0.23	+0.98	0	−2.84
9.3x62	s.p.	285.5	152	326	524	2329	2017	3436	2582	+0.71	0	−3.19	−9.37	+0.12	0	−2.60	−8.19
	r.n.									+1.69	+2.20	0	−5.08	+0.90	+1.81	0	−4.68
9.3x74R	s.p.	285.5	154	331	531	2297	1987	3342	2503	+0.71	0	−3.35	−9.72	+0.12	0	−2.76	−8.54
	r.n.									+1.85	+2.20	0	−5.28	+1.06	+1.81	0	−4.88
9.3x74R	H-m.	257.7	133	282	447	2613	2329	3913	3103	+0.43	0	−2.36	−6.85	−0.16	0	−1.77	−5.67
	l.p.									+1.22	+1.58	0	−3.74	−0.43	−1.18	0	−3.35

Columns: Cartridge; Bullet Style; Bullet Weight (Grain); Time in Flight (in 1000th of Sec.) at yards — 110, 220, 330; Velocity (feet per Sec.) — Muzzle, 110 yards; Energy (foot-pounds) — Muzzle, 110 yards; Height of Trajectory in inches when zeroed at a given range — Iron sights (yards) 55/110/165/220, Telescope sights (yards) 55/110/165/220.

D.W.M. Ballistics for Center Fire Rifle Cartridges

Cartridge	Style	Weight grs.	100	200	300	Muzzle	100 yards	Muzzle	100 yards	F&R 50	F&R 100	F&R 200	F&R 300	Tel 50	Tel 100	Tel 200	Tel 300
5.6x52R 22HP	soft pt.	71	120	250	380	2840	2430	1270	930	+0.2	0	−5.7	−17.4	−0.4	0	−4.5	−15
	solid pt.									+1.5	+2.8	0	− 8.9	+0.6	+2.2	0	− 8.3
6.5x57 6 5x57R	soft pt.	93	100	210	340	3310	2820	2260	1640	+0.1	0	−3.6	−13.1	−0.5	0	−2.4	−10.7
	solid pt.									+0.9	+1.8	0	− 7.7	0	+1.2	0	− 7.1
7x57 7x57R	soft pt.	139	130	270	430	2550	2230	2010	1540	+0.5	0	−6.7	−22.4	−0.1	0	−5.5	−20
	solid pt									+2.2	+3.5	0	−12.3	+1.3	+2.9	0	−11.7
7x64 Brenneke	Brenneke	162	110	230	360	2940	2620	3110	2470	+0.1	0	−4.4	−14.4	−0.5	0	−3.2	−12
	soft pt.									+1.2	+2.1	0	− 8.3	+0.3	+1.5	0	− 7.7
8x56 M. Sch.	soft pt.	200	150	320	520	2180	1850	2110	1510	+0.9	0	−4.9	−32.6	+0.3	0	−3.7	−30.2
	round pt.									+3.5	+5.1	0	−17.3	+2.6	+4.5	0	−16.7
8x57JS	soft pt.	196	120	260	420	2720	2310	3220	2320	+0.4	0	−6.2	−20.8	−0.2	0	−5	−18.4
	solid pt.									+2	+3.1	0	−11.5	+1.1	+2.5	0	−10.9
8x57JRS	soft pt.	196	130	280	450	2480	2140	2680	1980	+0.4	0	−7.7	−25.3	−0.2	0	−6.5	−22.9
	solid pt.									+2.8	+4	0	−13 3	+1.9	+3.4	0	−12.7
8x60S	soft pt.	196	120	260	400	2580	2160	2900	2030	+0.4	0	−6.7	−22.5	−0.2	0	−5.5	−20.1
	solid pt.									+1 6	+3.4	0	−12 4	+0.7	+2.8	0	−11.8
9.3x74R	soft pt.	285	142	303	490	2330	1980	3460	2490	+0.3	0	−8.1	−27.4	−0.3	0	−6.9	−25
	solid pt.									+2.3	+4 1	0	−16 6	+1.4	+3.5	0	−16

Columns: Cartridge; Bullet Style; Bullet Weight grs.; Time of Flight 1/1000 sec. For Yds. — 100, 200, 300; Velocity Feet per Sec. — Muzzle, 100 yards; Energy Foot Pounds — Muzzle, 100 yards; Path of Bullet in Inches Above or Below Line of — Front and Rear Sight 50/100/200/300, Telescope 50/100/200/300.

TABLE XIX
Loads and Shot Sizes

SUGGESTED SHOT SIZES FOR GAME

GAME	SHELL	SHOT SIZE	SUGGESTED CHOKES
DUCKS	High Base	4, 5, 6	FULL—For Pass Shooting MODIFIED—Oxer Decoys
GEESE	High Base	BB, 2, 4	FULL
PHEASANTS	High Base	5, 6	MODIFIED FULL—For Long Cornfield Shots
GROUSE, PARTRIDGE	High Base or Low Base	5, 6 7½, 8	IMPROVED CYLINDER—OR MODIFIED— For Brush Work. FULL—For Open Ranges
QUAIL	Low Base	7½, 8, 9	IMPROVED CYLINDER OR MODIFIED
DOVES, PIGEONS	Low Base or High Base	6, 7½, 8	MODIFIED
WOODCOCK	Low Base	7½, 8, 9	IMPROVED CYLINDER OR MODIFIED
RABBITS	Low Base or High Base	4, 5, 6	IMPROVED CYLINDER OR MODIFIED—For Brush FULL—For Long Open Shots
SQUIRRELS	High Base	5, 6	MODIFIED
RAIL	Low Base	7½, 8, 9	IMPROVED CYLINDER
TURKEY	High Base	BB, 2, 4	FULL
FOX	High Base	BB, 2	FULL
DEER, BLACK BEAR, WOLF	High Base	Rifled Slug and Buck Shot	For rifled slugs . . . any choke For buckshot loads . . . full choke

SHOT AND ITS MANUFACTURE

The forerunner of modern shot is the old grape shot of the middle ages which is mentioned as far back as 1420. By the year 1510 this was employed in the earliest handguns. Actual manufacture in the form of balls dates back to the British Patent No. 725 of the year 1758 whereby the shot was poured and then polished in drums. Manufacture of shot is based on the British Patent 1347 of the year 1782. The first shot tower was constructed in Austria in 1818. The exact composition of shot varies but is principally of lead with some arsenic added which has the property of not only making the lead harder but to make it flow more readily. The arsenic content in the small size shot may run approximately .2% and in larger shot sizes nearly twice that amount. This alloy is made up into blocks which are then used for shot manufacture which is usually carried out in one of two manners.

No. 1—The melted alloy is poured through a sieve-like container from which the ball shape drops fall from a considerable height into a tank of cold water. In the course of the fall the shot becomes rounded and the size depends upon the sieve. For very small sizes the drop is usually 100 ft. and for larger sizes as much as 100 yards.

No. 2—The melted alloy falls upon a quickly rotating metal disc from which the pellets are thrown by centrifugal force against an apron and then dropped into water. The size of the shot depends upon the speed of the revolving disc. The sorting of the shot for sizes is accomplished by rolling them down a surface with various size openings. The shot which have thus been sorted are mixed with very finely ground graphite and placed in revolving drums. This completely rounds the shot and covers them with a coat of graphite which protects them from oxidation. Hard shot contains in addition to the arsenic about 2% antimony. Such shot retain their form better than soft shot and consequently are less apt to stray away from the central shot mass and thus give better pattern with greater penetration. The most essential point is that the shot be round which is much more important than exact sizes. The characteristic of hard shot is enhanced by copper plating but this adds considerably to the cost and relatively little to performance.

SHOT				BUCKSHOT		
NUMBER	DIAM. IN INCHES	APPROX. PELLETS IN 1 OZ.		NUMBER	DIAM. IN INCHES	APPROX. PELLETS IN 1 LB.
12	.05	2385		4	.24	340
9	.08	585				
8	.09	410		3	.25	300
7½	.09½	350				
6	.11	225		1	.30	175
5	.12	170				
4	.13	135		0	.32	145
2	.15	90				
BB	.18	50		00	.33	130

TABLE XX
Damascus Barrels

Damascus barrels consist of a combination of forged iron and steel. Strips of iron and steel are braided in different forms into a band. This is then wound around a mandrel and welded. The manufacture proceeds little by little; the form is worked with light hammering until all the small rods or wires are joined into a solid piece. The mandrel used as a form is then removed by boring it out. Depending upon how the wires are braided and twisted, there appears upon the finished barrel after browning or bluing, a more or less fine Damascus-like figure. The finer and more regular these appear, the greater the worth of the barrel.

The cheapest Damascus barrels were the so called "band" Damascus barrels. Better types according to the quality are the so called "Horseshoe," "Rose," "Bernard," "Crolle," "Moire," and "Laminette." Other fine types of Damascus included those made in England, known as "Laminated

Steel," and the genuine English Damascus produced in Marshall's workshops in Birmingham. Confidence in the quality of Damascus was so great that even ordinary steel barrels were either painted or covered with decalcomania showing Damascus patterns. These imitation Damascus are even now occasionally to be found.

The improvements in barrel steels have now, however, practically driven Damascus off the market. Until the year 1900 approximately one third to a half of all Belgian guns were produced with Damascus barrels. In Suhl, however, the switch over to the use of the much superior open-hearth steel type, the elastic limits of which even in the very cheapest types, are equal to the very best Damascus barrels, i.e. about 45 kilograms per square millimeter, was undertaken considerably earlier.

BAND (above)
BERNARD (below)

HORSESHOE (above)
LAMINETTE (below)

ROSE (above)
LAMINATED STEEL (below)

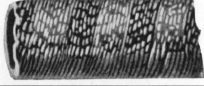

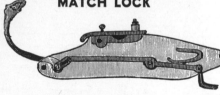

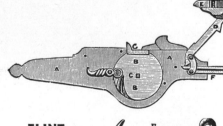

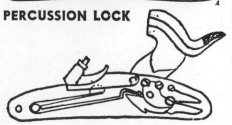

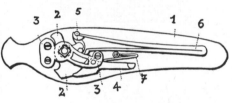

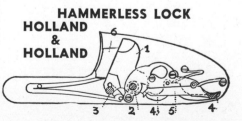

MATCH LOCK

WHEEL LOCK

FLINT LOCK

PERCUSSION LOCK

Gun Locks
MATCH LOCK
The illustration shows a rather advanced sample of the Match Lock which represents the earliest type of gun lock. The serpentine with the burning match is lowered by the trigger into the priming in the touch hole and the gun discharged.
WHEEL LOCK
Was invented in Germany in 1515. Its principal parts consist of a grooved steel wheel with serrated edge, motivated by a chain and spring. The wheel was wound up with a key and upon pressure on the trigger, the wheel was spinned against the pyrite, producing sparks and igniting the priming.
FLINT LOCK
Following the Wheel Lock came the Flint Lock, which was in general use through the beginning of the 19th century. The flint (f) in the hammer (e) strikes the battery (g) causing sparks, igniting the priming mixture in the flash pan (h). The flash is carried into the chamber through the touch hole and in turn ignites the actual powder charge.
PERCUSSION LOCK
In this type of lock, the hammer upon being released strikes the hollow nipple of which the hood shaped percussion cap has been placed. The flame thus enters into the powder chamber through the priming channel.
BACK ACTION LOCK
BAR LOCK, & SEMI BAR LOCK
The Back Action Lock and Semi Bar Lock have a main spring (#6) in back. The Bar Lock has the main spring in front. The Bar Locks have a disadvantage in that they require just that section of the action to be milled out which should be strongest. On the other hand, the Bar Lock is stronger and, therefore, the modification in the form of the Semi Bar Lock is preferable. All modern locks of this type are made so that the hammer, after firing, springs back into a safe position and cannot touch the firing pin in this position. The number of parts are #1—Side Plate, #2—Nut, #3—Housing, #4—Sear, #5—Stirrup, #6—Main Spring, #7—Sear Spring.
HOLLAND & HOLLAND HAMMERLESS LOCK
This represents the most modern form of the English Hammerless Side Lock, a feature of which is the double sear, which prevents accidental discharge.

BACK ACTION LOCK

SEMI BAR LOCK

BAR LOCK

HAMMERLESS LOCK
HOLLAND & HOLLAND

TABLE XXI
Stock Types and Measurements

The normal shotgun or rifle is factory fitted with a pistol grip stock with a length of about 14", a drop at the comb of about 1¾" and at the heel of 2¾". Distance from trigger to pistol grip about 4⅝". Pitch about 3", cast off about ¼". These specifications seldom vary more than ¼". The average shooter will have no trouble adapting himself to such a gun.

In special cases, particularly if a man is either very tall or very short or heavy or thin, he will shoot better if the stock is made to his individual requirements.

When an expensive gun is built to order, and this seldom applies to guns under $200, it is advisable to have the stock built to measure. This usually involves extra cost. The extra cost depending on how great the variation from normal. When ordering a gun with a special stock, the best way to be assured of satisfaction is to take the measurements from a gun of similar type that fits well. If such is not available, then body measurements should be given. These permit the experienced stock maker to produce a perfectly fitted stock.

MOST POPULAR STOCK TYPES

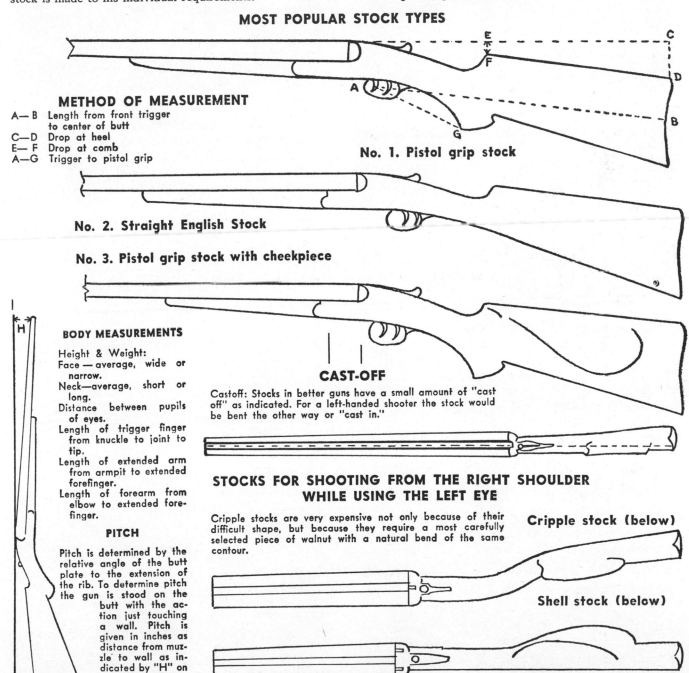

METHOD OF MEASUREMENT

A— B Length from front trigger to center of butt
C—D Drop at heel
E— F Drop at comb
A—G Trigger to pistol grip

No. 1. Pistol grip stock

No. 2. Straight English Stock

No. 3. Pistol grip stock with cheekpiece

BODY MEASUREMENTS

Height & Weight:
Face — average, wide or narrow.
Neck—average, short or long.
Distance between pupils of eyes.
Length of trigger finger from knuckle to joint to tip.
Length of extended arm from armpit to extended forefinger.
Length of forearm from elbow to extended forefinger.

PITCH

Pitch is determined by the relative angle of the butt plate to the extension of the rib. To determine pitch the gun is stood on the butt with the action just touching a wall. Pitch is given in inches as distance from muzzle to wall as indicated by "H" on sketch at left.

CAST-OFF

Castoff: Stocks in better guns have a small amount of "cast off" as indicated. For a left-handed shooter the stock would be bent the other way or "cast in."

STOCKS FOR SHOOTING FROM THE RIGHT SHOULDER WHILE USING THE LEFT EYE

Cripple stocks are very expensive not only because of their difficult shape, but because they require a most carefully selected piece of walnut with a natural bend of the same contour.

Cripple stock (below)

Shell stock (below)

263

TABLE XXII

Notable Dates in Firearms History
c — abbreviation for circa (about)

c1200

gunpowder, believed first compounded early in 13th century

1248

gunpowder, first authentic record of its existence by Bacon of England

1313

gunpowder, first recorded use as a propellent for a cannon projectile

c1324

hand held firearm, with a cannon lock known to be in use

1339

multi-barrel arrangement used to fire several cannons simultaneously, the predecessor of the machine or Gatling gun

c1350

gunpowder, use in cannon experimented with by Berthold Schwartz (1310-1384) a German monk, often erroneously credited with the invention of gunpowder

1386

hand gun, first use of the term found in English records

1411

matchlock, first authentic record of its existence

c1450

gun lock, a mechanical means attached to a gun for applying match to powder
corned powder supplanted serpentine powder

1475

matchlock, appeared with levers, springs and short sear

1498

rifled gun barrels with straight grooves by Kollner of Vienna

c1500

button lock an improved form of matchlock

c1517

wheel lock said to have been invented by Kiefuss in Nuremburg or Vienna

c1521

pressure lock an improved form of matchlock

1550-1570

snaphaunce, first firearm to use striking action of the cock to generate sparks

c1570

snap lock, also called "tinder lock" or "tube lock" came into use

c1575

cartridges of paper containing ball and powder in use

c1600

miquelet lock and English lock made appearance

1608

telescope invented by Lippershey of The Netherlands

c1615

flintlock invented by Marin le Bourgeoys of France

1629

game law, Virginia first of colonies to pass a game law

1639

gunpowder mill, grant of 500 acres of land made to Edward Rawson in the American Colonies for construction of a gunpowder mill.

1662

detonation, principle of, known to British

1690

Brown Bess officially adopted by British

1700

flintlocks being produced in the American Colonies with both smooth bore and rifled barrels

(Continued on following page)

1730

breech loading flintlocks known to have existed but not in general use

c1760

flintlock grenade launcher made in Tower of London Armory to fire a spherical grenade

1776

breech loading flintlock of improved form invented by Ferguson of England

1778

Springfield Armory established as an ammunition laboratory in Springfield, Massachusetts

1790

Seven barrel flintlock made with ignition system whereby one stroke of flint ignited a powder train and all seven barrels fired within one minute

1793

detonating powders experimented with by Rev. Alexander John Forsyth, a Presbyterian minister of Scotland

1795

muskets, manufacture of began at Springfield Armory

1796

game law, first Federal, passed May 19th by Congress

1801

duelling, Tennessee first state to pass a law dealing with duelling

1807

pill lock using detonating pellets patented by Forsyth of England

1808

paper fulminate device detonated by piercing with needle, by Pauly of Switzerland

1811

breechloader, first fairly successful design, by Hall of the U. S.

1816

copper percussion cup, by Shaw of England
copper tube primer, by Manton of England

1818

flintlock revolver, a single action flintlock gas sealed repeater patented by Collier of the U. S.

1822

lathe for duplicating irregular shapes, by Blanchard of the U. S.

1825

Deringer, first pistol produced using new percussion cap, by Deringer of the U. S.

1835

revolver, first practical one to rotate cylinder by cocking hammer, by Colt of the U. S.

1836

pinfire cartridge, first to provide successful combination of breech loading cartridge and gun with true breech seal, by Le Faucheux of France

1837

bolt action, first really successful one in production, by Dreyse of Germany

1838

nitric acid action on cotton, recognized by Pelouze

1845

nitrated cotton as explosive recognized by Schonbein of Germany
paper tape primer developed by Maynard of the U.S.
rimfire caps like BB cap, by Flobert of France
popular pepperbox pistol patented by Ethan Allen of the U.S.

1846

nitroglycerin by Sobrero of Italy

1848

breechloading percussion system, most famous and successful, by Sharps of the U.S.

1849

repeating rifle, first reasonably successful, by Jennings of the U.S.

1851

solid frame revolver, first successful one patented in England by Robert Adams
steel gun, first all steel gun exhibited by Alfred Krupp of Germany

(Continued on following page)

1852

disc primer by Sharps of the U.S.

1855

revolver combining single and double action hammer system patented in England
revolver with bored through cylinders patented by White of the United States

1856

steel manufacturing process by Bessemer of England

1857

rimfire cartridge, first really practical one in production, by Smith and Wesson
center fire cartridge, initiator of modern development patented in France

1858

center fire cartridge improved by Morse of the U.S.

c1860

game preserve, first in the U.S., a private preserve by Judge John Dean Canton of Ottawa, Illinois

1860

repeating rifle, first really successful, by Spencer of the U.S.
Boxer primer by Boxer of England

1861

center fire cartridge, first one widely used, patented in England, by Schnieder of France

1862

machine gun, first successful mechanical, manually operated, by Gatling of the U.S.

1863

smokeless powder by Shultze of Germany

1864

hunting license fee, first required by law in the U.S., by New York State

1866

dynamite by Nobel of Sweden

1870

Berdan primer by Berdan of the U.S.

1871

The National Rifle Association formed in New York City with 35 members

1872

Peacemaker, Colt single action revolver, first put into production

1873

Shooting meet, first held by The National Rifle Association

1878

bolt action magazine arm, (by Hotchkiss), first to be adopted by U.S.

1880

clay pigeon target patented in U.S. by George Likowsky of Cincinnati, Ohio

1883

machine gun, first truly successful automatically functioning firearm, by Hiram S. Maxim of the U.S.

1885

smokeless powder improved by Vieille of France

1888

ballistite, first of type having nitrocellulose dissolved in nitroglycerin

1889

revolver with swing-out cylinder introduced by Colt

1890

fully automatic shooting gallery, first one in the U.S. invented by Charles Wallace Parker of Abilene, Kansas

1891

alloy steel by Harvey of the U.S.

1892

self loading pistol, first practical, by Schonberger

1893

trap shooting meet, first in the U.S. at Jamaica, New York; live birds used
semiautomatic pistol, first in production in Germany, by Borchardt of the U.S.

1895

automatic arm, first successful gas-piston operated, by Hotchkiss Company

1898

semi-automatic pistol, toggle action, patented by Luger of Germany

(Continued on following page)

Table XXII, Continued

1900

trap shooting, first with clay pigeons at Queens, New York

International Revolver Tournament, first, between U.S. and French teams, held as to each team in Greenville, New Jersey and Paris, France, respectively, the U.S. team won

1901

high speed alloy steel, by Taylor and White of the U.S.

machine gun, water-cooled, short recoil operated, patented by J. M. Browning of the U.S.

1906

thermosetting man-made plastic, patented by Dr. Leo Hendrik Baekeland of the U.S.

1909

silencer by H. P. Maxim of the U.S.

1916

stainless steel by Brearly of England

1926

Garand rifle patented by John C. Garand of the U.S.

1930

firearms identification, first scientific research and instructional laboratory for forensic ballistics opened in the U.S. at Northwestern University

1937

game preserves, first Federally authorized in the U.S.

TABLE XXIII

U.S. Registered Trademarks

Under conditions prescribed by Federal Law, trademarks may be registered in the United States Patent Office where they are grouped in "classes" according to the nature of the goods to which they are applied. Class 9 embraces "Explosives, firearms, equipments, and projectiles." Abstracted from the official records of the Patent Office and listed herein are most of the trademarks in Class 9 encountered in the firearms art. Each abstract sets out the basic information found in the registration certificate, in the following order:

THE TRADEMARK	Registration Number
General description of goods	
Registrant	
Date of first use	Date of Registration

Copies of registered trademarks are sold by the U.S. Patent Office, Washington, D. C. 20231 at the price of twenty cents each.

Trademarks containing a letter, word, or phrase

AA INC. *in design form* — 704806
Ordnance
Aircraft Armaments, Inc.
3/6/52 — 9/27/60

ACCU-RANGE — 801164
Telescope rifle sights with distance indicator
Redfield Gun Sight Co.
5/18/64 — 1/4/66

ACCU-RISER — 745648
Pistol grips
Allan F. Barney d/b as Fitz
1/5/62 — 2/26/63

ACE *in a diamond outline* — 288609
Pistols
Colt's Manufacturing Co.
6/20/31 — 11/3/31

AC-KRO-GRUV — 778869
Rifling in gun barrels
O.F. Mossberg & Sons, Inc.
March 1959 — 10/20/64

ACME — G75848
Shotgun shell loader
Acme Industries, Inc.
11/1/55 — 3/24/59

ADJUSTOMATIC — 667922
Shot Gun chokes
Hartford Gun Choke Co.
10/30/57 — 10/7/58

AERO-DYNE SUPER POLY CHOKE — 511790
Barrel chokes
The Poly Choke Company, Inc.
July 1940 — 7/5/49

AEROMET — 399477
Firearms
Remington Arms Company, Inc.
7/31/41 — 1/12/43

AETNA — 51706
Dynamite Cartridges, etc.
Hercules Powder Company
March 1880 — 4/24/06

Continued on following page

Table XXIII, Continued

AG   651353
Firearms
Industria Armi Galesi
1910   9/10/57

AGENT   628517
Revolvers
Colt's Manufacturing Company
3/24/55   6/12/56

AGUIRRE Y ARANZABAL   611230
Firearms
Aguirre y Aranzabal, S.R.C.
July 1939   8/23/55

AI *in a triangular outline*   571023
Ammunition
N.V. Nederlandsche Machinefabriek
"Artillerie Inrichtingen"
Prior to 1951   2/24/53

AIR-O-MATIC   390139
Air rifles
A.B.T. Manufacturing Corp.
3/1/41   9/9/41

AIRSEARCH *with design*   G14159
Ammunition feed booster, for machine guns
The Garrett Corporation
December 1948   10/18/55

AIR-WEDGE   718079
Shotshell wads
Alcan Company, Inc.
4/19/59   7/11/61

AIRWEIGHT   585831
Revolvers
Smith & Wesson, Inc.
11/21/52   2/16/54

AL *and design*   667011
Shotshells, wads, primers, etc.
Alcan Paper Co., Inc.
1954   9/16/58

ALDENBILT   565231
Firearms and Ammunition
Aldens, Inc.
12/26/49   10/14/52

ALL RUBBER SLIP ON   509618
with manufacturer's name in a triangle
Recoil pads
Jostam Manufacturing Co.
1/6/30   5/10/49

ALTITE   618847
Shotgun shell wads
Federal Cartridge Corporation
2/25/55   1/10/56

AMERICAN 50 *with eagle design*   822226
Handworked rifle and shotguns as
collector's items
Robert C. Kain
12/4/64   1/17/67

AMERICAN EAGLE   781203
22 caliber ammunition
Federal Cartridge Corporation
1/1/36   12/8/64

AMERICAN EAGLE   808747
Center fire cartridges
Federal Cartridge Corporation
4/8/65   5/24/66

AMERICAN EAGLE *and design of eagle*   783485
.22 caliber ammunition
Federal Cartridge Corporation
1/1/36   1/19/65

AMERICAN EAGLE *and picture of eagle*   267303
Shotgun shells
Federal Cartridge Corp.
1/1/24   2/18/30

AMRON   678308
Cartridge and spring mechanism for
discharging pilot and seat from aircraft,
gun feeders and cartridge cases
Amron Corp.
7/28/58   5/12/59

AMRON *and design*   678309
Cartridge and spring mechanism for
discharging pilot and seat from aircraft,
etc.
Amron Corp.
8/29/58   5/12/59

AMWAL   836547
Gun stocks
American Walnut Co., Inc.
6/21/66   10/10/67

ANSCHUTZ *on designed background*   697663
Firearms
J.G. Anchutz G. m.b.H.
Prior to 1956   5/17/60

Continued on following page

ANTI-FLINCH	175462
Recoil pads for guns	
Jostam Manufacturing Co.	
3/13/15	11/6/23

ANTI-FLINCH (*block letters*)	501013
Recoil pads	
Jostam Manufacturing Co.	
3/13/15	7/13/48

AR-15	825581
Rifles	
Colt's Inc.	
5/11/64	3/14/67

ARMALITE	661814
Firearms	
Fairchild Engine and Airplane Corp.	
5/23/55	5/20/58

ARMALITE *and reticule design*	820574
Firearms	
Armalite, Inc.	
7/1/61	12/20/66

ARROW	49614
Cartridges and shells	
Remington Arms Co., Inc.	
2/25/01	2/13/06

ARROW EXPRESS	218859
Ammunition	
Remington Arms Company, Inc.	
2/26/26	10/5/26

ARROW-MATIC	386558
Air rifles	
A.B.T. Manufacturing Corp.	
9/27/40	4/15/41

ASTRA *within a design*	805409
Firearms	
Astra, Unceta y Cia, S.A.	
Prior to 1914	3/15/66

AUSTIN, *etc. and design*	303311
Powder, pellet powder, dynamite, etc.	
Austin Powder Company	
5/1/10	11/28/33

AUTOGUN *and design*	140318
Pistols, rifles, etc.	
Auto Ordnance Corp.	
3/23/20	3/15/21

AUTO MASTER	705802
Firearms	
Remington Arms Company, Inc.	
2/2/59	10/18/60

AUTOMATIC *on a colored shield*	441674
Firearms, projectile and grenade parts	
U.S. Automatic Corp.	
8/7/42	12/28/48

AUTO-ORD-CO *and design*	128002
Firearms, machine guns and ordnance	
Auto Ordnance Corp.	
3/28/19	12/23/19

AUTOPISTOL *and design*	140319
Pistols	
Auto Ordnance Corp.	
3/23/20	3/15/21

AUTORIFLE *and design*	128926
Rifles	
Auto Ordnance Corp.	
3/28/19	1/20/20

AYA *on a shield*	609796
Firearms	
Aguirre y Aranzabal, S.R.C.	
Prior to 1944	8/2/55

B *and design*	205824
Pistol grips and butt plates	
Bakelite Corp.	
12/1/24	11/17/25

B *and design*	646979
Firearms, explosives, ordnance, etc.	
Aktiebolaget Bofors	
Prior to 1953	6/18/57

BAKELITE	210093
Pistol grips and butt plates	
Bakelite Corp.	
6/12/18	3/9/26

BALLISTITE	51566
Explosives	
Du Pont Co.	
1892	4/17/06

BALL POWDER	G40884
Propellant explosives	
Olin Industries, Inc.	
11/27/40	2/5/57

Continued on following page

Table XXIII, Continued

BALL POWDER *on W design*   723447
Gun powder
Olin Mathieson Chemical Corporation
9/15/60   11/7/61

BANKERS SPECIAL   821005
Revolvers
Colt's Inc.
5/7/28   12/27/66

BAR-O   710417
Gun sights
Benjamin Air Rifle Company
10/20/59   1/31/61

BAR-V   710416
Gun sights
Benjamin Air Rifle Company
10/20/59   1/31/61

BAYARD *and likeness of a Knight*   84806
Pistols, rifles, etc.
Anciens Establissements Pieper
6/9/1892   1/9/12

BELKNAP   796938
Shotguns and rifles
Belknap Hardware and Mfg. Co.
5/17/63   9/28/65

BENJAMIN   639534
Air and gas guns, pellets, etc.
Benjamin Air Rifle Company
6/20/99   1/8/57

BENJAMIN FRANKLIN   641237
Air and gas guns
Benjamin Air Rifle Company
4/27/34   2/12/57

BERETTA   587716
Firearms and parts
Berben Corp.
3/14/52   3/30/54

BERNS-MARTIN   797970
Cartridge belts and holsters
J.A.F. Corp.
9/6/32   10/26/65

BETHLEHEM   155383
Artillery and Naval guns
Bethlehem Steel Corp.
11/1/21   10/3/22

BI-OCULAR   813693
Gun sights
Trius Products Inc.
2/5/65   8/23/66

BLACKHAWK   654650
Revolvers
Sturm, Ruger & Co., Inc.
9/13/55   11/19/57

BLACK PRINCE   68123
Shotguns
Shapleigh Hardwood Co.
March 1902   3/10/08

BLACK SHEEP   785434
Firearm equipment
Buddy Schoellkopf Products, Inc.
3/1/53   2/23/65

BL-C   742843
Rifle powder
B. E. Hodgdon, Inc.
5/5/57   1/1/63

BLUE GRASS   586747
Recoil pads and gun covers
Belknap Hardware and Manufacturing
Company
1947   3/9/54

BONOCORD   832813
Ammunition and explosives
Aktiebolaget Bofors
1/10/34   8/1/67

BREDA *within an outline*   773051
Firearms and ordnance
Breda Meccanica Bresciana S.p.A.
Prior to 1961   7/14/64

BRENNEKE   727867
Rifles, bullets, shotgun slugs and cartridges
Wilhelm Brenneke Kommanditgesellschaft
1898   2/27/62

BRIXIA   836955
Ordnance
Societa Metallurgica Italiano
Prior to 1968   10/24/67

BROWNING (*Block letters*)   708894
Firearms and equipment
Browning Arms Company
1870   12/27/60

Continued on following page

271

BROWNING *with portrait*   283189
Firearms and gun cases
J.M. & M.S. Browning
8/8/29   5/19/31

BRUSHMASTER   735158
Firearms
Remington Arms Co., Inc.
2/13/61   7/31/62

B.S.A.   68285
Firearms
The Birmingham Small Arms Co., Ltd.
January 1884   3/24/08

BUCKBUSTER   837409
Shotguns
Ithaca Gun Co., Inc.
4/19/67   10/24/67

BUDGET POWER   729055
Rifles
Speigel, Inc.
9/16/56   3/27/62

BULLS EYE   668200
Air guns, shot, and air gun scopes
Daisy Manufacturing Company
1/1/16   10/14/58

BULL'S EYE   61982
Powder for small arms
Laflin & Rand Powder Company
1900   4/16/07

BULL'S EYE *and design*   114207
Steel shot
American Ball Company
1/1/16   12/5/19

CANUCK   768998
Ammunition
Canadian Industries Limited
Prior to 1925   5/5/64

CAP-CHUR EQUIPMENT   688538
Projectiles containing tranquilizers, or etc.,
compositions and guns for propelling them
Palmer Chemical & Equipment Co. Inc.
April 1957   11/24/59

CAP-TURE   755784
Guns and projectiles for stunning drugs
Palmer Chemical & Equipment Company, Inc.
2/2/61   9/13/67

CASH   703106
Firearms and ammunition for stunning
animals
Accles & Shelvoke Limited
12/31/13   8/23/60

CASTLE *in an oval*   48405
Firearms
Webley & Scott Ltd.
1/1/1869   12/26/05

CATRON *in a design*   786249
Shotgun shells
Catron of Carmel, Inc.
5/22/63   3/9/65

CCI   831313
Rifle ammunition and primers
Cascade Cartridge, Inc.
7/3/57   7/4/67

CD *within a shotgun barrel illustration*   795860
Shotguns
Charles Daly, Inc.
8/15/63   9/14/65

CENTAURE   655140
Firearms, parts and ammunition
Fabriques d' Armes Unies de Liege
Prior to 1950   12/3/57

CENTENNIAL   767380
Firearms other than metallic cartridge
weapons
Centennial Arms Corp.
6/8/60   3/31/64

CH   712710
Shell reloading equipment
Charles R. Heckman, d.b.a. C.H. Die Company
Nov. 1949   3/21/60

CH *on a shield*   745278
Firearms, ammunition and equipment
Harvan Sporting Goods Co., Inc.
5/1/62   2/19/63

CHALLENGER   408712
Pistols
Colt's Patent Fire Arms Manufacturing Co.
5/26/43   8/29/44

Continued on following page

CHAMPION 68386
Rifles, shotguns, etc.
Iver Johnson's Arms & Cycle Works
1/8/1882 4/7/08

CHARLES DALY 546912
Shotguns and rifles
Charles Daly, Inc.
5/10/28 8/21/51

CHARLES DALY 639532
Firearms, air guns and parts
Charles Daly, Inc.
1928 1/8/57

CHARLES HARVAN *on shield* 745278
Firearms and ammunition
Harvan Sporting Goods Co., Inc.
5/1/62 2/19/63

CHEROKEE *and likeness of an Indian* 86425
Pistols, revolvers, etc.
C.M. McClurg Co.
1882 5/7/12

CHUCKSTER 719100
Rifles and parts
O.F. Mossberg & Sons, Inc.
9/19/59 8/1/61

C-I-L *and design* 833887
Sporting ammunition
Canadian Industries Limited
Prior to 1956 8/22/67

CLAYBIRDER 714591
Shotguns
Stoeger Arms Corporation
9/11/59 5/2/61

C-LECT-CHOKE 792046
Chokes as part of shotgun barrels
O.F. Mossberg & Sons, Inc.
January 1950 7/6/65

CLIMAX 83450
Cartridges
United States Cartridge Company
4/25/11 9/12/11

CLIPPER KING *and crown design* 674400
Firearms
The Marlin Firearms Company
8/15/58 2/24/59

CLUB 49611
Cartridges and shells
Remington Arms Co., Inc.
July 1885 2/13/06

CO₂ 200 816478
Semi-automatic gas pistols
Daisy Manufacturing Company
6/20/63 10/11/66

COBRA 651917
Firearms
Colt's Patent Fire Arms
Manufacturing Company, Inc.
7/14/51 9/24/57

COLT 49430
Pistols
Colt's, Inc.
1889 2/6/06

COLT 58249
Rifles and guns
Colt's, Inc.
1889 12/11/06

COLT 736237
Firearms
Colt's Patent Fire Arms
Manufacturing Co., Inc.
1889 8/21/62

COLT *with likeness of a colt* 52904
Pistols
Colt's, Inc.
May 1893 5/22/06

COLT 436574
with figure of colt and manufacturer's name
Firearms
Colt's Manufacturing Company
6/23/47 2/10/48

COLT *within a design* 830861
Rifles
Colt's, Inc.
6/3/62 6/27/67

COLT AR-15 827453
Rifles
Colt's, Inc.
5/11/64 4/18/67

Continued on following page

COLT AR-15 *with colt design* 830862
Rifles
Colt's, Inc.
6/30/62 6/27/67

COLT BUNTLINE SPECIAL .45 695146
Firearms
Colt's Patent Fire Arms Manufacturing
Company, Inc.
9/11/57 3/29/60

COLT'S PT. F.A. MFG. 50584
CO. HARTFORD CT. U.S.A.
Pistols
Colt's Inc.
1873 3/27/06

COLT'S PT. F.A. MFG. 58278
CO. HARTFORD CT. U.S.A.
Rifles and guns
Colt's Inc.
1873 12/11/06

COLT COLT'S PT. F.A. MFG. 163464
CO. HARTFORD CT. U.S.A.
and likeness of a colt
Firearms
Colt Patent Fire Arms Manufacturing Co.,
5/17/22 1/16/23

COMBOWAD 721508
Shotgun shell wad columns
Alcan Company, Inc.
12/30/60 9/16/61

COMMANCHE 792456
Rifles and parts
Stoeger Arms Corporation
6/3/64 7/13/65

COMMANDER 406461
Firearms
Colt's Patent Fire Arms Manufacturing Co.
10/8/43 4/4/44

COMMANDO 399749
Revolvers
Colt's Patent Fire Arms Manufacturing Co.
9/21/42 1/26/43

COMP 339820
Gas porting devices for firearms
R. M. Cutts, Jr.
6/23/36 10/20/36

COMPENSATOR 557114
Gas porting devices for firearms
Richard M. Cutts
April 1926 4/8/52

CONDOR 686528
Rifles and ammunition
Jose Ramon Somavia
June 1955 10/13/59

COOEY 768340
Guns
Winchester-Western (Canada) Ltd.
2/1/63 4/21/64

CO-OP *within a design* 396454
Firearms, air rifles, ammunition, etc.
National Co operatives, Inc.
December 1929 7/21/42

CORAL 698803
Firearms
Aguirre y Aranzabsl, S.R.C.
Prior to 1959 6/7/60

CORDEAU 183894
Detonating fuse
Ensign-Bickford Company
1914 5/6/24

CORDEAU BICKFORD 183893
Detonating fuse
Ensign-Bickford Company
1914 5/6/24

COUGAR 657335
Pistols
J.L. Galef & Son, Inc.
5/20/52 1/21/58

CRACK SHOT 173158
Rifles
Savage Arms Corporation
1/1/1900 9/18/23

CRANBERRY *and picture of a horseshoe* 86426
Firearms
C. M. McClung Co.
1882 5/7/12

CROSMAN *and design of target* 617687
Air and gas guns, etc.
Crosman Arms Company, Inc.
1925 12/20/55

Continued on following page

CROWN	428276
Guns and parts	
The L.C. Smith Gun Company, Inc.	
1912	3/18/47

CROWN PRINCE	674052
Firearms	
The Marlin Firearms Company	
8/1/58	2/17/59

C.R.P.	655139
Air and gas guns	
Crosman Arms Company, Inc.	
8/5/56	12/3/57

CUB	655908
Pistols	
Astra, Unceta y Cia, S.A.	
Prior to 1957	8/19/58

CUTTS *within a diamond outline*	268328
Compensator for firearms	
Richard M. Cutts	
1/1/29	3/11/30

CYCLONE	695898
Shotgun chokes	
Hartford Gun Choke Co., Inc.	
6/11/58	4/12/60

DAISY	82309
Air rifles	
Daisy Manufacturing Company	
1889	6/20/11

DAISY	695896
Air rifles, parts, B.B. shot and accessories	
Daisy Manufacturing Company	
7/1/1889	4/12/60

DAKOTA	834222
Revolvers and parts	
Intercontinental Arms, Inc.	
8/6/62	8/29/67

DEERSLAYER	693008
Rifles and shotguns	
Ithaca Gun Company, Inc.	
1/2/59	2/16/60

DEFENDER	396205
Air rifles	
Daisy Manufacturing Company	
1/22/42	6/30/42

DEFIANCE	212211
Ammunition	
Remington Arms Company, Inc.	
October 1924	4/27/26

DETECTIVE SPECIAL	267150
Revolvers	
Colt's Manufacturing Company	
1/6/26	2/11/30

DIAMONDBACK	834943
Pistols and revolvers	
Colt's, Inc.	
5/27/66	9/12/67

DIANA *with representation of a figure*	560458
Air guns	
Millard Brothers Ltd.	
October 1948	6/24/52

D-MANTEL *and design*	650346
Explosives, ammunition, etc.	
Dynamit-Actien-Gesellschaft	
Prior to 1955	8/20/57

DOMINION	774801
Ammunition	
Canadian Industries, Limited	
Prior to 1913	8/11/64

DOUBLE-NINE	673727
Revolvers and parts	
The High Standard Manufacturing Co.	
4/12/58	2/10/59

DREAD NAUGHT	173958
Shotguns	
Savage Arms Corp.	
1/1/13	10/2/23

DUAL-CORE	762463
Cartridges and bullets	
Antiebolaget, Norma Projektilfabrik	
Oct. 1961	12/31/63

DUO-VENT	757570
Shotgun chokes	
Hartford Gun Choke Co., Inc.	
6/28/61	10/1/63

DU PONT *in an oval outline*	616031
Firearms and ammunition	
E. I. duPont de Nemours & Co.	
8/17/33	11/15/55

Continued on following page

DU PONT FNH   295517
Military Smokeless Powder
E. I. duPont de Nemours and Company
8/13/23   7/5/32

DU PONT MX   298331
Smokeless shotgun powder
E. I. duPont de Nemours and Company
12/11/31   10/25/32

DU PONT NH   295518
Military Smokeless Powder
E. I. duPont de Nemours and Company
10/4/27   7/5/32

DURA-MATIC   630250
Pistols and parts
The High Standard Manufacturing Corp.
9/3/54   7/10/56

DWM *and design*   354202
Firearms, explosives, etc.
Deutsche Waffen and Munitionsfabriken
Aktiengesellschaft
Prior to 1936   2/8/38

DYNA-MAGIC   656679
Barrel chokes
The Multy-Choke Company
1/28/57   1/7/58

EBL *on design of shield*   53747
Cartridges
Eley Brothers Limited
August 1874   6/12/06

E.C.
Smokeless powder
E. I. duPont de Nemours and Company
1884   2/9/09

ECONOMAX   673042
Shotgun shells
Alcan Shells, Inc.
1/29/58   1/27/59

EIG *in design form*   718081
Firearms
Saul Eig d/b/as Eig Cutlery
5/20/57   7/11/61

ELB *with design*   49434
Cartridges
Imperial Metal Industries, Ltd.
August 1874   2/6/06

ELEY GRAND PRIX   711411
Shotgun cartridges
Imperial Chemical Industries Ltd.
1904   2/21/61

E. REMINGTON *and his portrait*   91602
Cartridges, etc.
Remington Arms Co., Inc.
12/1/11   5/13/13

EXCELSIOR   48217
Cartridges
American Smelting & Refining Co.
8/20/1885   12/19/05

EXCELSIOR   774802
Shotguns and shells
Fabbriche Italo-Americane Montaggi,
S.p.A.
7/15/61   8/11/64

EXPLORER   707090
Firearms
Fairchild Engine and Airplane Corporation
12/14/59   11/15/60

EXPRESS *and design*   200954
Ammunition
Remington Arms Company
11/12/24   7/14/25

EZ FIT GRIP   715190
Hand grips
Anthony Manzo
7/1/59   5/9/61

EZXS   327755
Ammunition
Winchester Repeating Arms Company
1/5/35   9/3/35

EZXS *on a W*   755303
Rifle and pistol cartridges
Olin Mathieson Chemical Corporation
9/1/61   8/27/63

FEATHERLIGHT   54130
Firearms and parts
Ithaca Gun Company, Inc.
1938   4/17/51

Continued on following page

FEATHERLIGHT   770201
Firearms and accessories
Ithaca Gun Company, Inc.
1938   5/26/64

FEDERAL   729948
Ammunition and components
Federal Cartridge Company
9/1/18   4/17/62

FELTAN-BLUESTREAK   679473
Shot shell wads
Alcan Paper Co., Inc.
1/29/58   6/2/59

FIELD   169970
Shot shells
Western Cartridge Company
1905   7/10/23

FIELDMASTER   346422
Firearms
Remington Arms Company, Inc.
9/17/36   5/25/37

FIELD TRIAL   792454
Gun accessories
Seaford Associates, Inc.
8/30/62   7/13/65

FINNBEAR   757571
Rifles
Firearms International Corp.
12/12/60   10/1/63

FIN 'N FEATHER CLUB   633003
Guns
Max McGraw d/b as Fin 'n Feather Club
7/6/55   8/21/56

FIRE BALL   797013
Ammunition
Remington Arms Company, Inc.
3/11/63   10/5/65

FITWELL   687043
Gun grips and handles
Marwyn Company
6/16/58   10/27/59

FITZ   630249
Firearms accessories and ammunition
reloading equipment
Allan F. Barney d/b/ as Fitz
12/30/53   7/10/56

FITZ AMMOSAFE *and design*   655142
Cartridge containers
Allan F. Barney
7/17/56   12/3/57

FLITE-KING   647687
Pistols and parts
The High Standard Manufacturing Corp.
8/26/53   7/2/57

FLITE-MAX   769363
Shot cups for shotgun cartridges
Alcan Company, Inc.
7/3/63   5/12/64

FLYERMAX   688544
Shotgun shells
Alcan Shells, Inc.
4/10/59   11/24/59

FN *in an oval outline*   588170
Firearms and ammunition
Fabrique Nationale d'Armes de Guerre
Societe Anonyme
8/4/06   4/13/54

FN *on design of butt plate*   248671
Automatic shotguns
J.M. & M.S. Browning Company
August 1923   10/30/28

FOIL   803319
Gas gun in pressurized container
Hill-Sentry of New England, Inc.
1/5/65   2/8/66

FORESTER   757572
Rifles
Firearms International Corp.
5/10/58   10/1/63

FOX   595060
Firearms and parts
Savage Arms Corp.
6/1/30   9/14/54

FRANZITE   419306
Grips, butt plates, etc.
Sports, Inc.
March 1940   2/12/46

Continued on following page

FRED PALMER'S POSITIVE SHOOT-   735857
ING
   Air rifles
   Fred N. Palmer d/b/ as Fred Palmer's
   Positive Shooting
   7/19/60   8/14/62

FRONTIER   622874
   Firearms and parts
   American Weapons Corporation
   3/25/55   3/13/56

FRONTIER SCOUT   755785
   22 Caliber pistols and revolvers
   Colt's Patent Fire Arms Manufacturing
   Company, Inc.
   1870 as to "Frontier"   9/3/63

FRONTIER SIX SHOOTER   626062
   Revolvers and parts
   American Weapons Corporation
   3/15/55   5/1/56

FULTON   425905
   Guns and parts
   The L.C. Smith Gun Company, Inc.
   1920   12/3/46

GALESI   663328
   Firearms
   Industria Armi Galesi
   1910   6/24/58

GALAHAD   153192
   Firearms
   Hadfields, Ltd.
   2/22/18   3/14/22

GAME GETTER   736646
   Guns and accessories
   Marble Arms Corp.
   3/31/10   8/28/62

GAMEMASTER   336056
   Firearms
   Remington Arms Company, Inc.
   1/17/36   6/23/36

GAMEMAX   718078
   Shotgun shells
   Alcan Shells, Inc.
   6/26/59   7/11/61

GARRETT *and design*   836956
   Ammunition feed boosters for machine guns, etc.
   The Garrett Corporation
   12/5/55   10/24/67

GEVARM *on black diamond background*   678306
   Rifles and rifle ammunition
   Gevelot Societe Anonyme
   5/14/54   5/12/59

GEVELOT   678307
   on a black diamond background
   Rifles and rifle ammunition
   Gevelot Societe Anonyme
   2/18/33   5/12/59

GLENFIELD   827078
   Guns
   The Marlin Firearms Company
   3/7/60   4/11/67

GOLDEN PHEASANT *and pheasant design*   64355
   Gunpowder
   E. I. duPont de Nemours Company
   1886   8/6/07

GOLD-N-LINE   700769
   Recoil pads, butt plates and spacers
   Pachymyr Gun Works, Inc.
   6/15/56   7/12/60

GREEN DOT   816827
   Smokeless shotgun powder
   Hercules Powder Company
   5/19/65   10/18/66

"GUARDSMAN"   671695
   Revolvers
   Harrington & Richardson, Inc.
   8/11/52   12/30/58

GUN ALL *with design of target*   799366
   Gun cleaning kits
   John W. Romaine
   8/1/63   11/30/65

GUN-CADDY   798219
   Rifle holster
   Marketable Ideas, Inc.
   1/30/64   10/26/65

GUNSLICK   714592
   Gun cleaning rods
   Outers Laboratories, Inc.
   June 1938   5/2/61

GYRO-JET   799701
   Sub-miniature ballistic rockets
   MB Associates
   4/7/61   12/7/65

Continued on following page

Table XXIII, Continued

H   44939
Cartridges
Olin Mathieson Chemical Corp.
                              8/1/05

"HAMMER THE HAMMER",   333293
illustrated
Firearms
Iver Johnson's Arm & Cycle Works
6/1/04   3/17/36

HANDICAP   196345
Ammunition
Remington Arms Company, Inc.
10/3/24   3/17/25

HARVEY .224 KAY-CHUK   697664
Handguns
Lakeville Arms Incorporated
8/27/57   5/17/60

HAWKEYE   766973
Pistols and revolvers
Sturm, Ruger & Company, Inc.
1/24/63   3/21/64

HAWKINS   428614
Recoil pads
The Cushion Pad Company
5/25/25   3/25/47

HAWTHORNE   746098
Firearms, ammunition and accessories
Montgomery Ward & Company, Inc.
7/15/58   3/5/63

H C BENJAMIN   648062
Pellets for air and CO_2 guns
Benjamin Air Rifle Company
5/8/41   7/9/57

HELLCAT   411741
Firearms and ammunition
Remington Arms Company, Inc.
6/17/44   1/30/45

HERCO   225253
Smokeless shotgun powder
Hercules Powder Company
7/9/26   3/15/27

HERCULES 2400   364632
Smokeless Powder
Hercules Powder Company
8/4/32   2/7/39

HERCULES RED DOT *on disc design*   377116
Propellent powder
Hercules Powder Company
10/26/39   4/16/40

HERCULES RED DOT   378961
Propellent powder
Hercules Powder Company
5/14/34   6/25/40

HERTER'S   638276
Gunshells, ammunition, parts, accessories, etc.
Herter's, Inc.
1/15/46   12/11/56

HIAWATHA   703763
Firearms
Gamble-Skogmo, Inc.
1/12/60   9/16/60

HIAWATHA (*in script*)   549284
Rifle cartridges
Gamble-Skogmo, Inc.
May 1949   10/9/51

HIGHWAY PATROLMAN   618465
Revolvers
Smith & Wesson, Inc.
4/15/54   1/3/56

HIJ *and concentric circles*   652254
Firearms and accessories
Sloan's Sporting Goods Company, Inc.
8/8/56   10/11/57

HI-POWER   588990
Ammunition
Federal Cartridge Corporation
9/1/18   4/27/54

HI-POWER *with design*   548328
Ammunition
Federal Cartridge Corporation
3/8/41   9/18/51

HI SHOK   765673
Bullets
Federal Cartridge Corporation
11/30/62   2/25/64

Continued on following page

HI-SKOR   740468
Smokeless powder
E. I. DuPont de Nemours and Company
11/9/61   11/13/62

HI-SPEED *distinctively printed*   201528
Ammunition
Remington Arms Company, Inc.
7/1/24   7/28/25

HI-STANDARD *and figure of an eagle*   608175
Pistols and parts
The High Standard Manufacturing Corp.
7/1/50   7/15/55

HI-STANDARD   535463
Pistols and parts
The High Standard Manufacturing Corp.
10/1/32   12/26/50

HIVEL   93598
Smokeless powder
Hercules Powder Company
4/18/13   9/30/13

HK   765314
Firearms and components
Heckler & Koch G. m.b.H.
Prior to 1962   2/25/64

H-MANTEL *with design*   664249
Explosives, ammunition, etc.
Dynamit-Actien-Gesellschaft
Prior to 1955   7/15/58

HOPPE'S *with target and gun design*   717070
Gun cleaning patches
Frank A. Hoppe, Inc.
1935   6/20/61

HOPPE'S *with design*   800152
Gun cleaning, patches, rods, etc.
Frank A. Hoppe, Inc.
10/14/60   12/14/65

HOPPE'S   638326
Gun cleaning patches and rods
Frank A. Hoppe, Inc.
September 1934   11/20/56

H & R ARMS CO.   66950
Shotguns, rifles and revolvers
Harrington & Richardson Arms Company
5/1/07   1/7/08

H & R ARMS COMPANY *on black disk*   535317
Firearms
Harrington & Richardson Arms Company
11/1/1899   12/26/50

H & R REISING   682050
Rifles and submachine guns
Harrington & Richardson, Inc.
1/2/41   7/21/59

HUDSON BAY   742842
Gun cases
Herter's, Inc.
November 1961   1/1/63

HUNTER   427699
Guns and parts
The L.C. Smith Gun Company, Inc.
1893   2/18/47

"HUNTSMAN"   809099
Shotguns
Harrington & Richardson, Inc.
8/6/56   5/31/66

HUSKY   748630
Firearms
Tradewinds, Inc.
3/23/62   4/30/63

HUSQVARNA   709819
Firearms
Husqvarna Vapenfabriks Akriebolag
1867   1/17/61

HYCON   603805
Rockets for propelling aircraft and
military projectiles
Hycon Manufacturing Company
11/15/51   3/29/55

HYDRO-COIL   776845
Recoil assemblies
Hydro-Coil, Inc.
7/15/63   9/15/64

Continued on following page

Table XXIII, Continued

HY-GUN   217646
Recoil pads for gunstocks
Jostam Manufacturing Co.
2/26/26   9/7/26

HYMAX   696268
Shotgun and small arms ammunition
Imperial Chemical Industries, Limited
Prior to 1958   4/9/60

I.C.I.   652934
Arms, ammunition, etc.
Imperial Chemical Industries Ltd.
Prior to 1941   10/15/57

IDEAL   116866
Loading Implements for cartridges
The Lyman Gun Sight Corp.
1887   5/29/17

IDEAL   710768
Ammunition loading and reloading equipment
The Lyman Gun Sight Corporation
1886   2/7/61

IMPERIAL   738096
Firearms
The High Standard Manufacturing Corp.
8/17/61   9/25/62

INDIAN *with rifle design*   64360
Gun powder
Hazard Powder Co.
1876   8/6/07

INNER-BELTED   716324
Ammunition
Remington Arms Company, Inc.
Jan. 1939   6/6/61

INSTINCT SHOOTING *with gun design*   804959
Small caliber rifles
Bobby Lamar (Lucky) McDaniel
8/1/64   3/8/66

INTERARMCO *and design*   671690
Firearms and ammunition
Interarmco Ltd.
June 1954   12/30/58

INTERNATIONAL   748626
Firearms
International Guns, Inc.
3/16/62   4/30/63

ITHACA   559787
Shotguns
Ithaca Gun Company, Inc.
1880   6/10/52

ITHACA (*block letters*)   776021
Shotguns and rifles
Ithaca Gun Company, Inc.
6/10/52   9/1/64

ITHACA (*block letters*)   827454
Firearms
Ithaca Gun Company, Inc.
1880   4/18/67

ITHACA RAYBAR   680633
Sight mechanism for shotguns and rifles
Ithaca Gun Company, Inc.
1/1/55   6/23/59

IVER JOHNSON   231365
Revolvers and shotguns
Iver Johnson's Arm & Cycle Works
9/1/1894   8/16/27

JAVETTE   803705
Sub-miniature ballistic rockets
MB Associates
9/29/64   2/15/66

J.C. HIGGINS (*in script*)   589858
Firearms and accessories
Sears Roebuck and Company
1/15/46   5/18/54

JEEP   411784
Shotguns and rifles
Charles S. Wheatley
September 1943   1/20/45

JET   736647
Ammunition
Remington Arms Company, Inc.
5/24/61   8/28/62

JET-AWAY   813283
Shotgun choke
Bernard Weiser
2/18/65   8/23/65

JETFIRE   687040
Pistols
J.L. Galef & Son, Inc.
4/29/52   10/27/59

Continued on following page

Table XXIII, Continued

JGR GUN SPORT   761199
Guns, ammunition, parts and accessories
JGR Gunsport Ltd.
Prior to 1961   12/10/63

JUNIOR SPECIAL   441503
Firearms and parts
Remington Arms Company, Inc.
2/24/47   11/30/48

K *within concentric circles*   406325
Machine gun chargers
Walter Kidde & Company, Inc.
October 1942   3/28/44

KANT-SPLASH *on an X*   795857
Cartridges
Olin Mathieson Chemical Corporation
7/1/60   9/14/65

KENTUCKY RIFLE GUNPOWDER   58013
and design
Gunpowder
DuPont Company
1886   12/4/06

KING   64855
Air rifles
Daisy Manufacturing Company
12/1/1890   8/27/07

KLAY BIRD   776846
Ammunition
Remington Arms Company, Inc.
8/23/40   9/15/64

KLEANBORE   223998
Ammunition
Remington Arms Company
10/7/26   2/15/27

KLEANBORE *and design*   223997
Ammunition
Remington Arms Company
10/7/26   2/15/27

KLEEN-TEST   415735
Firearms and ammunition
Oakes & Co., (also as Tru-Test)
5/25/44   8/14/45

KNOCK-ABOUT   54954
Shotguns
Abercrombie & Fitch Co.
1896   8/7/06

KRUMBLE BALL   616735
Ammunition
Remington Arms Company, Inc.
4/14/33   11/29/55

KRUZELL *and design with scope*   638207
Scope mounts
George R. Kruzell d/b Kruzell Gunsmithing Works
4/20/55   12/4/56

KWIK-SERT   770203
Shot cups for shotgun cartridges
Alcan Company, Inc.
6/4/63   5/26/64

LAFLIN & RAND   58022
Explosive powder
Hercules Powder Company
8/21/1869   12/4/06

LANCER   714038
Firearms
"Star" Bonifacio Echeverria, S.A.
1956   4/18/61

LA SALLE   714037
Shotguns
Firearms International Corp.
7/24/58   4/18/61

LATIGO   676554
Rifle and shotgun slings
Frank Royce Brownell II, d/b/
Bob Brownell's
2/23/57   4/7/59

L.C. SMITH   427698
Guns and parts
The L.C. Smith Gun Company, Inc.
1893   2/18/47

LEADER   47351
Paper shell cartridges
Olin Industries, Inc.
4/19/1894   10/31/05

LEADER IN THE FIELD   791244
Firearm equipment
Buddy Schoellkopf Products, Inc.
3/1/53   6/22/65

LECCO   764893
Chemical warfare guns, shells, etc.
The Lake Erie Chemical Company
1935   2/18/64

Continued on following page

Table XXIII, Continued

LEVERMATIC   616402
Guns
The Marlin Firearms Company
10/11/54   11/22/55

LIFE SAVING SERVICE   58012
Cannon powder
Du Pont Company
1886   12/4/06

LIFETYME   722477
Reloading dies
Paul C. Knepp, d.b.a. Carbide Die & Mfg. Co.
Sept. 1946   10/20/61

LIGHTNING   669479
Pistols
J. L. Galef & Son, Inc.
12/8/56   11/11/58

LIGHTNING   61984
Powder for small arms
Lufkin & Rand Powder Co.
1898   4/16/07

LITTLE ATOM   594091
Miniature blank cartridge firing pistols
and blank cartridges
Gold-Silver & Company, Inc.
11/25/50   8/24/54

LLAMA   722476
Pistols
Gabilondo and Company
6/6/50   10/10/61

LONGHORN   737715
Firearms
The High Standard Manufacturing Corp.
9/2/60   9/18/62

LUBALOY   153054
Bullets
Western Cartridge Company
1/1/21   3/7/22

LUBALOY   153053
Bullets
Olin Mathieson Chemical Corp.
1/1/21   3/7/22

LUBALOY   500211
Bullets
Olin Industries, Inc.
1/1/21   5/11/48

LUB-RA SEAL *in a circle*   737714
For lubricating shot shell over powder wads
Carl C. Cook
6/10/61   9/18/62

LUCKY McDANIEL *and design*   804959
Small caliber rifles
Bobby Lamar (Lucky) McDaniel
8/1/64   3/8/66

LUGER   269834
Firearms and parts
A.F. Stoeger, Inc.
2/1/1895   4/22/30

LYMAN   64526
Gun sights
The Lyman Gun Sight Corp.
1885   8/13/07

LYMAN   721211
Ammunition loading equipment and muzzle devices
The Lyman Gun Sight Corporation
October 1947   9/12/61

MAGICLICK   721503
Shotgun barrel cleaners
Minnesota Rubber Company
7/28/60   9/19/61

MAGNAMAX   662423
Shotgun shells
Alcan Company, Inc.
9/28/56   6/3/58

MAGNUM   324894
Revolvers
Smith & Wesson, Inc.
12/28/34   6/4/35

".357" MAGNUM   323654
Revolvers
Smith & Wesson, Inc.
12/28/34   4/23/35

MANNLICHER SCHOENAUER   535120
Rifles
Stoeger Arms Corporation
2/1/47   12/19/50

MARAUDER   748625
Firearms.
The Marlin Firearms Company
2/13/62   4/30/63

Continued on following page

Table XXIII, Continued

MARBLE'S   507352
Guns, sights, and accessories
Marble Arms Manufacturing Company
4/1/11   3/8/49

MARK V   710119
Firearms
Weatherby's, Inc.
8/1/58   1/24/61

MARK XXII   810346
Rifles
Weatherby's, Inc.
January 1962   6/28/66

MARKSMAN   212602
Rifle cartridges
Olin Industries, Inc.
7/1/21   5/11/26

MARKSMAN   173149
Rifles
Savage Arms Corp.
1/1/12   9/18/23

MARLIN   55158
Shotguns, rifles and revolvers
Marlin Firearms Company
1870   8/7/06

MATADOR   757574
Firearms, air guns and parts
Aguirrey Aranzabal S.R.C.
Prior to 1962   10/1/63

MATCHMASTER   358968
Firearms
Remington Arms Company Inc.
3/31/38   7/26/38

MATCH TARGET *with target design*   736236
Automatic pistols
Colt's Patent Fire Arms Manufacturing
Company, Inc.
7/7/38   8/21/62

MATCH TARGET   522532
Automatic pistols
Colt's Manufacturing Company
6/7/38   3/21/50

MATCH TARGET   388938
Automatic pistols
Colt's Patent Fire Arms Manufacturing
Company, Inc.
6/7/38   7/15/41

MATCH TARGET *with outline of a target*   388937
Automatic pistols
Colt's Patent Fire Arms Manufacturing
Company, Inc.
6/7/38   7/15/41

MAUSER   608135
Firearms and ammunition
Mauser Kommandit-Gesellschaft
Prior to 1953   6/28/55

MAUSER *and design*   807725
Firearms, accessories, ammunition and
ordnance
Mauser-Werke Aktiengesellshaft
Prior to 1961   5/3/66

MAUSER *with design*   727864
Firearms and ammunition
Mauser-Werke Aktengesellschaft
Prior to 1925   2/27/62

MAUSER-OBERNDORF   807724
Firearms, accessories, ammunition and
ordnance
Mauser-Werke Aktiengesellshaft
Prior to 1962   5/3/66

MAX-FIRE   717071
Shot shell primers
Alcan Company, Inc.
5/4/59   6/20/61

MAXIFLUX   418878
Electrical apparatus for firing mechanism
of guns
Dunlop Rubber Company, Ltd.
February 1944   1/15/46

MAXIFORT   418879
Electrical apparatus for firing mechanism
of guns
Dunlop Rubber Company, Ltd.
February 1944   1/15/46

MAX-SPEED   769802
Shotgun shells
Alcan Company, Inc.
7/9/63   5/19/64

"MEDALIST"   805410
Rifles
Harrington & Richardson, Inc.
September 1946   3/15/66

Continued on following page

MERCURY 680255
Firearms
Tradewinds, Inc.
8/24/55 6/16/59

M.F.A. CO. 56280
Shotguns, rifles and revolvers
Marlin Firearms Company
1881 9/4/06

MICRO CHOKE 688490
Chokes and guns with chokes
The Marlin Firearms Company
4/15/57 11/17/59

MICRO-GROOVE 579235
Firearms
The Marlin Firearms Company
5/16/52 8/25/53

MIDVALE 288603
Naval and Army guns, projectiles
The Midvale Company
3/1/1881 11/3/31

MINIMAX 139426
Shot shells, cartridges, etc.
Olin Mathieson Chemical Corp.
7/10/19 2/1/21

MINX 687443
Pistols
J.L. Galef & Son, Inc.
6/10/52 11/3/59

MOLD-TITE 719098
Wads for shot shells
Remington Arms Company, Inc.
10/4/60 8/1/61

MONARK 509767
Ammunition
Federal Cartridge Corp.
9/15/25 5/10/49

MONARK *with figure of a duck* 639894
Shotgun shells and air rifle shot
Federal Cartridge Corporation
9/1/18 1/15/57

MONTE CARLO 522484
Firearms, air guns parts and accessories
J.L. Galef & Son, Inc.
1923 3/21/50

MOOSE BRAND 530383
with representation of a moose's head
Gun and ammunition carriers, etc.
Brauer Brothers Manufacturing Co.
1898 9/5/50

MOSSBERG 513951
Firearms and parts
O.F. Mossberg & Sons, Inc.
January 1937 8/23/49

MOUNTIE 583967
Rifles and parts
The Marlin Firearms Company
12/24/52 12/22/53

MULTY-CHOKE 606176
Shotgun chokes
The Multy-Choke Company
3/1/50 5/17/55

MUSKETEER 760889
Rifles
Firearms International Corp.
5/1/62 12/3/63

MUSTANG 416686
Firearms
Colt's Patent Fire Arms Manufacturing
Company
1/19/45 9/25/45

MUSTANG 832056
Rifles
Colt's Inc.
1/7/66 7/18/67

N A CO. *in an anchor and cannon design* 738098
Replicas of Civil War weapons
Navy Arms Company, Inc.
1/15/59 9/25/62

NATCHEZ 737716
Firearms
The High Standard Manufacturing Corp.
9/2/60 9/18/62

NATIONAL MATCH 295029
Pistols
Colt's Manufacturing Company
2/12/32 6/14/32

Continued on following page

NEW CHIEF	98601
Cartridges, etc.	
Western Cartridge Company	
2/16/06	7/21/14
NEW CLUB	49610
Cartridges and shells	
Remington Arms Company, Inc.	
December 1891	2/13/06
NEW RIVAL	44938
Paper shell cartridges	
Winchester Repeating Arms Company	
1/25/1899	8/1/05
NEW SERVICE	32536
Firearms	
Colt's Manufacturing Company	
June 1898	2/21/99
NEW SERVICE	50585
Pistols	
Colt's Inc.	
June 1898	3/27/06
NITRO CLUB	49606
Cartridges and shells	
Remington Arms Co. Inc.	
2/25/01	2/13/06
NITRO EXPRESS	216743
Ammunition	
Remington Arms Company, Inc.	
2/19/26	8/17/26
NO KICK COMING	508315
Recoil pads	
Jostam Manufacturing Company	
1914	4/5/49
NORKA	149388
Gun recoil pads for rifles, etc.	
B.F. Goodrich Company	
1913	12/31/21
NORMA	609388
Ammunition and components	
Aktiebolaget Norma Projektifabrik	
1/15/49	7/26/55
NOROC	835763
Protective personnel, etc. armor	
Norton Company	
12/6/65	9/26/67

NUBLACK	45730
Shot shells and cartridges	
Olin Industries, Inc.	
3/9/05	8/29/05
NUM-RITE	774800
Livestock stunning cartridges	
Olin Mathieson Chemical Corporation	
12/14/62	8/11/64
NYDAR	430175
Non-telescope gun sights	
Swain Nelson Company	
11/2/45	6/10/47
O *and design*	45249
Cartridges	
Olin Industries, Inc.	
5/1/1884	8/8/05
OERLIKON *and design*	609797
Firearms, parts and ammunition	
Oerlikon Machine Tool Works, Buehrle &	
Company	
Prior to 1943	8/2/55
OFFICERS MODEL	522531
Revolvers	
Colt's Manufacturing Company	
1904	3/21/50
OFFICIAL POLICE	522530
Revolvers	
Colt's Manufacturing Company	
5/13/27	3/21/50
O.F. MOSSBERG & SONS INC.	511758
Firearms and parts	
O.F. Mossberg & Sons, Inc.	
March 1945	7/5/49
O.K.H.	395647
Cartridges	
O'Neil, Keith and Hopkins	
1/1/38	6/2/42
OLYMPIC	562299
Pistols and parts	
The High Standard Manufacturing Corp.	
10/14/49	7/29/52
OL' SARGE *with representation of a man*	443614
Gun equipment such as cleaning rods	
Universal Engineering Company	
1/4/46	12/13/49

Continued on following page

ORANGE EXTRA   57995
Gun powder
Hercules Powder Company
1881   12/4/06

OZITE   247789
Gun wadding
American Hair Felt Company
6/12/28   10/2/28

P *in a circle*   68209
Ammunition
Remington Arms Company, Inc.
January 1895   3/17/08

PACHMAYR *(script)*   803320
Gun accessories
Pachmayr Gun Works, Inc.
1931   2/8/66

PACKAGED POWER   661265
Gas generating cartridges
Olin Mathieson Chemical Corp.
9/1/54   2/18/58

PALMA   195472
Ammunition
Remington Arms Company, Inc.
October 1921   2/24/25

PALOMINO   694100
Rifles and parts
O.F. Mossberg & Sons, Inc.
5/27/59   3/8/60

PARASHOOT   400433
Automatic firearms
Harrington & Richardson Arms Company
9/14/42   3/9/43

P. BERETTA *with design*   704153
Firearms
Fabbrica d'Armi P. Beretta, S.P.A.
Prior to 1959   9/13/60

PEACEMAKER   626745
Revolvers and parts
American Weapons Corporation
3/25/55   5/15/56

PEACEMAKER SIX SHOOTER   626063
Revolvers and parts
American Weapons Corporation
3/25/55   5/1/56

PEERLESS   608174
Firearms parts
Stoeger Arms Corporation
3/1/34   7/5/55

PELLGUN   617688
Air and gas guns, etc.
Crosman Arms Company, Inc.
5/7/54   12/20/55

PETERS   60728
Cartridges
Remington Arms, Inc.
1/1/1888   2/19/07

PETERS   324506
Ammunition
Remington Arms Company, Inc.
1/1/1888   5/21/35

PETERS VICTOR NO 12 *and design*   192015
Shotgun shells
Remington Arms Company, Inc.
1895   11/25/64

PGS   725228
Shotshell wads
Alcan Company, Inc.
2/28/61   12/19/61

PHILIP'S   541100
Gun swivels
Philip Magid
11/1/39   4/17/51

PIC *and scene with pickax*   736235
Firearms
Precise Imports Corp.
12/9/54   8/21/62

PLAINSMAN   712711
Pistols
Healthways
1950   3/21/61

PLINKERS *with design*   726419
Bullets
Vernon D. Speer
3/2/61   1/16/62

PLINK-O-MATIC   739886
Air guns
Crosman Arms Company, Inc.
9/12/61   10/30/62

Continued on following page

PMC THE CALIFORNIAN (*script*)   741487
Gunstocks
Carl Richard Peterson d/b as Peterson
Machine Carving
3/13/61   12/4/62

POCKET POSITIVE   50125
Pistols
Colt's Inc.
7/12/05   3/6/06

POLICE POSITIVE   50460
Pistols
Colt's, Inc.
7/12/05   3/20/06

POLICE POSITIVE SPECIAL   285374
Revolvers
Colt's Manufacturing Company
8/4/08   7/28/31

POLY CHOKE   436169
Barrel chokes
The Poly Choke Company, Inc.
1/1/32   1/27/48

POLY-MATIC   667919
Barrel choking devices
The Poly Choke Company, Inc.
9/30/57   10/7/58

POLYVENT   758589
Shotgun chokes
Hartford Gun Choke Company, Inc.
7/26/61   10/15/63

PONY   416687
Firearms
Colt's Patent Fire Arms Manufacturing
Company
1/19/45   9/25/45

POSSE   737717
Firearms
The High Standard Manufacturing Corp.
9/2/60   9/18/62

POWERLET   612019
Power cylinders for gas powered firearms
Crosman Arms Company, Inc.
6/11/54   9/13/55

POWER-LOKT   818517
Ammunition
Remington Arms Company, Inc.
7/22/65   11/15/66

POWER-MATIC   617689
Firearms
Remington Arms Company, Inc.
12/28/54   12/20/55

POWER-POINT   697326
Ammunition
Olin Mathieson Chemical Corporation
7/16/59   5/10/60

POWER WITHOUT POWDER   707312
Gas guns, projectiles and targets
Crosman Arms Company, Inc.
1926   11/15/60

POW-R-SET   762569
Powder loads
Olin Mathieson Chemical Corporation
3/16/61   1/7/64

"PRESENTATION MODEL"   819739
Recoil pads
Pachmayr Gun Works, Inc.
2/11/65   12/6/66

PRECISIONEERED   776018
Reloading equipment
R.C.B.S., Inc.
9/18/61   9/1/64

PROTECTO KADDY *and design*   834946
Plastic gun carrying cases
Protecto Plastic, Inc.
December 1962   9/12/67

PUMA   687442
Pistols
J.L. Galef & Son, Inc.
4/3/52   11/3/59

PYTHON   795431
Hand guns
Colt's, Inc.
6/2/55   9/7/65

"QUAILS FARGO"   767803
Shotguns
Simmons Gun Specialities, Inc.
10/14/62   4/7/64

QUICKIE   721757
Rear shotgun sight
P. W. Gray Co., Inc.
September 1958   9/26/61

Continued on following page

Table XXIII, Continued

R *on a shield*	606274
Ammunition	
Dynamit-Actien-Gesellschaft	
Prior to 1925	5/24/55
RANGEMASTER	336055
Firearms	
Remington Arms Company, Inc.	
1/17/36	6/23/36
RANGER	191702
Paper shot shells and cartridges	
Western Cartridge Co.	
2/1/18	11/18/24
RANGER	191722
Shot shells and cartridges	
Olin Mathieson Chemical Corp.	
2/1/18	11/18/24
RAYBAR	682379
Gun sights	
Ithaca Gun Company, Inc.	
6/11/54	7/28/59
RCBS	820178
Reloading tools	
RCBS, Inc.	
6/1/43	12/13/66
REBEL	689704
BB shot, air rifles	
International Distributors, Inc.	
April 1957	12/15/59
REDFIELD PRECISION *on reticule design*	771012
Sights, mounts and accessories	
Redfield Gun Sight Company	
1/10/62	6/9/64
RED HEAD	240827
Ammunition	
Montgomery Ward & Company, Inc.	
July 1922	4/10/28
REDI REST	810344
Firearm equipment	
Ten Ring Manufacturing Corp.	
10/9/64	6/28/66
REGENT	748634
Revolvers	
Firearms International Corp.	
8/8/61	4/30/63

RELODER *and design*	816841
Smokeless rifle powder	
Hercules Powder Company	
5/19/65	10/11/66
REMINGTON (*block letters*)	745041
Firearms and ammunition	
Remington Arms Company, Inc.	
Prior to 1889	2/12/63
REMINGTON	187871
Firearms	
Remington Arms Company, Inc.	
1889	8/12/24
REM U M C *in a circle*	94697
Paper shot shells	
Remington Arms Company, Inc.	
7/28/13	12/23/13
REMINGTON	60248
Shotguns, pistols, revolvers etc.	
Remington Arms Company, Inc.	
1/1/1888	1/29/07
REMINGTON UMC	133792
Firearms, etc.	
Remington Firearms Company	
2/1/11	8/3/20
REMINGTON U M C *in a red circle*	90304
Firearms	
Remington Arms Company, Inc.	
2/1/11	2/18/13
REMINGTON *on a red disk*	419302
Firearms and ammunition	
Remington Arms Company, Inc.	
1934	2/12/46
REPEATER	28463
Shotgun shells	
Olin Industries, Inc.	
March 1896	6/23/96
REVELATION	754867
Ammunition and gun cases	
Western Auto Supply Company	
5/15/54	8/20/63
REVELATION	706133
Firearms	
Western Auto Supply Company	
12/8/59	10/4/60

Continued on following page

Table XXIII, Continued

REVELATION	735537		**RWS-MAGNUM**	796615

REVELATION   735537
  Gun cleaning patches and kits
  Western Auto Supply Company
  3/8/61   8/7/62

RIFLE RANCH   757568
  Guns, parts and accessories
  James S. Williamson
  August 1947   10/1/63

RIFLE SPORT   430437
  Air rifles
  A.B.T. Manufacturing Corp.
  5/8/44   6/10/47

RIFLE SPORT *and outline of a target*   502753
  Air rifles
  A.B.T. Manufacturing Corp.
  3/1/45   10/5/48

RING-WAXED   716696
  Shot shell wads
  Alcan Company, Inc.
  1954   6/13/61

ROMAX   83451
  Cartridges
  United States Cartridge Company
  4/25/11   9/12/11

ROSSI   821744
  Revolvers
  Stoeger Arms Corporation
  7/10/65   1/31/67

ROTO FORGED   801163
  Shotguns and rifles
  Ithaca Gun Company, Inc.
  January 1963   1/4/66

RUBY   722475
  Revolvers
  Gabilondo and Company
  8/13/57   10/10/61

RUGER   618055
  Handguns and ammunition
  Strum, Ruger & Company, Inc.
  10/7/49   12/27/55

RWS *with figure of a man and legend*   740808
  Small arms ammunition
  Dynamit Nobel Aktiengesellschaft
  Prior to 1960   11/20/62

RWS-MAGNUM   796615
  Ammunition
  Dynamit Nobel-Genschow G.m.b.H
  Prior to 1862   9/28/65

S *within a design*   790579
  Machine guns, rifles, carbines and pistols
  Cadillac Gage Company
  5/31/62   6/8/65

SABLE   629354
  Revolvers
  J.L. Galef & Son, Inc.
  6/10/55   6/26/56

S A CO. *in design form*   733231
  Replicas of Civil War weapons
  Service Armament Company
  1/15/59   6/26/62

SADDLEGUN   740467
  Guns
  Ithaca Gun Company, Inc.
  11/1/60   11/13/62

SAFARI   748624
  Firearms
  Parker-Hale, Limited
  Prior to 1961   4/30/63

SANTA FE   697966
  Ammunition
  Golden State Arms Corporation
  7/7/59   5/24/60

SARASQUETA   731712
  Firearms
  Victor Sarasqueta S.A.
  7/13/09   5/22/62

SAVAGE   595059
  Firearms, ammunition and accessories
  Savage Arms Corporation
  7/1/06   9/14/54

SAVAGE *with Indian head design*   595393
  Firearms, and parts and ammunition
  Savage Arms Corp.
  1/15/39   9/21/54

SAVAGE QUALITY *and design*   100629
  Rifles, pistols, etc.
  Savage Arms Corp.
  1/1/06   10/20/14

Continued on following page

Table XXIII, Continued

SAVAGE	813282
Reloading equipment	
Emhart Corporation	
12/5/63	8/23/66
SCOREMASTER	354023
Firearms	
Remington Arms Company, Inc.	
9/10/37	1/24/38
SCOUT *in a rectangle*	87688
Cartridges	
Olin Industries, Inc.	
3/18/11	7/30/12
SEARS	732022
Explosives, firearms, ammunition, accessories, etc.	
Sears Roebuck and Company	
1/15/59	5/29/62
SECS PLASTIC AMMO *with design*	748622
Plastic bullets	
Systems, Engineering & Component Sales, Inc.	
1/12/62	4/30/63
SEDGLEY *within a shield*	405141
Firearms and parts	
R.F. Sedgley, Inc.	
5/15/43	1/11/44
SELBY	52629
Shot	
American Smelting & Refining Company	
1865	5/15/06
SENTINEL	621989
Pistols and parts	
The High Standard Manufacturing Corp.	
1/20/55	2/28/56
SHELL CRACKER	687444
Remote exploding, delayed action firearm projectiles	
United Commercial Company	
8/14/56	11/8/59
SHELLMASTER	710771
Shotgun shell loading devices	
Charles R. Heckman	
March 1958	2/7/61
SHELL PAC	651322
Shotgun shell holder	
S. Wallace Amundson	
8/20/65	9/3/57

"SHIRTPOCKET" *(script)*	703433
Cleaning implements for firearms	
Benjamin C. Higham	
9/1/59	8/30/60
SHOOTING MASTER	288610
Revolvers	
Colt's Manufacturing Co.	
5/4/31	11/3/31
"SIDE-KICK"	639533
Revolvers	
Harrington & Richardson, Inc.	
2/13/65	1/8/57
SIERRA *with scenic design*	560618
Bullets and front sight ramps	
Harris Machine Company	
1/31/46	6/24/52
SIG *in an oval outline*	612016
Firearms	
Swiss Industrial Company	
1931	9/13/55
SILVERTIP	602601
Rifle Cartridges	
Olin Industries, Inc.	
4/1/40	3/1/55
SINGLE-SIX	658423
Revolvers	
Sturm, Ruger & Company, Inc.	
12/15/53	2/18/58
SKEETMAX	674051
Shotgun shells	
Alcan Shells, Inc.	
6/18/58	2/17/59
SKEET "N" FIELD	714593
Gun holsters	
Michael Yavello	
7/20/60	5/2/61
SKODA	673042
Ordnance	
Zavody V. I. Lenina Plzen, Narodni Podnik	
Prior to 1956	1/27/59
SKYSHOOTER	748628
Fireworks	
Clipper Pyrotechnic Corp.	
1938	4/30/63

Continued on following page

SLUGSTER 765315
Gun barrels
O.F. Mossberg & Sons, Inc.
2/20/63 2/25/64

SMITH & WESSON 95164
Revolvers, etc.
Smith & Wesson, Inc.
1857 2/3/14

SNIPER 411742
Firearms and ammunition
Remington Arms Company, Inc.
6/17/44 1/30/45

SOURDOUGH 802924
Gun sights and mountings
Redfield Gun Sight Company
6/25/46 2/1/66

SPATTERPRUF 590038
Ammunition
Olin Industries, Inc.
7/11/32 5/18/54

SPECIALTY 437751
Guns and parts
The L.C. Smith Gun Company, Inc.
1912 3/30/48

SPEEDIES 818516
Reloading dies
Micro-Precision Company
2/1/64 11/15/66

SPEEDMASTER 336054
Firearms
Remington Arms Company, Inc.
1/17/36 6/23/36

SPIT 659209
Cartridges
Societe de Prospection et d'Inventions
Techniques Spit
Prior to 1953 3/11/58

SPITFIRE 411743
Firearms and ammunition
Remington Arms Company, Inc.
6/17/44 1/30/45

SPORT-KING 565238
Pistols and parts
The High Standard Manufacturing Corp.
12/26/50 10/14/52

SPORTMASTER 336058
Firearms
Remington Arms Company, Inc.
1/17/36 6/23/36

SPORTSMAN 279904
Firearms
Remington Arms Company, Inc.
9/5/30 2/31/31

SPORTSWAYS 836183
Shotgun shell reloading devices
Sportsways, Inc.
1/15/66 10/3/67

SPR 637586
Device for muzzle of a gun
Richard M. Cutts
1/1/46 11/27/56

SR, *intertwined* 546918
Pistols
Sturm, Ruger & Company, Inc.
10/13/49 8/21/51

STAG *with antler design* 770202
Rifle and shotgun stocks
Eugene D. Depue and Lester E. Depue
12/17/62 5/26/64

STAGECOACH 834947
Rifles
Colt's, Inc.
2/23/66 9/12/67

STANDARD 48379
Cartridges
American Smelting & Refining Company
7/30/1885 12/26/05

STAR *and star design* 683862
Firearms and ordnance
Star, Bonifacio Echeverria, S.A.
2/17/33 8/25/59

STARLET 729936
Firearms
"Star" Bonifacio Echeverria, S.A.
1956 4/17/62

STAYNLESS 231726
Ammunition
Winchester Repeating Arms Company
3/21/27 8/23/27

Continued on following page

Table XXIII, Continued

STAYSET 592552
Adjusting knobs for gun sights
The Lyman Gun Sight Corp.
3/10/48 7/13/54

STEVENS 91391
Firearms
Savage Arms Corp.
January 1864 4/29/13

STEYR *with a figure of concentric circles* 778667
Firearms
Steyr-Daimler-Puch Aktiengesellshaft
2/13/19 10/20/64

STOEGER 788361
Firearms, parts and attachments
Stoeger Arms Corporation
9/1/28 4/20/65

STORM KING 681665
Lens covers for scopes
Harvey B. Anderson d/b as The Anderson
Gun Shop
4/1/57 7/14/59

STUN SAFE 726418
Humane stunning cartridges
Remington Arms Company, Inc.
5/6/60 1/16/62

SUBMACHINE GUN *and design* 140320
Machine guns
Auto Ordnance Corp.
3/23/20 3/15/21

SUNSPOT 665589
Sights for firearms
The Poly Choke Company, Inc.
8/1/57 8/12/58

SUPER *imposed on an X* 500223
Ammunition
Olin Industries, Inc.
11/1/21 5/11/48

SUPER .38 AUTOMATIC 260616
Pistols
Colt's Manufacturing Company
2/11/29 8/27/29

SUPER B-B 792385
Air rifle shot
Crosman Arms Company, Inc.
1/28/64 7/6/65

SUPER BB REPEATER *with design* 686503
Gas rifles
Crosman Arms Company, Inc.
5/19/58 10/6/59

SUPER "C" 439108
Recoil reducing compensators
Olin Industries, Inc.
4/12/47 6/1/48

SUPERCLEEN 716694
Ammunition
Golden State Arms Corporation
7/7/59 6/13/61

SUPER KANT-SPLASH *on Y* 795858
Cartridges
Olin Mathieson Chemical Corporation
9/1/60 9/14/65

SUPER MATCH 565201
Ammunition
Olin Industries
4/7/33 10/14/52

SUPER-MATCH X *and design* 706173
Ammunition
Olin Mathieson Chemical Corporation
4/27/60 10/25/60

SUPERMATIC 566919
.22 caliber pistols and parts
The High Standard Manufacturing Corp.
2/28/51 11/18/52

SUPERMATIC CITATION 676846
Pistols and parts
The High Standard Manufacturing Corp.
2/8/58 4/14/59

SUPERMATIC TOURNAMENT 676845
Pistols and parts
The High Standard Manufacturing Corp.
2/8/58 4/14/59

SUPERMATIC TROPHY 676197
Pistols and parts
The High Standard Manufacturing Corp.
2/18/58 3/31/59

SUPERSINGLE 802421
Shotguns
Ithaca Gun Company, Inc.
August 1962 1/18/66

Continued on following page

Table XXIII, Continued

SUPER SPEED		530145
Ammunition		
Olin Industries, Inc.		
1930		9/15/50

SUPER-X — 573211
Ammunition
Olin Industries, Inc.
11/1/25 — 4/14/53

SUPER X *and design* — 159784
Shot shells
Olin Mathieson Chemical Corp.
11/1/21 — 10/3/22

"SUPREME"
Ammunition
Amerex Trading Corporation
12/30/60 — 2/18/64

SURE GRIP — 776019
Gun accessories
Firearms Accessories, Inc.
1931 — 9/1/64

S W — 93767
Revolvers, pistols, etc.
Smith & Wesson, Inc.
1/29/1879 — 10/14/13

SWAG-O-MATIC — 710770
Bullet-forming tools
Charles R. Heckman
3/19/60 — 2/7/61

TACK-HOLE — 153277
Cartridges
Remington Arms Corp, Inc.
2/8/21 — 3/14/22

TACKHOLE DOT *and target design* — 391643
Rifle sight
T.K. Lee
4/25/41 — 11/18/41

TARGET — 33053
Ammunition
Remington Arms Co.
5/1/1899 — 6/6/99

TARGET — 65656
Cartridges, shells, etc.
Remington Arms Company
5/1/1899 — 10/15/07

TARGET GRIP — 69039
Revolvers, pistols, etc.
Harrington & Richardson Arms Company
October 1907 — 5/19/08

TARGETEER — 518535
Air guns and parts
Daisy Manufacturing Company
4/20/37 — 12/6/49

TARGETMASTER — 364490
Firearms and ammunition
Remington Arms Company, Inc.
4/20/38 — 1/31/39

TARGO *with representation of a rifle* — 440820
Firearms and parts
O.F. Mossberg & Sons, Inc.
7/17/45 — 9/28/48

TED WILLIAMS *(block letters)* — 745615
Firearms ammunition and accessories
Sears Roebuck and Company
8/30/61 — 2/26/63

TED WILLIAMS — 745614
(script) and facsimile of face
Firearms ammunition and accessories
Sears Roebuck and Company
8/30/61 — 2/26/63

TED WILLIAMS *(script) in a design* — 746062
Firearms, ammunition and accessories
Sears Roebuck and Company
8/30/61 — 3/5/63

TEN-O-GRIP *on target design* — 651919
Firearms, accessories
Allan F. Barney d/b/ as Fitz
1/21/56 — 9/24/57

TEXAN — 609798
Firearms and parts
The Marlin Firearms Company
2/7/52 — 8/2/55

TEXAS RANGER — 632062
Pistol holsters and cartridge belts
Tex Tan of Yoakum
4/13/49 — 8/7/56

TEXLOAD — 771378
Shotgun shells
Vawter Ammunition, Inc.
9/25/62 — 6/16/64

Continued on following page

Table XXIII, Continued

"THE COLTEER 1-22"   678305
.22 caliber rifles
Colt's Patent Fire Arms Manufacturing
Company, Inc.
12/10/57   5/12/59

THE FRONTIER   753166
Revolvers
Colt's Patent Fire Arms Manufacturing
Company, Inc.
1870 as to "Frontier"   7/23/63

THE FRONTIER *and figure of a colt*   755302
Revolvers
Colt's Patent Fire Arms Manufacturing
Company, Inc.
1870 as to "Frontier"   8/27/63

THE MINUTEMAN   823264
Pellet air rifle
Precision Engineered Products Corp.
11/16/64   1/31/67

THE ORIGINAL SIGHT-EXCHANGE   383608
Telescopic sight
Wilbur P. Klapp, Jr.
5/31/40   12/17/40

THE PEACEMAKER   753165
Revolvers
Colt's Patent Fire Arms Manufacturing
Company, Inc.
1870 as to "Frontier"   7/23/63

THE PEACEMAKER *with figure of a colt*   757133
Revolvers
Colt's Patent Fire Arms Manufacturing
Company, Inc.
1870 as b "Frontier"   9/24/63

THE SIGN OF A MARLIN *& design*   72755
Shotguns and rifles
The Marlin Firearms Company
January 1908   2/16/09

THE WOODSMAN   264898
Pistols
Colt's Manufacturing Company
3/9/27   12/10/29

THOMPSON *and design*   149828
Rifles, pistols, etc.
Auto Ordnance Corp.
7/18/21   12/27/21

THUNDERBOLT   411744
Firearms and ammunition
Remington Arms Company, Inc.
6/17/44   1/30/45

TOMMY   395567
Machine guns
Auto Ordnance Corp.
7/26/41   6/2/42

TOMORROW'S RIFLES TODAY   824725
Rifles
Weatherby, Inc.
9/15/64   2/28/67

TOP NOTCH   608538
Bullets
Savage Arms Corporation
1/2/41   7/12/55

TOPPER   806234
Shotguns
Harrington & Richardson, Inc
May 1943   3/29/66

TRADEWINDS   732330
Gun sights
Tradewinds, Inc.
8/26/59   6/5/62

TRAP   49607
Cartridges and shells
Remington Arms Company, Inc.
January 1890   2/13/06

TRAPMAX   683107
Shotgun shells
Alcan Shells, Inc.
6/18/58   8/11/59

"TRI-CLAD"   732049
Ammunition
Aktiebolaget, Norma Projektilfabrik
6/1/60   5/29/62

TRIM-TRU *and design*   800050
Shot shell cartridge trimmers
George L. Steebler d.b.a. Sports Industries
10/3/63   12/7/65

TROUND   718799
Ammunition
Dardick Corporation
9/13/58   7/25/61

Continued on following page

TRUAIM 810342
Rifle rest
R. M. Stevenson & E. W. Knight
July, 1964 6/28/66

TRUFLITE 637585
Gas porting device for gun muzzle
Richard M. Cutts
9/8/48 11/27/56

TRU-LOCK 668860
Scope mounts
The Lyman Gun Sight Corp.
7/24/57 10/28/58

TRW 788907
Rifles
Thompson Ramo Wooldridge, Inc.
11/18/63 5/4/65

T-WAD 773456
Wads for cartridges
The R & K Plastic Industries, Inc.
March 1963 7/21/64

TW FORTUNA-SUHL *and design* 834221
Firearms
VEB Ernst-Thalmänn-Werk Suhl
1956 8/29/67

U 49500
Cartridges
Remington Arms Company, Inc.
October 1885 2/6/06

U *in a circle* 49617
Cartridges
Remington Arms Company, Inc.
October 1885 2/13/06

U *in a circle* 65031
Cartridges and primers
Remington Arms Company, Inc.
12/1/1894 9/3/07

ULTRAMAX 662422
Shotgun shells
Alcan Shells, Inc.
12/14/56 6/3/58

ULTRARIFLED 629730
Rifle barrels
Gerald R. Douglas
10/7/53 6/26/56

U.M.C. 49616
Cartridges
Remington Arms Company, Inc.
January 1869 2/13/06

U.M.C. *in an oval* 49619
Cartridges
Remington Arms Company, Inc.
1/1/1893 2/13/06

UNDERCOVER 795430
Pistols
Charter Arms Corp.
4/7/64 9/7/65

UNIQUE 99306
Smokeless rifle powder
Hercules Powder Company
December 1903 8/25/14

UNI-SEAL 721507
Wad columns
Alcan Company, Inc.
12/30/60 9/19/61

VAL-KEEN 416720
Firearms and ammunition
Oakes and Company also as Tri-Test
9/15/44 9/25/45

VALMET 560166
Firearms and ammunition
Valmet Oy-Valmet Ab
Prior to 1949 6/17/52

VALOR *on shield* 735855
Firearms
Valor Sales Corp.
12/9/56 8/14/62

VANDALEE 810343
Shotgun shell powder wads
Herter's
12/12/63 6/18/66

VARI-CHOKE 589348
Shotgun chokes
Herter's Inc.
September 1950 5/4/54

VARMINTER 377073
Rifles, ammunition and loading tools
J. E. Gebby
10/1/37 4/16/40

Continued on following page

VARMINT KING *and crown design* — 687445
Firearms
The Marlin Firearms Company
3/3/58 — 11/3/59

VARMINTMASTER — 794650
Firearms and ammunition
Weatherby, Inc.
1/15/63 — 8/24/65

VICTOR — 601805
Ammunition
Remington Arms Company, Inc.
March 1894 — 2/8/55

VICTOR — 197695
Shotgun shells
Remington Arms Company, Inc.
1895 — 4/21/25

VIRONDA *and design* — 619653
Gun chokes
Italo D. Vironda
October 1952 — 1/17/56

VIXEN — 757573
Rifles
Firearms International Corp.
9/12/59 — 10/1/63

VOSTOK — 825969
Sporting rifles and pistols
Vsesojuznoje Export no-Importnoze
Objedinenije "Raznoexport"
September 1963 — 3/21/67

W — 47093
Shot shells, cartridges, etc.
Olin Industries, Inc.
1879 — 10/24/05

W — 60620
Guns
Olin Industries, Inc.
6/28/06 — 2/12/07

W — 36422
Firearms and ammunition
Winchester Repeating Arms Co.
1879 — 5/14/01

W *with RANGER superimposed* — 705413
Ammunition
Olin Mathieson Chemical Corporation
4/13/60 — 10/11/60

W *with superimposed* **EZXS** — 755303
Cartridges
Olin Mathieson Chemical Corp.
9/1/61 — 8/27/63

W *with superimposed* **LEADER** — 755304
Cartridges
Olin Mathieson Chemical Corp.
9/1/60 — 8/27/63

W *with superimposed* **SPATTERPRUF** — 755306
Cartridges
Olin Mathieson Chemical Corp.
9/1/61 — 8/27/1963

W *with* **SUPER SPATTERPRUF** — 768081
superimposed
Cartridges
Olin Mathieson Chemical Corp.
9/1/61 — 4/14/64

W. SUPER-SPEED *with design* — 708278
Ammunition
Olin Mathieson Chemical Corporation
7/16/59 — 12/13/60

W *with superimposed* **WINCHESTER** — 755305
Cartridges
Olin Mathieson Chemical Corp.
9/1/60 — 8/27/63

WALTHER *and design* — 303701
Ordnance and small arms
Carl Walther
1910 — 6/6/33

W & C SCOTT & SON — 48404
Firearms
Webley & Scott Ltd.
January 1883 — 12/26/05

WEATHERBY *(script)* — 688539
Firearms
Weatherby's, Inc.
9/15/45 — 11/24/59

WEAVER CHOKE *and design* — 753936
Firearms chokes
William R. Weaver d/b/ as W. R. Weaver
Co.
11/15/40 — 8/6/63

WEBLEY — 163486
Revolvers and pistols
Webley & Scott, Ltd.
1840 — 1/16/23

Continued on following page

WESTERN 224874
Small arms ammunition
Western Cartridge Company
1/1/96 3/8/27

WESTERN *(arced)* 500213
Ammunition
Olin Industries, Inc.
1/1/1896 5/11/48

WESTERN *(script)* 500224
Ammunition
Olin Industries, Inc.
June 1906 5/11/48

WESTERN *and design* 142347
Shot shells, cartridges, etc.
Olin Mathieson Chemical Corp.
January 1908 3/10/21

WESTERN *on a red diamond* 505178
Ammunition
Olin Industries, Inc.
January 1908 12/28/48

WESTERN FIELD 209759
Shot shells
Western Cartridge Company
January 1905 3/2/26

WETPROOF 175229
Shot shells
Remington Arms Company, Inc.
2/11/16 10/30/23

WHITE FLYER 149544
Target and traps
Western Cartridge Company
11/1/1897 12/13/21

WHITE LINE *with design of recoil pad* 665687
Recoil pads and butt plates
Mershon Company, Inc.
February 1937 8/12/58

WHITNEY 662045
Pistols
The Whitney Firearms Company
10/1/55 1/11/56

WHIZ-BANG 768999
Ammunition
Canadian Industries Limited
Prior to 1931 5/15/64

WINCHESTER 47094
Shot shells and cartridges
Olin Industries, Inc.
1867 10/24/05

WINCHESTER 53994
Shotguns and rifles
Olin Mathieson Chemical Corp.
1867 6/19/06

WINCHESTER 142353
Firearms
Olin Mathieson Chemical Corp.
1901 5/10/21

WINCHESTER W *with design* 755305
Rifles and pistol cartridges
Olin Mathieson Chemical Corporation
9/1/61 8/27/63

WINGMASTER 541094
Firearms
Remington Arms Company, Inc.
9/29/49 4/17/51

WIN-LITE 700348
Firearms barrels
Olin Mathieson Chemical Corp.
8/8/59 7/5/60

WIN-WAD 770204
Wads for shotshells
Olin Mathieson Chemical Corporation
7/29/63 5/26/64

WOODMASTER 336059
Firearms
Remington Arms Company, Inc.
1/17/36 6/23/36

WP *in an oval* 52927
Shotguns and rifles
Olin Mathieson Chemical Corp.
7/17/05 5/22/06

W.R.A. CO. 47352
Shot shells and cartridges
Olin Industries, Inc.
1867 10/31/05

W.R.A. CO. 36424
Firearms, ammunition, etc.
Olin Industries, Inc.
1867 5/14/01

Continued on following page

Table XXIII, Continued

XL	549896
Shotgun shells and air rifle shot	
Federal Cartridge Corp.	
6/1/28	10/23/51

"X-L"	261977
Shotgun shells	
Federal Cartridge Corp.	
6/1/28	9/24/29

XPERT	500221
Ammunition	
Olin Industries, Inc.	
1/16/24	5/11/48

XPERT	199903
Shot shells	
Olin Mathieson Chemical Corp.	
1/16/24	6/23/25

XPERT *on* X	705414
Ammunition	
Olin-Mathieson Chemical Corporation	
5/2/60	10/11/60

YAMA WOOD	723250
Gun stocks	
Richard Emanuel Longarini	
7/15/54	10/31/61

Z *in concentric circles*	245178
Ordnance of wide variety	
Zbrojovka Brno, Naradni Podnik,	
(Brno Arms Factory, National Corp.	
Brno, Czechoslovakia)	
7/29/25	8/17/28

ZEPHYR	706864
Firearms and ammunition	
Stoeger Arms Corp.	
5/21/36	11/8/60

220 MAX-FIRE	767801
Shot shell primers	
Alcan Company, Inc.	
8/29/62	4/7/64

Trademarks consisting only of a design

Acorn in a circle	606273
Ammunition	
Dynamit-Actien-Gesellschaft	
Prior to 1896	5/24/55

Anvil outline	801162
Shotguns and rifles	
Ithaca Gun Company, Inc.	
Jan. 1963	1/4/66

Bird design	536786
Pistols	
Sturm, Ruger & Co., Inc.	
10/13/49	1/16/51

Bird in a circle	280632
ordnance of wide variety	
Limited Company formerly The Skoda-Works	
3/26/25	2/24/31

Black disk surrounded by a white band	429575
Rifles and shotguns	
The Marlin Firearms Company	
12/5/21	5/6/47

Blacksmith's figure	785463
Rifles, parts and ammunition	
Firma Gebruder Merkel & Co., G.m.b.h.	
Prior to 1964	2/23/65

Centaur design on target background	655141
Firearms, parts and ammunition	
Fabriques d'Armes Unies de Liege	
Prior to 1950	12/3/57

Circle with red lines	87177
Firearms, etc.	
Remington Arms Co., Inc.	
2/1/11	7/2/12

Circular dots	289898
Propellent powder	
Hercules Powder Company	
3/25/31	12/15/31

Colt, figure of with arrows	52903
Pistols	
Colt's, Inc.	
1865	5/22/06

Continued on following page

Colt, figure of with arrows	58277
Rifles and guns	
Colt's, Inc.	
1865	12/11/66
Colt, figure of with arrows	738097
Firearms	
Colt's Patent Fire Arms Mfg. Co., Inc.	
1865	9/25/62
Colt, figure of with arrows, within oval outline	821006
Handguns	
Colt's, Inc.	
1877	12/27/66
Colt, figure of with arrows in a circle	830861
Rifle	
Colt's, Inc.	
6/30/62	6/27/67
Deer and gunsight	61393
Gun sights	
The Lyman Gun Sight Corp.	
1886	3/9/06
Diamond outline	514003
Rifle cartridges	
Olin Industries, Inc.	
1/1/08	8/23/49
Diamond outline	268486
Rifle cartridges	
Olin Industries, Inc.	
1/1/08	3/18/30
Dogs and design	57418
Gunpowder	
Dupont G.	
1894	11/13/06
Eagle, drawing of an	595057
Ammunition	
Federal Cartridge Corp.	
1/1/24	9/14/54
Eagle, drawing of an	782263
.22 caliber ammunition	
Federal Cartridge Corp.	
1/1/36	12/29/64
Eagle, drawing of an	808748
Center fire cartridges	
Federal Cartridge Corp.	
4/8/65	5/24/66

Flag within a wreath	61981
Powder for small arms	
Lufkin & Rand Powder Company	
1/1/1896	4/16/07
Frontiersman holding gun	293798
Rifle cartridges	
Federal Cartridge Corp.	
12/15/31	5/3/32
Frontiersman with rifle, bust of	780538
Firearms and accessories	
Ithaca Gun Company, Inc.	
5/11/54	11/24/64
Geometric design	757569
Firearms	
J. P. Sauer & Sohn G.m.b.h.	
Prior to 1956	10/1/63
Gunsmith, figure of	785463
Rifles, ammunition and parts	
Firma Gebruder Merkel & Co., G.m.b.h.	
Prior to 1964	2/23/65
Helmet, drawing of	600881
Firearms	
Noble Manufacturing Co., Inc.	
August 1949	1/18/55
Indian head design	812824
Reloading equipment	
Emhart Corp.	
12/5/63	8/16/66
Indian head, drawing of	595392
Firearms and parts and ammunition	
Savage Arms Corp.	
1/15/39	9/21/54
Owl's head	68389
Rifles, shotguns, etc.	
Iver Johnson's Arms & Cycle Works	
7/1/1893	4/7/08
Ram's head	783045
Firearm equipment	
Buddy Schoellkopf Products, Inc.	
3/1/53	1/12/65
Ram's head within a circle	792457
Firearm equipment	
Buddy Schoellkopf Products, Inc.	
3/1/63	7/13/65

Continued on following page

Table XXIII, Continued

Recoil pad design — 817631
Recoil pads
Pachmayr Gun Works, Inc.
1932 — 11/1/66

Recoil pad outline — 727865
Recoil pads, butt plates and spacers
Pachmayr Gun Works, Inc.
6/15/56 — 2/27/62

Red band design — 207284
Ammunition
Remington Arms Company, Inc.
4/15/25 — 12/29/25

Revolver, representation of — 207951
Revolvers and pistols
Smith & Wesson, Inc.
1856 — 1/12/26

Rifles, stacked — 89812
Firearms
The Birmingham Small Arms Co., Ltd.
March 1881 — 1/14/13

Rodent within a sight design — 768578
Reloading tools
R.C.B.S., Inc.
11/16/60 — 4/28/64

Shield, picture of — 349294
Firearms and ammunition
Jacques L. Galef
3/10/25 — 8/24/37

Shell with wings — 50353
Guns, rifles, pistols, etc.
Webley & Scott, Ltd.
5/10/1876 — 3/13/06

Shotgun shell, picture of — 275927
Shotgun shells
Federal Cartridge Corp.
5/1/30 — 10/7/30

Shot shell — 233089
Shot shells
Federal Cartridge Corp.
7/1/18 — 9/20/27

Shot shells, crossed — 45729
Shot shells
Olin Industries, Inc.
8/29/05 — 8/28/05

Squirrel in a circle — G24738
Ammunition
Dynamit-Actien-Gesellscheft
1898 — 4/10/56

Target, shattered — 600234
Ammunition
Federal Cartridge Corp.
3/17/53 — 1/4/55

Trapshooter — 236385
Shotgun shells
Federal Cartridge Corp.
1/8/26 — 12/13/27

TABLE XXIV
References

Classified below are a few of the many specialized references consulted in the preparation of this lexicon and to which the reader is referred for detailed treatment of certain broad divisions of the firearms art. Selection of books for this listing has been based upon comprehensive treatment, relatively recent publication and availability in most public libraries. Following the classified list of books is a list of the publications of The National Rifle Association that cover the firearms field important to the shooter.

Antique Firearms

ANTIQUE FIREARMS — 220 pp. . . . . *Ronald Lister*
COLLECTING OF GUNS — 272 pp. . . . . *James E. Serven*
COMPLETE BOOK OF GUN COLLECTING — 222 pp. . . . . *Charles Edward Chapel*
ENCYCLOPEDIA OF FIREARMS — 366 pp. . . . . *Harold L. Peterson*
SHOOTER'S BIBLE GUN TRADER'S GUIDE — 190 pp. . . . . *Paul Wahl*

Ballistics and Design

BULLET'S FLIGHT, THE — 416 pp. . . . . *Dr. Franklin W. Mann*
HATCHER'S NOTEBOOK — 640 pp. . . . . *Maj. Gen. Julian S. Hatcher*
SHOTGUN BALLISTICS — 159 pp. . . . . *Rolla B. Boughan*
SMALL ARMS DESIGN AND BALLISTICS — 2 Vols. 690 pp. . . . . *Col. Townsend Whelen*

Gunsmithing

GUNSMITHING — 740 pp. . . . . *Roy F. Dunlap*
MODERN GUNSMITH, THE — 2 Vols. 943 pp. . . . . *James V. Howe*
MODERN GUNSMITHING — 525 pp. . . . . *Clyde Baker*
PROFESSIONAL GUNSMITHING — 740 pp. . . . . *Walter J. Howe*

History of Firearms

AGE OF FIREARMS, THE — 220 pp. . . . . *Robert Held*
GUNS — 254 pp. . . . . *Dudley Pope*
HISTORY OF GREEK FIRE AND GUNPOWDER — 380 pp. . . . . *J. R. Partington*
TREASURY OF THE GUN — 252 pp. . . . . *Harold L. Peterson*

Military Arms

INTERNATIONAL ARMAMENT — 2 Vols. 954 pp. . . . . . . *George B. Johnson* & *Hans Bert Lockhoren*
SMALL ARMS OF THE WORLD — 723 pp. . . . . *W. H. B. Smith* & *Joseph E. Smith*

Modern Firearms

ENCYCLOPEDIA OF MODERN FIREARMS — 1059 pp. . . . . *F. Robert Brownell*
GUN DIGEST — 400+ pp. — an annual publication of The Gun Digest Company . . . . . . *John T. Amber*
SHOOTER'S BIBLE — 570+ pp. — an annual publication of Shooter's Bible, Inc. . . . . *John Olson*

Pistols and Revolvers

BOOK OF PISTOLS AND REVOLVERS — 762 pp. . . . . *W. H. B. Smith* & *Kent Bellah*
PISTOLS, A MODERN ENCYCLOPEDIA — 380 pp. . . . . *Henry M. Stebbins*
SHOOTER'S BIBLE PISTOL & REVOLVER GUIDE — 192 pp. . . . . *George C. Nonte*

Reloading

COMPLETE GUIDE TO HANDLOADING — 695 pp. . . . . *Philip B. Sharpe*
HANDBOOK FOR SHOOTERS AND RELOADERS — 2 Vols. . . . . *P. O. Ackley*
PRINCIPLES AND PRACTICE OF LOADING AMMUNITION — 952 pp. . . . . *Earl Naramore*
SHOOTER'S BIBLE RELOADER'S GUIDE — 190 pp. . . . . *R. A. Steindler*

Table XXIV, Continued

Rifles

BOOK OF RIFLES — 668 pp. .... *W. H. B. Smith & Joseph E. Smith*
RIFLE BOOK, THE — 332 pp. .... *Jack O'Connor*
RIFLES, A MODERN ENCYCLOPEDIA — 376 pp. .... *Henry M. Stebbins*
RIFLES AND SHOTGUNS — 477 pp. .... *Jack O'Connor*

Shotguns

RIFLES AND SHOTGUNS — 477 pp. .... *Jack O'Connor*
SHOTGUN BOOK, THE — 332 pp. .... *Jack O'Connor*
MODERN SHOTGUN, THE — Vol. I, 242 pp. .... *Maj. Sir Gerald Burrard, Bt.*

National Rifle Association Publications

FIREARMS AND AMMUNITION FACT BOOK .... 352 pp.
FIREARMS ASSEMBLY HANDBOOK .... 2 Vols. 336 pp.
FIREARMS HANDLING HANDBOOK .... 80 pp.
FIREARMS LAWS AND COURT DECISIONS .... 112 pp.
GUN COLLECTORS HANDBOOK .... 48 pp.
HUNTERS HANDBOOK .... 128 pp.
INTERNATIONAL SHOOTING HANDBOOK .... 56 pp.
QUESTIONS AND ANSWERS HANDBOOK .... 45 pp.
RELOADING HANDBOOK .... 224 pp.
SHOOTING HANDBOOK .... 224 pp.
SHOOTERS GUIDE .... 72 pp.
SHOTGUN HANDBOOK .... 128 pp.

TABLE XXV
Directory of American Manufacturers

Abercrombie & Fitch
(Griffin & Howe Mounts)
Madison & 45th Streets
New York, New York

P. O. Ackley
(Custom barrels, reamers)
2235 Arbor Lane
Salt Lake City 17, Utah

Advance Onyx Trophies
(Sporting trophies)
254 Flushing Avenue
Brooklyn, New York

Airguide Instrument Company
(Weather instruments, compasses)
2210 Wabansia Avenue
Chicago 47, Illinois

Aladdin Laboratories, Inc.
(Jon'e Warmers)
620 So. 8th Street
Minneapolis, Minnesota

Alcan Company, Inc.
(Reloading components)
Alton
Illinois

Allcock Manufacturing Company
(Havahart Traps)
North Water Street
Ossining, New York

Bob Allen
(Shooting clothing)
211 Court Street
Des Moines, Iowa

Alley Supply Corporation
(Site-Aline Collimator)
P. O. Box 458
Sonora, California

American Optical Company
(Ear protectors)
P. O. Box 1408
Philadelphia, Pennsylvania

The American Pad & Textile Company
(Sleeping bags)
6230 Bienvenue
New Orleans 17, Louisiana

Anderson Gun Shop
(Storm King Lens Covers)
1203 South 3rd Avenue
Yakima, Washington

Animal Trap Company of America
(See Woodstream Corporation)

Armalite, Inc.
(AR rifles and shotguns)
118 East 16th Street
Costa Mesa, California

The Banton Corporation
(Ranger Spotting Scopes)
9 First Street
San Francisco, California 94105

Behr-Manning Company
(Oilstones, abrasives)
Green & North Streets
Teterboro, New Jersey

Belding & Mull
(Reloading tools)
P. O. Box 428
Centre County
Philipsburg, Pennsylvania

Benjamin Air Rifle Company
(Air and gas guns)
1525 South 8th Street
St. Louis, Missouri

E. C. Bishop & Son, Inc.
(Gunstocks)
P. O. Box 7
Warsaw, Missouri

Bobwhite Target Co.
(Clay targets)
2101 Harrison Street
Kansas City 8, Missouri

Table XXV, Continued

Brauer Brothers Mfg. Company
(Holsters, gun cases)
817-19 North 17th Street
St. Louis 6, Missouri

Bob Brownell
(Gunsmithing supplies)
3rd & Main
Montezuma 3, Iowa

Browning Arms Company
(Firearms)
St. Louis, Missouri

Maynard Buehler
(Scope Mounts, safeties)
17 Orinda Way
Orinda, California

Bushnell Co.
(Scopes, binoculars)
1178 Bushnell Building
Pasadena, California

Cascade Cartridge, Inc.
(C.C.I. primers)
P. O. Box 282
Lewiston, Idaho

C & H Die Company
(Reloading tools)
1600 West 166th Street
Gardena, California 90247

Coleman Company, Inc.
(Stoves, lanterns)
113 W. Hunting Park Avenue
Philadelphia, Pennsylvania

Colt's Manufacturing Company
(Firearms)
Hartford, Connecticut

Craft Industries
(Gunsmithing tools)
719 N. East Street
Anaheim, California

Crosman Arms Company
(Air and gas guns)
E. Church Street & Turk Hill Road
Fairport, New York

Daisy Manufacturing Company
(Air guns)
P. O. Box 210
Rogers, Arkansas

Deeks, Inc.
(Rubber decoys)
P. O. Box 2309
Salt Lake City, Utah

Dill Manufacturing Company
(Presto-Oiler)
700 E. 82nd Street
Cleveland, Ohio

M. B. Dinsmore
(Shooting glasses)
Box 21
Wyomissing, Pennsylvania

G. R. Douglas Company, Inc.
(Custom barrels)
5504 Big Tyler Road
Charleston, West Virginia

E. I. DuPont de Nemours & Company
(Gun powder)
Empire State Building
New York, New York

Reinhart Fajen, Inc.
(Gunstocks)
Warsaw, Missouri

Faulks Game Calls
616-18th Street
Lake Charles, Louisiana

Federal Cartridge Corporation
(Ammunition)
2700 Forshay Tower
Minneapolis 1, Minnesota

Fitz
(Handgun grips)
P. O. Box 49797
Los Angeles 49, California

Flaigs Hunters Lodge
(Ace trigger shoes)
Babcock Blvd. & Thompson Run Road
Millvale, Pennsylvania

Forster Appelt Mfg. Co., Inc.
(Reloading tools)
Lanark, Illinois

Freeland's Scope Stands, Inc.
3737 14th Avenue
Rock Island, Illinois

"Gee" Manufacturing Company
(Auto gun racks)
P. O. Box 4152
Houston, Texas

Grace Metal Products
(Gunsmiths screwdrivers)
115 Ames Street
Elk Rapids, Michigan

Gun Club
(Shooting clothes)
214 S.W. Jackson Street
Des Moines, Iowa

Harrington & Richardson Arms
(Firearms)
Worcester, Massachusetts

Hercules, Inc.
(Gun powder)
900 Market Street
Wilmington, Delaware

Hi-Standard Manufacturing Co.
(Firearms)
1817 Dixwell Avenue
Hamden, Connecticut

Hollywood Gun Shop
(Reloading tools)
6116 Hollywood Blvd.
Hollywood, California

Frank A. Hoppe, Inc.
(Gun cleaning equipment)
123 York Road
P. O. Box 687
Jenkintown, Pennsylvania 19046

Hornaday Manufacturing Company
(Bullets)
216 W. Fourth Street
Grand Island, Nebraska

The Hunter Corporation
(Holsters, belts)
12-15 12th Street
Denver, Colorado

Intercontinental Arms, Inc.
(Muzzle loading firearms)
10927 West Pico Blvd.
Los Angeles 64, California

Ithaca Gun Company, Inc.
(Firearms)
Box 700
Ithaca, New York

Iver Johnson Arms
(Firearms)
Fitchburg, Massachusetts

Paul Jaeger
(Mounts and triggers)
21 Leedom Street
Jenkintown, Pennsylvania

Jet-Air Corporation
(G-66 Cleaning Products)
Paterson 4, New Jersey

Johnson Arms, Inc.
(Firearms)
104 Audubon Street
New Haven, Connecticut

Johnson Gartman Custom Guns
(Custom rifles)
U.S. Route 1, Washington Street
Wrentham, Massachusetts

Phil Judd
(Swivels)
83 E. Park Street
Butte, Montana

Justrite Manufacturing Co.
(Carbide lamps)
2061 North Southport Avenue
Chicago 14, Illinois

Kesselring Gun Shop
(Scope mounts)
Route #1
Burlington, Washington

Table XXV, Continued

Kuharsky Brothers
(Scope mounts)
2425 W. 12th Street
Erie, Pennsylvania

The George Lawrence Company
(Holsters, leather products)
306 S.W. 1st Avenue
Portland 4, Oregon

Lee Custom Engineering
(Reloading tools)
Route #2
Hartford, Wisconsin

Leupold & Stevens Instrument Co.
(Scopes & mounts)
4445 N.E. Glisan Street
Portland 13, Oregon

Lohman Mfg. Co.
(Game calls)
Neosho, Missouri

Lyman Gun Sight Corporation
(Reloading tools and sights)
Middlefield, Connecticut

Marble Arms Co.
(Sights, knives)
Gladstone, Michigan

Markell, Inc.
(Lead bullets)
2347 35th Avenue
San Francisco 16, California

Marksman Products
(Air guns)
2101 Barrington Avenue
P. O. Box 25396
Los Angeles, California

Marlin Firearms Corporation
(Firearms)
New Haven, Connecticut

Mayville Engineering Company
(MEC Loading Tools)
Box 267
Mayville, Wisconsin

MB Associates
(Rocket guns)
P. O. Box 196
San Ramo, California

Merit Gun Sight Company
(Sight discs)
6144 Madanock Way
Oakland, California

Michaels of Oregon
(Swivels)
2011 S.E. Lambert
Portland 2, Oregon

Micro Sight Company
(Pistol sights)
242 Harbor Blvd.
Belmont, California

Mill-Run Products Company
(Cleaning equipment)
1360 West 9th Street
Cleveland 13, Ohio

Mitchell Shooting Glasses
Wilson Long Bldg.
Waynesville, Missouri

Moody Machine Products Co., Inc.
(Miniature tools)
42-46 Dudley Street
Providence 5, Rhode Island

Morgan Adjustable Recoil Pad Co.
240 Norwood Avenue
Youngstown, Ohio

O. F. Mossberg & Sons
(Firearms)
7 Grasso Avenue
P. O. Box 479
North Haven, Connecticut

National Research Corp.
(Space blanket)
70 Memorial Drive
Cambridge, Massachusetts 02142

Nimrod Company
(Gun racks)
350 Sprague Road
Narberth, Pennsylvania

Table XXV, Continued

Nobel Manufacturing Company
(Firearms)
P. O. Box 208
Haydenville, Massachusetts

Norma Precision Company
(Ammunition)
South Lansing, New York

Nosler Partition Bullet Company
(Custom bullets)
P. O. Box 671
Bend, Oregon

Numrich Arms Corporation
(Firearms, gun parts)
West Hurley, New York

Olin-Mathieson Chemical Company
Winchester-Western Division
(Firearms and ammunition)
New Haven, Connecticut

P. S. Olt
(Game calls)
Pekin, Illinois

Pachmayer Gunworks, Inc.
(Recoil Pads, mounts)
1220 So. Grand Avenue
Los Angeles, California

Pacific Gun Sight Company
(Reloading tools)
Box 4495
Lincoln, Nebraska

Penguin Associates, Inc.
(Gun cases, tear gas)
Box 97
Parkesburg, Pennsylvania

The Polychoke Company
(Adjustable shotgun chokes)
Box 296
Hartford, Connecticut

Potter Engineering Company
(Reloading tools)
1410 Santa Anna Drive
Dunedin, Florida

R. C. B. S., Inc.
(Reloading tools)
P. O. Box 729
605 Oroville Dam Blvd.
Oroville, California

Redding Hunter, Inc.
(Reloading tools)
Box 524
Cortland, New York

Redfield Gun Sight Company
(Sights, scopes and mounts)
5800 East Jewell Avenue
Denver, Colorado

Remington Arms Company, Inc.
(Firearms and ammunition)
939 Barnum Avenue
Bridgeport, Connecticut

Rugged Grip Products
(Plastic handgun grips)
104 South Street
Hackensack, New Jersey

Saeco
(Reloading tools)
3270 E. Foothill Blvd.
Pasadena, California

Savage Arms Company
(Firearms)
Springdale Road
Westfield, Massachusetts

Scotch Game Call Company
60 Main Street
Oakfield, New York

Jay Scott, Inc.
(Wooden handgun grips)
81-85 Sherman Place
Garfield, New Jersey

Sheridan Products, Inc.
(Air guns)
Gun Department
Racine, Wisconsin

Table XXV, Continued

Shooter's Accessory Supply
(Powder dripper)
Box 205
North Bend, Oregon

Sierra Manufacturing Company
(Custom bullets)
10532 South Painter Avenue
Santa Fe Springs, California

Sigma Engineering Company
(Ear valves)
1608 Hillhurst Avenue
Los Angeles 27, California

Silva, Inc.
(Compasses)
LaPorte, Indiana

Smith & Wesson, Inc.
(Pistols and revolvers)
P. O. Box 520
Springfield, Massachusetts

Speer Bullet Company
(Custom bullets)
Box 224
1023 Snake River Avenue
Lewiston, Idaho

Sturm Ruger Company
(Firearms)
Southport, Connecticut

Ten-X Manufacturing Company
(Shooting Clothing)
100 Southwest Third Street
Des Moines 9, Iowa

Trius Products Company
(Mechanical target throwers)
Box 25
Cleves, Ohio

J. Unertl Optical Company
(Scopes and mounts)
2551-2555 East Street
Pittsburgh 14, Pennsylvania

Weatherby's Sporting Goods
(Custom rifles and ammunition)
2781 Firestone Boulevard
South Gate, California

The Weaver Company
(Scopes and mounts)
7125 Industrial Avenue
El Paso, Texas

Williams Gun Sight Company
(Sights, scopes and mounts)
7389 Lapeer Road
Davison, Michigan

Will Burt Company
(Versa-Vise)
P. O. Box 530
Oroville, Ohio

L. E. Wilson
(Reloading tools)
404 Pioneer Avenue
P. O. Box 324
Cashmere, Washington

Winchester Repeating Arms Corporation
(See Olin-Mathieson)